ENERGY TRANSFORMATION

ENERGY TRANSFORMATION

AN OPPORTUNITY FOR EUROPE

CLAUDE TURMES

IN COLLABORATION WITH
JÉRÉMIE ZEITOUN

TRANSLATED FROM THE FRENCH BY
DAVID AND NAOMI BUICK

FOREWORD BY
MARTIN LIDEGAARD

Biteback Publishing

First published in Great Britain in 2017 by
Biteback Publishing Ltd
Westminster Tower
3 Albert Embankment
London SE1 7SP
Copyright © Claude Turmes 2017
Copyright in the translation © David and Naomi Buick

ISBN 978-1-78590-257-4

10 9 8 7 6 5 4 3 2 1

A CIP catalogue record for this book is available from the British Library.

Set in Minion Pro

Printed and bound in Great Britain by
CPI Group (UK) Ltd, Croydon CR0 4YY

MIX
Paper from
responsible sources
FSC® C020471
FSC
www.fsc.org

CONTENTS

FOREWORD

While Europe is struggling to decide on its energy transition pathway to have a slight chance of maintaining global warming well below 2 degrees by the end of the century, a country like Denmark has already undergone no less than three energy revolutions over the past few decades. And the Danish experience has shown that energy transition is more possible than ever today. Lessons learned lead to focus on three pillars: energy efficiency, renewable energy sources and market opening thanks to flexible options and cross-border interconnections between countries. All of that with the indispensable involvement of citizens to stimulate public ownership of the change of paradigm.

The history of Danish energy policy starts in the 1970s with the oil crisis. Denmark then relied on oil for transport, for the heating sector, and for electricity production. But we soon found that it was definitely not sustainable from any perspective; neither economically, nor geopolitically. And this was well before climate change was high on the political agenda. Denmark therefore initiated a massive cross-sector transition into coal … Not very smart from an environment perspective, but this radical change was accomplished in only five years, thanks to a strong political will. Soon after that, we found gas in the North Sea. This led to a second rapid transition into gas. And later on, our third energy transition, the one which is still ongoing, was triggered by the shift to renewables and market opening.

At the times of our first (coal) and second (gas) energy transition, we had to explain our decision to the general public by raising their awareness of the likelihood that we may not receive any oil from the OPEC any more. But the truth was that we simply wanted to be energy independent in the way we had been before 1973. That implied to both left- and right-wing governments at the time that we would need to diminish our absolute energy consumption and to increase the efficiency of our economy. This initiative came before the climate discussion: it was mostly a security question at that time, based on the observation that scarce resources would never allow a country like Denmark to be energetically autonomous.

It was during the 1980s that the whole idea of sustainable development entered political discourse. The knowledge and understanding of how big climate change is was gaining momentum. This marked the arrival of our third energy revolution: the current one, the green one. We changed not only our energy consumption and production, but the whole system. This revolution was launched by the centre-right and rapidly embraced by the whole political spectrum. We developed a strong technological basis, which is one of the key factors of the success of our energy transition.

In 1993 minister Svend Auken, who was clearly in favour of renewable energy sources, came into office under the left-wing ruling government, where he stayed until 2001. He played a crucial role in shaping the Danish transition by initiating this third energy revolution. He brought to reality the old idea of energy market liberalisation coming from the first EU energy package of 1996. Indeed, energy policy always encountered cross-party support. Because he thought that the right-wing parties had too little ambition, he made an agreement to launch three big offshore wind parks: the first ones in the country.

In 2001 we had had five years of right-wing government led by Anders Fogh Rasmussen, which were basically five years of energy black out. The ruling party made a big mistake, and heavy consequences of it are still felt today: that was cancelling these new permits for offshore installations. This was a blow to the Danish renewable industry and to the whole climate policy. After five years of energy 'ignorance', Fogh's government reverted to a greener energy path.

In 2011, I came into office as a minister for climate. Until 2012, both the industry and utilities were backward-looking, so I set myself a challenge: to gain their support for the energy agreement for the period 2012–2020 that was already on the table at that time, but about which they were reluctant. And the first thing I did as minister was to enter into discussions with them to identify problems and agree on possible solutions able to secure their backing.

I presented the revised energy agreement in 2012 and it was, of course, criticised for being too ambitious. However, the industry eventually supported me, thanks to their prior inclusion in the process. They supported the plan and, at the end, not only the right-wing party were convinced but also the budget ministry, the industry ministry and sceptics from all sides. This fostered such a sense of ownership that these groups are now the strongest defenders of our ambitious energy policy. In the next energy agreement, I hope we will set ourselves the objective to reach '100 per cent renewables', not only in the power sector but also to a much higher degree in heating and transportation sectors, where electricity demand is rising.

Energy efficiency has always been the first pillar of the Danish green energy transition: it justified the shift to coal and then gas – for security reasons at the time. Energy efficiency required the deep renovation of buildings so that consumption was reduced dramatically. It resulted in a large majority of Danish households being connected to district heating networks using waste heat and heat from high-efficiency combined heat and power (CHP) plants fuelled by gas and by residual waste combustion.

The second pillar of this green revolution lies with the deployment of renewables. A crucial element allowed that to happen: during the 2000s, the balance between industrial sectors benefiting from this development and the old industry tilted in favour of the former, which became stronger and stronger. A whole new industrial basis emerged.

It is only with their support that we were able to change our production patterns.

The third pillar is market access, liberalisation and interconnectivity. This pillar is very important as it makes renewable energy less expensive than traditional means. From the Danish perspective, you can see that when you have interconnectivity and a market-based system, renewables are definitely cheaper. Wholesale electricity prices in Denmark are lower than the EU average, thanks to the large penetration of renewables and to a flexible, interconnected market. High retail prices stem from a political choice of heavy taxation established to generate income necessary to finance our welfare state. Back-up is only needed at a very limited scale if the system is sufficiently interconnected and flexible. It means that even capacity payments are not necessary. The message conveyed by some old fossil-fuel utilities that the more variable renewable electricity you have, the more you need capacity payments, is what I call blackmailing. The Spanish example is interesting: their biggest problem is that it takes too much time to build a decent interconnection to France, allowing them to export their surplus wind-generated electricity. In Denmark, when we have a surplus, we can export to neighbouring countries and generate income for Danish producers. Today almost 98 per cent of produced electricity is sold on the market, although curtailment remains the exception; and when we lack domestic production, we import. These are the benefits of a truly integrated market.

The success and the rapidity of the energy transition in Denmark are also due to another fundamental factor: citizens' involvement. There is no doubt that the civil society sector and the commitment from a large proportion of Danes to invest in wind and solar cooperatives have been extremely important in the '80s and '90s. There is a special system in Denmark where project developers are obliged to offer a share of the ownership to local communities when building such an infrastructure. A wind farm is almost never owned by a single or a handful of investors. Thousands and thousands of individual Danes, including myself, own at least a small number of shares of wind farms. That is a very important part of the Danish story as it is a very democratic way of producing energy.

But after that came a dilemma in Denmark. We suddenly had to develop large-scale offshore wind parks. And the financial market came along. Large institutional investors, businesses, pension funds, and private sectors took equity in these projects. In short, big money came in. As a result, we lost the public support we used to have for onshore wind, thanks to the participative model. But the positive impact is that the arrival of institutional investors helped achieving massive cost reduction. The level of budgetary support to offshore wind has been reducing in a spectacular way and has reached a level as low as fifty euros/MWh. This allowed Danish industry to gain market shares abroad via a strong export strategy: today 25 per cent of all wind turbines produced in the world are Danish!

The way to solve our dilemma and to get citizens back on board, while also relying on large investors, is the *prosumer* approach. Everyone who wishes will be involved in the market. It will be in a new way of producing and consuming energy in a decentralised way with PV or small solar plants that could be increasingly important, together with storage.

What is about to happen in the coming few years will be crucial, and even more important than what happened over the past fifteen years. Now we need scale in smart grids, renewables and efficiency investments. And we need a vision for interconnecting Europe. This is indispensable for economic reasons and for security reasons. A common vision does not exclude flexibility, but we will allow different regions in Europe to have different solutions on the concrete mix of renewables. Let us decide to expand offshore wind projects in the Baltic region or with Sweden and Poland, and let us calculate how cheap that actually comes out. Let's do the same with the seas in Southeast Europe and in the Mediterranean region. This way, people will see the cost of not acting together and visualise the benefits of cooperation through the establishment of a truly common market.

Climate knights, as I like to call them, are people – just like Claude

Turmes – who dedicate their lives to energy transition, because they know the planet cannot wait. They want to get things done as quickly and efficiently as possible. I am convinced that energy transition is not only good for the climate, but also for the economy. If we can prove that renewables are the best solution for the climate and the cheapest option to decarbonise our economy, there would be no fight against it anymore. The good news is that today, we are very close to that.

Martin Lidegaard

INTRODUCTION

The place: Strasbourg. The date: 17 December 2008. European Parliament President Hans-Gert Pöttering brings down his gavel: '632 votes for, 25 against, 25 abstentions. The report is hereby adopted. Congratulations, Mr Turmes.' I weep – for joy, out of relief, and from exhaustion. As a former sports teacher, I'm very familiar with how a victorious decathlete feels after having given my all during each event and crossed the final finishline; the finishline in this case being the final vote on the Renewable Energy Directive in a plenary session of the European Parliament. This measure was to give a huge boost to the policy of energy transition. It marked a paradigm shift in EU energy policy, opening up the way for thousands of wind turbines and solar panels to be installed. I wept because I recalled the years spent as an activist in Luxembourg, building solar thermal panels with my friends, dreaming of changing the world. Today, I thought, here I am at the heart of the European decision-making process, where the future of a resource that is vital for both individuals and companies is in play: the future of energy.

One might ask what, if any, relationship could there be between the future of the European Union and energy transition. The question is a vital one, and answering it has been at the centre of my battle as an MEP for over fifteen years now. First and foremost, it's a battle for the climate. Scientists the world over agree that climate change due to greenhouse gas emissions is a reality. The most sophisticated forecasting models tell us that if the air temperature rises by more than 1.5°C before the end of this century, irreversible phenomena will be triggered, forcing enormous upheaval on the biosphere. However, there is still time to change the game if we change how we produce and consume energy – starting now. We cannot do it on behalf of everyone, but as industrialised nations we should do our bit. We should do so because we have an ecological debt, incurred as a result of a development model which is unsustainable for a planet that could be home to some ten billion people by 2050.

It is also a battle to preserve our industrial leadership. Europe is a world leader in many green technologies, including onshore and offshore wind power, as well as in the cables used in power lines to improve the transmission of electricity produced from renewable sources to wherever it's needed. Our emphasis has shifted from heavy industry to cutting-edge technology. Transition therefore offers incredible opportunities to export and disseminate our know-how worldwide, both in terms of the technologies themselves and in terms of how they are integrated in systems (for instance, in green cities). There is, however, fierce competition from both North America and the Far East. Naturally, we need to continue to invest in research and innovation, but that won't be enough to keep us in the race. Above all, we need to establish the right conditions for green technologies to flourish here, with a dynamic domestic market that allows for the large-scale deployment of renewable energy, positive-energy buildings and green transportation; all with the help of a digital energy system featuring smart grids, the Internet of things and so on.

It is also a battle for employment. While an expanding sector of the economy leads to new jobs, much-needed changes in the energy sector will doubtless involve sacrifices in some traditional sectors, such as the closure of coal mines in France, Belgium and many other European countries. But at the same time, a renewal – if not an explosion – in the number of positions to be filled in other sectors can be expected. Energy transition brings with it the promise of sustainable jobs. These positions offer labourers and tradespeople the potential for career conversion. Europe is faced with very high levels of endemic unemployment, so opportunities like this need to be seized. All the more so as these jobs, as with all roles relating to energy efficiency, cannot be relocated. The same principle applies to biogas production, which works to maintain more profitable and sustainable farming through the creation of new prospects.

Lastly, this is a battle for democracy. What can be done to change things? When it comes to making change happen, we simply cannot trust the all-powerful market without any checks and balances, nor the highly select club of the oligopolies who control the flow of energy. Indeed, we are hostage to economic and geopolitical interests that are beyond our reach. I want to put power back in the hands of ordinary people when it comes to decisions about energy because, at the end of the day, it is we as citizens who pick up the bill. The era of customers who have no option but to be passive, blind and, above all, dumb, with no influence on decisions and their consequences, is over. Energy consumers are now an integral part of the system: active and aware, they must be allowed the option of producing their own electricity, individually or as part of a cooperative, and decide how they are going to use their smart meter. Instead of simply assenting to decisions made by the oligopolies, policymakers must allow private individuals to have their say.

Brussels has a role to play too

In this book, I have sought to review the political battles fought over the last fifteen years concerning energy transition for the 450 million citizens of the EU. The issues in terms of climate, economics and democracy relating to this transition extend far beyond local and national boundaries: the battle is a European one. The EU has powerful resources at its disposal to implement change. Treaties grant it powers to make laws that protect the environment, combat climate change, promote energy efficiency and renewable energy, structure the internal energy market, ensure security of supply and provide for infrastructure and interconnection. The EU also has financial resources capable of tipping the scales to stimulate innovation in the fields of energy and transportation.

The EU institutions are complex and sometimes lacking in transparency, but they allow for in-depth discussion between all the stakeholders concerned – civil society, the business world and national governments. Familiarity with all their workings is undoubtedly necessary if they are to be used to the greatest effect. Contrary to the stereotypes put about by national governments keen to set themselves apart from 'Brussels', however, legislation adopted by the EU institutions is greatly influenced by member states as well as by enterprises and civil society.

The European Parliament has been able to enact laws in its own right since the Maastricht and Lisbon Treaties. In this capacity, it is naturally the subject of intense lobbying on the part of industry and NGOs. But the twenty-eight national governments that meet together in the EU Council of Ministers are also involved in this law-making process. Their interests are extensively taken into account in the subtleties of each piece of EU legislation, and lobbying is largely carried out at the national level. In other words, 'Brussels' does not make decisions in isolation: most decisions are taken with the approval of Paris, Berlin, London and so on. In this book, the extent to which the influence of certain governments has played a determining role in EU energy policy orientations will be made clear.

A couple of things about green energy

The industrial revolution and the development of Western countries over the past 150 years have been founded on the use of fossil fuels. Their extraction and combustion produce greenhouse gases which, among other things, are responsible for global warming and air pollution. In addition, some countries have been using nuclear power for some forty years now, and the resulting radiation leaves a legacy of tens of thousands of tonnes of dangerous radioactive waste for future generations.

We have also inherited an energy system that is in the grips of oligopolistic companies keen to preserve their revenue from this state of affairs, and reluctant to agree to any reduction in their impact on the environment. They include EDF and Engie in France, Enel in Italy, CEZ in the Czech Republic, Endesa and Iberdrola in Spain, EDF, E.ON and Centrica in the UK and the 'Big Four' in Germany (E.ON, RWE, EnBW and Vattenfall).

There are three criteria that can be used to ensure our energy system acquires more respect for the environment, the climate and humanity. These are consumption, production and the infrastructures linking them. As regards the first of these, the cheapest and most abundant energy is the energy we don't actually use. Waste can be avoided through better-insulated buildings, lower-energy industrial processes and household appliances, and fewer spendthrift behaviours – thus decreasing our overall energy needs.

As for production, we can change the game by producing clean energy from renewable sources: wind power, the heat and light of the sun, the carbon components of plants, the heat of the earth, wind and river currents and the gases given off by decomposing organic waste. One day, we may also be able to harness osmotic power and the carbon compounds produced by algae.

Lastly, by making the power grid denser and smarter thanks to digital technology, production and consumption sites can, virtually, be brought closer together. Storing more electricity within the grid would allow us to benefit from the abundant supply of renewable energy at any time, and enable consumers themselves to become energy producers.

We have focused our efforts on these three areas to achieve energy transition in Europe and to change the rules of the game when it comes to energy geopolitics. So much has been done already that many aspects of energy transition now come as second nature to us. But that was far from the case in the late 1990s. Some people refused to believe. Too bad for them.

'Architects' versus 'saboteurs'

I am of course referring to those who have been seeking to obstruct these efforts: the major energy corporations, including the CEOs who joined forces to form the Magritte Group, an obscure but influential body when it comes to preserving vested interests of oligopolies. And too, the powerful European bosses' lobby BusinessEurope, which allied itself with the electricity firms in an attempt to scupper energy transition. And they could never have implemented their Machiavellian tactics without the aid of the conservative governments in the UK, Spain and Poland, or the then French government, all at once pro-renewables and pro-nuclear. Above all, by stitching up the European Commission, these transition saboteurs could rely on faithful henchmen; in particular, during José Manuel Barroso's second term, he was aided and abetted by Commission Secretary-General Catherine Day.

Fortunately, transition has also had its architects to whom I wish to pay tribute here: European commissioners, ministers, mayors, top civil servants, MEPs, innovative entrepreneurs, visionaries of all stripes, grassroots organisations and many others besides.

EU legislation on energy transition spans several periods, and it is worth noting these in order to have a clear view of the political state of battle as it is today. In the beginning, there were the 'Enlightenment' years, during which the architects laid the foundations, not without difficulty. These reached their apogee in 2008 with the adoption of the Climate and Energy Package, and the 20-20-20 goals for 2020. Next came the 'Dark Ages', during which the 'saboteurs' imperilled transition particularly by undermining support for renewable energy and the drive for energy efficiency. Lastly, there is the present day, at which we have reached a turning point. We will see how the new resources at our disposal can be brought to bear in making a firm commitment to energy transition. These include the outcome of the COP21, the loose concept of an Energy Union, the Junker plan to stimulate investment and, above all, the new EU legislation put forward by the Commission in November 2016 to establish a framework for action through to 2030.

This transition is inevitable. But it should be noted that it will never be a welcome prospect for those who deny the urgency of climate concerns, or those who seek to preserve their grip on the supply of energy to each and every one of us.

PART ONE

FROM THE ENLIGHTENMENT TO THE DARK AGES

CHAPTER 1

AN OUTMODED
BUSINESS MODEL

On 22 May 2013, a European Council meeting was held at which Europe's energy policy for 2020 to 2030 was discussed. The day before, at the invitation of Gérard Mestrallet, the CEO of the GDF-Suez group (now Engie), eight leading European energy industry bosses had gathered in Brussels at the museum dedicated to the famous Belgian surrealist artist, René Magritte,[1] of which GDF-Suez is the 'founding patron'. On this occasion, the CEOs of GDF-Suez, German groups RWE and E.ON, Spanish firms Iberdrola and Gas Natural Fenosa, Italian companies Eni and Enel and GasTerra from the Netherlands declared themselves to be the victims of a 'perfect storm' affecting the profitability of their investments. They noted the threats to the security of Europe's energy supply and threatened blanket blackouts unless the EU reversed the policy that had emerged from the 2008 Climate and Energy Package.

Indeed, it was a dark hour for Europe's electricity oligopolies. They had forecast demand for electricity growing by 2–5 per cent each year but, in fact, it was stable or even decreasing; in particular thanks to energy efficiency measures implemented by the EU, such as labelling and eco-design. To their surprise, for the first time since the Second World War the energy consumption of an entire continent was falling.

---

[1]   'Call of eight leading energy companies to EU leaders for a revitalized energy policy', 21 May 2013, www.engie.com.

The pie was getting smaller. Worse still, it would have to be carved up between many more stakeholders. The EU's Renewable Energy Directive of 2009 and its mechanisms for supporting producers of green energy, set to increase the share of renewables to 20 per cent of final energy consumption across Europe – 35 per cent of our electricity in 2020 – had led to the emergence of unexpected competition, since anybody and everybody could now produce electricity. The directive established the right to set up targeted state aid, such as guaranteed green electricity feed-in tariffs. On the ground, it had produced practical effects from the moment it was adopted. In Germany alone, the four major electricity providers E.ON, RWE, Vattenfall and EnBW no longer held all the cards; in 2007, they controlled 85 per cent of conventional electricity output but by 2015, these same companies were to control only 5 per cent of renewable output.[2] Suddenly, these oligopolies are faced with millions of producers, and thus with competitors, too: some 50 per cent of electricity production capacity in Germany from renewable sources is in the hands of citizens (individually or as part of cooperatives), farmers and small businesses.

Faced with this threat, the key demands of the Magritte Group were clear: scaling back the pace of development of renewable energy after 2020 by setting the lowest and least binding targets for 2030; doing away with renewable energy subsidies; and setting up subsidies to existing conventional power stations through new, so-called 'capacity markets'.

The economic crisis and the failure of the COP15 negotiations in Copenhagen were reason to believe that Europe would no longer invest in renewables. But the statistics show that 2010, 2011 and 2012 were boom years, with a peak of 23GW of solar power installed in 2011 and 12GW of wind power in 2012. Investments in the sector remained unaffected by the crisis, starting to level off only from 2013/2014 before a spectacular decline in 2015 – a consequence of the oligopolies' efforts.

---

2   At that time, renewables accounted for the following shares of their business portfolios: E.ON, 9 per cent; RWE, 8 per cent; Vattenfall, 6 per cent; and bringing up the rear, EnBW, with just 1 per cent.

What comparative advantage do major electricity providers have? Of course, they know how to manage highly complex projects in terms of authorisations, construction, maintenance and, above all, funding. They are also aware of the risks relating to major installations, which are diluted in their huge asset portfolios. However, this advantage has been roundly eliminated by the EU directive, which favours the adoption of national laws on guaranteed prices, enabling anyone to invest in the production of electricity from biogas, solar energy and wind power. This enables the risk to be covered by the state, which sets a price (feed-in tariff) or additional remuneration (feed-in premium) for producers, be they cities, local authorities, individuals, cooperatives or farmers.

Electricity firms in disarray

What is more, the margins of electricity oligopolies have melted away due to a fall in prices, dragged down by overcapacity on the European market. Indeed, the huge addition of renewable energy production capacity in the form of wind and solar power has not been accompanied by an equivalent decrease in conventional capacity. Here again, this paradox is the result of the oligopolies' stubbornness and the implementation of a twofold strategy on their part. On the one hand, they have refused to remove their ageing coal-fired (RWE, Iberdrola, Enel) and nuclear (EDF, Engie) power plants from the market, despite these having paid for themselves long ago, hoping instead to operate them until the bitter end. At the same time, they are committing to energy transition but only outside their domestic markets, whose economic rent they jealously guard.

Iberdrola has long ceased investing in Spain, preferring instead to fund wind power in the US, Brazil, Mexico and Chile. In doing so, the company has managed to position itself as a champion of renewable energy, despite 61 per cent of its business in this sector being outside its home country. The same logic applies to EDF Énergies Nouvelles with only 15 per cent of its business in France. And let us not forget Enel Green Power; at a recent event staged by the European Wind

Energy Association (EWEA), its CEO, Francesco Venturini, made the following complaint:[3]

> I am European; I am Italian; and so I regret the fact that over 90 per cent of the €2 billion that we are investing annually at the moment is leaving this continent ... We would love to come back to Europe, that would be wonderful, but we need a vision ... and it is not up to us to have a vision; that is up to policymakers.

These are crocodile tears in view of the efforts on the part of the Magritte Group – of which Enel is a founding member – to scupper EU policies that favour renewables.

OVERCAPACITY LEADS EU POWER PRICE DOWN

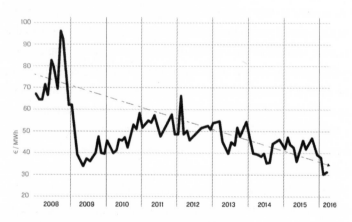

Source: PLATTS © REVOLVE MEDIA

In short, the mantra of the oligopolies is basically along the lines of 'renewables, but not in my home market'; a kind of NIMBYism pushed to extremes. In actual fact, there are few problems with renewables in Europe in terms of public acceptance; it is the major market players who have acceptance issues.

---

3   Paris, 17 November 2015.

Demand is falling, production capacity is increasing and collapsing prices are the mechanical result of this state of affairs.[4]

What is more, 'merit order' or order of precedence is a market mechanism that engages production capacity in order of increasing marginal costs. These are virtually nil for renewables because, after a significant initial investment, renewable 'fuel' (the wind and the sun) is available abundantly and free of charge, unlike coal and gas. This means that they come first in the order of precedence, followed by nuclear power and fossil fuels. Among the latter coal now takes precedence over gas in the order of merit, following the collapse in coal prices and the failure of the European carbon market. As a result, wholesale market prices at any given time are often pegged to the costs of generating electricity using coal and lignite. These wholesale market prices are reflected in over-the-counter trades. Indeed, power exchanges account for only a tiny part of the electricity supply market (for instance, just 25 per cent in Germany in 2014), but they set the baseline price on which over-the-counter transactions between suppliers and consumers[5] are indexed. Looking at the fall of wholesale electricity prices, EDF, E.ON and ENEL's dreams of making significant margins out of their old coal-fired and nuclear plants is vanishing. But instead of adapting to this market signal and progressively phasing out their old assets, oligopolies demand a new support policy: new subsidies to avoid blackouts in a European market already in severe overcapacity.

Another element that impacts the financial health of oligopolies that operate nuclear fleets (or have done so in the past) is a lack of funds to decommission power plants and safely manage radioactive waste.

---

4   However, household bills are not going down. To understand this, a distinction needs to be drawn between wholesale and retail prices. Wholesale prices are those practised on electricity markets. Retail prices offered to households include various taxes, charges for use of the grid, VAT and other specific contributions that together add up to more than the price of the power itself. On average, the latter accounts for only 37 per cent of the final bill in the European Union (actual proportions range from 15 per cent in Denmark, where taxes are highest, to 77 per cent in Malta, where there is very little taxation). As a result, retail prices do not necessarily fall when wholesale prices do. In addition, most electricity providers sell their output two or three years in advance, on the basis of futures contracts. This means there is a lag between wholesale market falls and any impact on households.

5   Over-the-counter (OTC) trades accounted for 65 per cent of all trades in the EU in 2013.

Indeed, not only are the relevant companies' finances inadequate in and of themselves, but to make matters worse they have often invested funds set aside for decommissioning in assets that are gradually losing value. No sooner had Germany confirmed that it would be abandoning nuclear power after the Fukushima disaster than the debate surrounding decommissioning of its nuclear fleet began; were the funds specified in law available and sufficient, or did they exist only on paper?

The 'polluter pays' principle that has featured in EU treaties since the Single Act of 1986 implies that funds for decommissioning and waste management should be incorporated into nuclear electricity production prices in such a way as to cover all costs. I subscribe to this viewpoint, which is designed to promote transparency in decommissioning funding. But since this principle has yet to be applied, who will end up footing the bill? The oligopolies are fumbling forwards short-sightedly, with this sword of Damocles dangling over their heads. Some companies have invested their decommissioning funds in assets whose market value is zero, such as coal and lignite mines (lignite is a fossil fuel that is even more of a pollutant than coal). These mines are condemned to close in the medium term since they are no longer profitable, and coal and lignite are energy sources that are too dirty for a world making a serious commitment to combating climate change. Moreover, the costs of restoring the land occupied by mines are enormous. For electricity companies, mines are therefore becoming more of a liability than an asset. Will oligopolies be able to bring to bear the financial reserves required when presented with the enormous bill for nuclear decommissioning? Nothing could be less certain. If they cannot, taxpayers run the risk of having to stump up. In the meantime, power plant operators clearly have an interest in extending their lifespan, in defiance of the risks they are imposing on society in doing so.

Trapped oligopolies

In short, electricity oligopolies are between a rock and a hard place. They only have themselves to blame; the tricky situation in which they find themselves is nothing other than the fruit of obvious strategic errors in their investment decisions. Hard though it may be to believe, groups like RWE were still investing in coal between 2011 and 2013. Resisting the energy transition, they failed to see coming what has now become a question of survival for them. They are seeking to slow the development of renewables and keep polluting power stations working as long as they can, in order to generate some cash.

This is happening despite the fact that when it comes to combating climate change, not to mention the related risks and costs to society, renewables are undeniably better placed than coal, nuclear power and gas. As a result, the oligopolies came together in the Magritte Group with a single aim in mind: sabotaging EU climate and energy policy implemented in the mid-2000s. The targets to be destroyed are the national support schemes for renewables and the promotion of energy efficiency. The resources brought to bear consist in relentless lobbying at the highest level of national governments and the European Commission. Certain conservative governments are among their allies, such as those in the UK, Poland and Spain, and the European bosses represented by BusinessEurope, in which electricity-intensive sectors such as the cement, lime, steel and glass industries are major drivers.

I have to admit to being constantly astounded by the blatant hypocrisy of European bosses. In June 2013, just a few weeks after the creation of the Magritte Group, BusinessEurope published the following spirited press release: 'Energy costs have risen to unprecedented levels in Europe at a time when our main competitor, the United States, is benefiting from increasingly lower energy costs … the energy prices impact of current support schemes [for renewables] is not viable for the EU's economy.'[6] Can this really be a coincidence? And besides, it is a blatant lie. By talking in terms of energy, BusinessEurope has deliberately maintained the confusion between gas and electricity prices. Gas prices have indeed increased in Europe, since they are indexed to oil prices. However, wholesale electricity prices are at historically low levels, thanks to EU policies favouring renewable energy. The report

---

6   'A competitive EU energy and climate policy', www.businesseurope.eu.

also fails to mention the huge exemptions from which electricity-intensive industries in Europe benefit, with the result that they do not have to pay into renewable support schemes. Like a stowaway, they therefore enjoy all the perks of a system to which they do not contribute in the slightest. So why do they attack it if they benefit from it? This might seem counter-intuitive, but I do have an explanation: I believe that the Magritte Group energy firms and the electricity-intensive industries in BusinessEurope have closed ranks in adversity. This unholy alliance between clients and suppliers has allowed them to launch a coordinated attack against the progressive policies initiated by the EU. The electricity firms are helping electricity-intensive companies to preserve their tax and levy exemption regime, while the electricity-intensive companies are helping electricity firms to restrict the progression of renewables, which are to their disadvantage.

The oligopolies believed that they could sabotage policy decisions taken by twenty-eight governments. They boycotted renewables and failed to understand that if they did not invest, others would step up to do so – as has indeed happened in energy services, with the entry of digital players such as Google and superstores such as IKEA onto the market. The oligopolies have staunchly refused to change their mind-set. Jürgen Grossmann, the former boss of RWE, embodied this short-sightedness with his soundbite about the promotion of solar power in Germany: 'It's like trying to grow pineapples in Alaska'.[7] Today, thousands of solar panels have been installed on German roofs – and for RWE, the joke has gone sour.

This, then, is the battle which concerns us: the end of a comfortable and well-paying business model for the oligopolies, and the emergence of a new system founded on the reappropriation of energy issues by individuals, cooperatives, cities and all the new stakeholders of the digital economy. But to understand what has been going on behind the scenes, we need to back up and take a look at what happened at the beginning of this success story.

---

7   'Großmann mahnt europäische Energiepolitik an', *Handelsblatt*, 17 January 2012.

CHAPTER 2

THE SPARK

During the winter of 1999–2000, the price of crude oil started to climb in a manner that had not been seen since the oil bust of 1986. After having fallen as low as $10/bbl (per barrel), within the space of a few months it rose to over $30/bbl. This may seem rather low in comparison with the spike of $147/bbl reached on 11 July 2008 a few weeks after Lehman Brothers went bankrupt. But at the time, it was far from painless. The European Commission, then headed up by Romano Prodi, had to respond; the EU is overdependent on its energy imports and therefore sensitive to oil price fluctuations, which impact both its balance of payments (since oil prices are quoted in dollars) and its trade balance – higher oil prices have an inflationary effect on its economy. However, the EU only has limited power over this phenomenon, which is external to the European economy.

The second oil shock had led to the creation of the Directorate-General Energy and Transport (DG Tren) in the European Commission in the late 1970s; once again, black gold was to spark in-depth examination of the need for a common energy policy in Europe. Historically, EU intervention in this field can be divided into three phases up to the year 2000: the setting up of a new Directorate-General as part of the Commission; a decision designed to decrease the share of oil in electricity production; and the incorporation of energy products when the internal market was set up (having previously been excluded by Delors in 1992). In short, one or two measures had been taken here and there, but without a genuinely shared philosophy on the table. There was little more than a rough outline of joint policy, based on Europe's needs to reduce its dependence on oil, and enshrined in the myth of the internal market being a panacea – an agenda largely inspired by the UK government. And so it was that the first Internal Electricity Market Directive was adopted in 1996 in order to set down common principles, such as the deregulation of tendering for new production capacity, and non-discriminatory access by various producers to power grids.

Nevertheless, it was left to Loyola de Palaciao, the Spanish vice president of the Commission who took office in September 1999 with the Energy and Transport portfolio, to provide the spark that ignited the flame of energy transition. The realisation that the EU also had a responsibility to address energy demand was a revolutionary one at the time. 'The powerlessness of politicians ... to restrict the demand for energy is just as much a weakness as the excessive influence of oil on the economy', she explained.

Loyola de Palacio was a tenacious political animal with very fixed ideas: a pro-nuclear environmentalist that I liked to describe as 'very active, but also highly radioactive'. Gifted with prodigious intelligence and a huge appetite for work, she worked incredibly well with her French director-general, François Lamoureux. She led the political battle while he sweated the paperwork. Together, they created a document that was to mark the start of proper in-depth work regarding the EU's energy system: the first energy Green Paper. Coming as they did from different political backgrounds, neither de Palacio nor Lamoureux were familiar with the details of the world of energy. As a result, drafting of the Green Paper was entrusted to Nina Commeau-Yannoussis, a DG Tren civil servant since 1987, later rewarded with a position as head of unit. 'Initially, I was free to draft the Green Paper as I wished', she told me. In time, François Lamoureux and Loyola de Palacio got to grips with the content and developed the principal measures put forward in the document. On this they were agreed: the EU's energy dependence was going to become hard to manage. 'Working on that basis, the means to be brought to bear – such as the promotion of renewables and demand reduction – naturally emerged.'

Some ten days before the Green Paper was published, François Lamoureux held an informal meeting with three journalists who were experts in European affairs, energy and the environment to put the finishing touches to the definitive text. It was a race against time. When it was published on 29 November 2000, it was on the large side and not written in the usual style of the Commission, but the message was clear: 'The Union must rebalance its supply policy by clear action in favour of a demand policy … the scope for action to address demand appears more promising.'

And for the first time, transport was brought into the mix. The genius of François Lamoureux was to come up with the term 'security of supply', to which the Commission as a whole signed up. Despite this, he was not rewarded for his labours and saw himself summarily pushed aside, having to give up his place to the German Matthias Ruete.[8] Was this the price to pay for not espousing the neoliberal vision of the internal market?

The Green Paper put the cat among the pigeons. François Lamoureux later published a brochure in every language of the EU to make sure the message got across: 'Let's control our dependence'. In it, he set out the two avenues to be explored to impact demand: 'making energy-efficient technologies (products, home automation etc.) available' and 'making consumers more responsible by raising their awareness of the degree to which their own consumer choices impact their environment'; in other words, eco-design, energy labelling, construction ('a priority sector when it comes to improving energy efficiency') and innovation on the one hand, coupled with green taxes on the other hand. He also noted that 'transport will be a key sector in terms of the strategies to be developed'. Everything was there in black and white.

---

8   *Mort d'un Européen*, Jean Quatremer, Libération, 27 August 2006.

The huge potential of demand reduction

François Lamoureux understood that impacting demand was vital when it came to decreasing energy dependence. Scarcely had he arrived at the head of DG Tren when he began to deploy the European legal arsenal to improve the energy efficiency of all the relevant consumer products. The consequences of this type of policy on global energy demand are not generally realised, but the potential is gigantic: measures concerning eco-design and energy labelling alone are equivalent to 175Mtoe (million tonnes of oil equivalent) of savings between now and 2020: the annual consumption of primary energy by a country the size of Italy, the tenth-largest economy in the world. Indeed, the concept took some time to take hold, and it was not until 2015 that the European Commission began systematically to highlight the fact that a 1 per cent increase in energy efficiency leads to a 2.6 per cent reduction in gas imports.

Of course, our daily energy-saving routines have an impact. But the largest savings in terms of volume occur when we buy consumer goods and equipment that consume less energy, when we live in better-insulated and better-built homes, and when we adopt alternative modes of travel because we have the option of doing so. The 'invisible hand' that allows us to do so is in fact that of EU legislation, which requires governments and industry to implement these powerful sources of leverage. François Lamoureux said as much at the launch of his Green Paper: 'The policies will be all the more powerful and legitimate because they will be decided at the EU level … Only binding policies such as taxation and regulatory measures will achieve concrete results.'

Eco-design and energy efficiency: an end to waste

It was in the late 1990s that the EU first began to address the issue of waste in consumer products with the first energy labels on fridges. For my part, I began my work as a MEP in 1999, acting as rapporteur for the draft directive drawing up performance requirements for ballast in fluorescent lighting. Having recently been elected, I met a number of civil servants at the European Commission with responsibility for eco-design and energy efficiency. Some of them had begun their careers in nuclear fusion in the 1980s before concluding that it would never work. I cannot but agree with them; the mantra of ITER, the international experimental thermonuclear reactor, is basically 'in fifty years' time' – and has been ever since the start. And even if ITER were eventually to succeed, it would come far too late to address climate change, whereas eco-design has very quickly generated energy savings corresponding to thirty or forty ITER reactors! The biggest waste when it comes to ITER is not so much the billions of euros it costs us each year, but the fact that it prevents perhaps thousands of researchers and scientists from working on practical solutions that could be put in place while there is still time.

A huge amount of potential waste reduction can be achieved through eco-design because it deals with the performance of all the equipment used in homes, offices and factories: boilers, AC units, fans, electric motors, lighting, fridges, freezers, washing machines, dishwashers, electronic machinery, office equipment and so on. Whether it is produced in the EU or elsewhere, any appliance that does not comply with these minimum performance requirements can no longer be marketed in the European Union.

Until the early 2000s, the EU had a distinct directive for each product. Then in 2005 it adopted a framework directive, revised in 2008. This set up a decision-making mechanism to incorporate new products and adjust requirement criteria in line with market changes, without having to repeat a cumbersome legislative process each time. The liberal Belgian MEP Frédérique Ries[9] was in the front line during these negotiations, with the full support of myself and Peter Liese.[10] Thanks to the Parliament's insistence, the EU adopted an exhaustive list of products for which the potential reduction in energy use was

---

9   Frédérique Ries, a former journalist for the Belgian channel RTL-TVI, first entered the European Parliament in 1999 and has been a member of the Environment Committee ever since.

10   Peter Liese is a German conservative MEP who is very influential on the European Parliament's Environment Committee, of which he has been a member since 1994.

the highest, and improved the transparency of the decision-making process by setting up the Ecodesign Regulatory Committee. This resulted in the application of a four-stage process. Firstly, the European Commission carries out studies to determine the standards that should be applied to each product. Next, these studies are presented to the Ecodesign Regulatory Committee and discussed, which allows industries to have their say, along with consumer associations and environmental NGOs.[11] Thirdly, the twenty-eight member states meet and decide on the applicable standard on the basis of this work by way of a qualified majority vote. Lastly, the European Parliament may approve or reject the decision. This represents genuine progress: the Committee is a venue where all parties can discuss the level of standards to be applied to each product, thus avoiding the possibility of the underhand manoeuvring so beloved of certain stakeholders. In short, it is democratic, transparent comitology that is not technocratic.

Using the list of products adopted by the Parliament and the Council, the European Commission moved to abandon incandescent light bulbs (which, with energy performance of just 5 per cent, represented a huge amount of waste). This prohibition did indeed have a proper technical justification; what is more, it opened up the way for the deployment of LEDs, which was a major innovation. This decision alone enabled Europe's electricity consumption to be reduced by an amount equivalent to the output of several coal-fired power stations. However, it is also a good example of the mixed messages that can sometimes surround a decision by the EU. When it was applied – and criticised by the gutter press – the Commission had not prepared any kind of media campaign; national governments collectively dived for cover and denied all responsibility, despite the fact that all of the twenty-eight member states had approved the measure in 2008. Communication to the public was therefore characterised by considerable confusion. Political courage, however, involves standing one's ground in the face of populism and defending a decision that is logical.

---

11   Particularly Ecos, a grassroots environmental organisation for standardisation, set up to provide alternative expertise to that of industrial interests.

In addition to measures concerning industrial and household electrical appliances, the EU also engaged in international cooperation on energy efficiency standards for office equipment: the Energy Star programme. Adopted jointly with the United States in 2001 (based on a programme devised by the US Environmental Protection Agency dating from 1992), it has since been updated twice, most recently in 2008. This agreement encourages the manufacture of equipment offering good energy performance, and the Energy Star label allows consumers to identify such devices. The innovative aspect is that the same requirements apply in both the EU and the United States.

Eco-design versus populism

Labelling and eco-design are therefore at the heart of Europe's energy efficiency policy. Thanks to these instruments, Europe has encouraged industrial innovation and improved consumer information. This has led to household energy bills decreasing, and the energy savings achieved account for a significant share of the energy efficiency effort required by 2020. And this is why I deplore the populist rhetoric of Jean-Claude Juncker during the most recent EU election campaign in April 2014:

> Yes, we can ensure that the EU no longer regulates the energy intensity of shower caps and coffee machines. But if we want to be honest about this, we will then have to abolish the EU's Ecodesign Directive, which had the support of a majority of member states and of the European Parliament. As Commission president, I will look into this question to see whether Europe is ready to abolish this legislation, in spite of our common commitment to a healthy environment and to fighting climate change. Yes, as Commission president, I will resist regulating the height of hairdressers' high heels.[12]

This type of talk echoes the scandalous attacks by his campaign manager during 2014: 'We are not going to be regulating toilet flush.'

---

12   'New growth without debt: my priorities as Commission president', juncker.epp.eu.

What is more, his vice president, Frans Timmermans, said something similar in September 2014 prior to his confirmation by the Parliament: 'Brussels should not be meddling with the power ratings of vacuum cleaners ... Is that really what we want? I don't think so. Should this be the EU's responsibility? I don't think so.'[13] This, despite the fact that the whole point of EU labelling on vacuum cleaners was to put an end to the myth (or indeed the contrick) according to which power equals suction power. And while we're on the topic, I invite you to watch the hilarious video of a vacuum cleaner contest between two Euro-MPs from the Parliament's Energy Committee, in which the less powerful one (the vacuum cleaner, not the MEP) actually performed better.

Eco-design has always been at the heart of the Eurosceptic offensive, as the campaign preceding the UK referendum on remaining in the EU demonstrated once again. In February 2016, the sovereigntist Euro-MP David Coburn went as far as to state the following: 'My toaster takes four attempts before bread goes brown and can put my Dundee marmalade on many thanks to EU.' This is a blatant lie, since there are no EU regulations on toasters (not that the Brexiteers were too bothered about how many lies they were telling). On the other hand, in September 2014, the founder of the eponymous brand of vacuum cleaners James Dyson recommended that the UK should leave the EU because its vacuum cleaner power regulations were not binding enough; the reason being that this allowed his German competitors plenty of scope for continuing to market power-hungry products, whereas his appliances used scarcely more than 1,400W. So, are the regulations too strict or too lax? Instead of being ashamed of regulating vacuum cleaners, the president of the Commission should be rejoicing in the fact that consumers all across Europe can, at a glance, distinguish appliances that perform well from those that waste energy. Few EU measures have been so visible and so beneficial for both citizens and environment.

My work on the first directive governing ballast for fluorescent

---

13   'Timmermans tegen EU-bemoeienis met stofzuiger', www.nu.nl.

lighting taught me three lessons about how European legislation is developed in Brussels and Strasbourg. Firstly, political alliances in the European Parliament are generally very broad and very permeable. There is a genuine culture of compromise that is rarely to be found in national parliaments, which tend to be highly polarised between a majority and an opposition, with clearly identified left- and right-wing blocs. For instance, Danish conservative Christian Rovsing is of an entirely different political persuasion to me, but was a precious ally when it came to energy efficiency. Secondly, industry is not a monolithic block, but is often divided when it comes to its lobbying strategies. It is up to MEPs to identify the most progressive companies and make the most of their capacity to mobilise – for example, Philips and Osram on the issue of low-energy bulbs. Lastly, EC civil servants are often highly competent and motivated, despite inertia and the occasional lack of political courage on the part of the hierarchy.

Beyond directives: mobilising the stakeholders

Legislation is important, but insufficient if there is no accompanying dynamic among stakeholders on the ground. In view of this, in 2003 we set up a new kind of institutional animal, the Intelligent Energy Europe programme (IEE). Energy transition – although it wasn't yet referred to as that at the time – called for the development of new technologies and the involvement of new actors for change: cities, field experts, urban planners, architects and so on. During a 2001 meeting in the office of Swedish conservative MEP Anders Wijkman, we submitted a six-page project along these lines to François Lamoureux. By the end of the meeting, he was enthusiastic: 'OK, let's do it, it's good.' We could not believe either our eyes or our ears: the network to fund energy transition stakeholders had been born in thirty minutes flat. And while he was at it, François Lamoureux also set up the separate budget line and the Executive Agency, which works flexibly with change actors.

What is more, since it is based on societal innovation, the programme was later linked in with the first European Strategic Energy

Technology (SET) plan in December 2007. This programme is a huge source of leverage across the EU for prospective studies, collaborative work and discussions relating to smart grids.

Energy transition concerns not only technical issues, but also sociological and political questions. The IEE is a subversive instrument, since it is a way of funding politically incorrect initiatives such as the Covenant of Mayors, and projects[14] that make appropriate recommendations to European institutions and member states for the implementation of their renewable energy and energy efficiency policies. They identify and disseminate the best practice, gather the various stakeholders into networks and promote regional cooperation.

During her time as secretary-general of the Commission, Catherine Day did everything she could to dismantle the IEE. She detested the programme, since it embodied the concept of 'soft law' and the 'bottom-up' approach. And indeed today, the IEE name has disappeared. It has been diluted into the Horizon 2020 Framework Programme for Research and Innovation, on the pretext of simplification, but above all to satisfy the marketing whims of the Directorate-General for Research, which wanted to promote a single instrument. This despite the fact that the IEE has nothing to do with research and development – it is a programme designed to accelerate the implementation of energy transition by identifying best practices and social, economic and regulatory innovation, and disseminating these throughout Europe. What a waste … A programme akin to the IEE absolutely must be restored in the EU's next multiannual financial framework review.

In April 2006, at the same time as the IEE programme was being set up, the EU adopted its first energy end-use efficiency and energy services directive. This piece of legislation put forward a suggested annual target of energy savings of 1 per cent. It replaced a former directive from 1993 that set up national energy saving programmes (Save) and for the first time, put ambitious European mechanisms in place based on the principle that energy efficiency could be improved 'by

---

14   Diacore, Build Up, and Better are just some of the great many projects funded by the IEE with benefits for policymakers and local authorities alike.

exploiting market forces'. To achieve this, energy suppliers had either to offer energy audits or services to consumers, or pay into a fund devoted to energy efficiency. There was not yet any binding agreement at that stage, but it did represent an initial conceptual advance: viewing energy efficiency as a profitable business enterprise. The directive did not lead to significant energy savings, but it did help raise the awareness of economic stakeholders and, in doing so, opened up the way for subsequent, more binding legislation.

The pillars of renewables policy

The arrival of Loyola de Palacio at the Commission in 1999 led to in-depth thinking and a fresh interest in European policy relating to renewable energy. When she became European Commissioner for Energy, a dossier prepared by her predecessor Christos Papoutsis was ready to be signed. It concerned the harmonisation across the EU of schemes to support renewable energy sources, replacing national and local support mechanisms. This dossier was coordinated by the very liberal Christopher Jones, director of the Directorate-General of Transport and Energy (DG Tren), and the architect of deregulation in the internal energy market. This led to howls of protest from industry in the sector, NGOs and the Green MEPs. As rapporteur, I made sure the European Parliament took a stance firmly opposed to this idea in an own-initiative report adopted in March 2000. The commissioner took it back on and asked for it to be thoroughly reviewed. And reviewed it was. In May 2000, she published her draft renewable energy directive, geared to strengthening national support schemes. A few months later, she drove the point home a little further: 'One avenue of investigation would be to envisage profitable energy derived from oil, gas and nuclear power funding the development of renewable energy, which has not as yet benefited from significant aid equivalent to that provided to other conventional sources of energy.'

On 13 March 2001, the German electricity firms staunchly opposed to the EU proposal suffered a major setback: in its 'PreussenElektra' ruling, the European Court of Justice upheld the legitimacy of national support schemes for renewables. Support for renewable energy has been one of the pillars of EU energy policy ever since. It was to be a significant part of the legacy of Loyola de Palacio, who sadly died in 2006. She was both an ardent pro-European and in favour of renewables, however strange that may seem for a conservative.

And therein hangs a tale. The first time I took part in an inter parliamentary meeting of the European Forum for Renewable Energy Sources (EUFORES) in the Canary Islands, I went to the opening drinks reception. When I first entered the room, I thought must have got the wrong venue: everyone was dressed much more smartly than I had expected for supporters of renewable energy! And so I learned that in Spain, renewables were the preserve of extremely rich, conservative families, many of whom had invested considerably in hydroelectric power. The first wind turbines were erected in Tarifa in southern Spain, a location known for its strong and steady wind streams making it a spot praised by surfers and windsurfers. But the actual industrial boom of wind energy took place in Navarra and Basque provinces, a market looked at by the company Gamesa, teaming up with Vestas to manufacture the first wind mills 'made in Spain'. The province of Galicia is then joining the club thanks to a system based on feed-in tariffs developed by the regional leadership of Manuel Fraga, who had formerly been Franco's Tourism Minister and Home Affairs Minister. Ironically, Spanish conservatives' support to renewables owes a lot to a former Francoist.

This was a great help to us at the beginning of the year 2000. During the preparation of my report on renewables, in addition to support from German Social Democrat MEP Mechtild Rothe,[15] I received the unexpected support of Spanish conservatives who were opposed to German conservatives – the latter having already attempted, via Brussels, to soften the German law on support for renewables that had just

---

15   Mechtild Rothe was a leading figure in the European Parliament, of which she was a member from 1984 to 2004. The spiritual daughter of Willy Brandt, she was vice president of the SPD delegation. A long-time supporter of renewable energy, she facilitated a great many legislative advances in the field.

been adopted by the Schröder–Fischer–Trittin government, piloted by a pair of visionary German MPs, Hermann Scheer and Hans-Josef Fell. It was thanks to the Spanish conservative MEP Alejo Vidal-Quadras[16] that we were able to see off these attacks. The report was an opportunity to insist on the need for a specific renewable energy directive over and above the internal market legislation. Adopted in March 2000 by the European Parliament's Industry, Research and Energy Committee (ITRE) by twenty-seven votes to three (with twenty-two abstentions), the report was highly critical of the European Commission's approach; the EC's working documents on renewables at that time were in their very early stages. These documents simply opted for the same approach as that of the internal market itself – which, ironically enough, implied that no specific directive or support mechanism were in fact required. In contrast, in my report I explained that member states were continuing to pay significant direct subsidies to conventional sources of energy, particularly coal and nuclear power. In view of this, the rare and modest subsidies already granted to renewable energy sources in most member states could in no way be deemed to constitute market distortion. If anything, they should be seen as a form of compensation for existing inequalities.

The report set out a roadmap for the adoption of a specific Renewable Energy Directive in 2001. This directive in turn marked a first step towards an increase in the share of renewables in the European energy mix, although it did leave member states to determine their own indicative national targets, despite the best efforts of the rapporteur Mechtild Rothe to make them mandatory (a position that had indeed been unanimously supported in the ITRE committee). The directive also set out the scope of a European framework for support mechanisms founded on common principles, such as the taking into account of technological particularities and geographical differences. Furthermore, it established guarantees of origin in order to ensure the traceability of renewable energy and specified that member states

---

16   Alejo Vidal-Quadras first entered the European Parliament in 1999 and was active until 2014 as part of the Industry, Research and Energy Committee.

should minimise the administrative barriers to it being deployed. The possibility for green electricity to be granted priority access to the grid was thus opened up, and its priority dispatch became mandatory. The text was supplemented in 2003 by a directive on the promotion of the use of biofuels, setting indicative targets of 2 per cent in 2005 and 5.75 per cent in 2010. However, sustainability criteria were notably absent from the directive.

Despite this progress, the legal arsenal was still relatively small. It was the 2008 Climate and Energy Package that really enabled renewables to start playing with the big boys.

CHAPTER 3

CLIMATE AND ENERGY POLICY TOWARDS 2020

On Friday 12 December 2008, the EU heads of state and government met in Brussels to discuss the conclusions of the twenty-seven member states, in particular as regards the 2020 Climate and Energy Package. This package of legislation was crucial to the implementation of energy transition in Europe. It was the second day of the meeting of the European Council, which also marked the close of France's presidency of the EU under the leadership of Nicolas Sarkozy. The French leader quickly grasped that making Europe the front-runner in combating climate change was a golden opportunity – not to be missed on any pretext – to chalk up another success attributable to his presidential mandate. And as the man who, under the influence of Nicolas Hulot, had organised the 'Grenelle' environmental summit in France and attempted to set up a superministry of the environment with far-reaching powers, it was also a question of personal pride.

As France's permanent representative to Brussels, Pierre Sellal, tells it, Sarkozy 'spent hours negotiating with the Poles, the Czechs, the Slovaks and Angela Merkel, accepting compromises in a bid to persuade them to seal the deal.'[17] The French President had the support of a ministerial duo, Jean-Louis Borloo and Nathalie Kosciusko-Morizet. France even stood up to Angela Merkel when the German Chancellor, doubtless

---

17   Catherine Nay, 'Le "grand moment" de la présidence de l'Union européenne, en 2008', 28 February 2012, www.lexpress.fr.

facing pressure from the heads of leading German companies – not least Jürgen Grossmann, the charismatic boss of RWE – called for the free allocation of pollution rights to electricity firms to be maintained.

At nine o'clock that morning, the EU leaders had 'a mediocre hotchpotch of compromises' on the table. Pierre Sellal takes up the story again:

> Sarkozy said to me: 'We have to get this over by lunchtime.' I replied: 'Mr President, we have to allow the delegations at least ten minutes to read the text.' He shot back: 'No way. We start now; sit down next to me.' We had scarcely got further than page three when hands were going up everywhere. The government leaders were out of their depth. They were all proposing amendments suggested by their technical advisors. I slid him counter-arguments on pieces of paper. He slid them back, saying: 'No, we're moving right along.' With unbelievable chutzpah, he shouted everyone down. If anyone so much as lifted a finger, he rebuffed them. Everyone around the table was left shell-shocked, while he charged forward. An hour and a half later, we had got through all thirty pages. At which point he gave a broad smile, and announced: 'Well, since I can see we're all agreed, let's sign it.' And do you know what happened? Everybody stood up – and applauded. It was literally a standing ovation. Everyone was happy to be finishing on a positive note. And they all signed, somehow happy to have been dragged kicking and screaming to do so. That's Sarkozy for you.[18]

And so it was that Nicolas Sarkozy's leadership enabled the Climate and Energy Package to be concluded. But at what cost? He had run roughshod over the joint decision-making process with an immediate consequence: significant amendments by the European Parliament concerning the EU carbon market[19] and burden-sharing[20] were

---

18   Ibid.
19   The EU's CO_2 emissions trading system, set up in 2005. The failure of the system is described in Chapter 6, pp. 76–94.
20   Burden-sharing is a system of sharing between member states that determines the greenhouse gas emission reduction levels to be achieved in sectors not subject to the ETS system, such as transportation, farming and construction.

summarily dismissed by the heads of state and government. This was to be a disastrous precedent in energy policy governance. Ever since, every time a government is afraid of being in the minority at the Council of Ministers in a qualified majority vote, it kicks the dossier upstairs to the European Council, where decisions by heads of state and government must be unanimous. On the face of it, the adoption of the Climate and Energy Package represented major progress in terms of content, but it bore within it the seeds of the energy policy renationalisation that reached its apogee in 2014.

The highly sensitive context in which this package was adopted also needs to be kept in mind. The US bank Lehman Brothers had been declared bankrupt just three months earlier, triggering a global economic and financial crisis from which the EU has yet fully to recover. Fortunately, nobody had as yet realised the scope of the consequences. Adoption of the Climate and Energy Package was facilitated by the momentum created by Al Gore's 2006 film *An Inconvenient Truth* and favourable media coverage of the issue. It was then or never. Witness the instinct to withdraw behind national lines which was prompted when the crisis really impacted Europe.

This set of legislation was the practical culmination of an examination of European energy policy following Energy Commissioner Andris Piebalgs's 2006 Green Paper, and of EU climate policy in the wake of Environment Commissioner Stavros Dimas's 2006 annual Environment Policy Review. Andris Piebalgs is an experienced politician and former minister in Latvia. He also led the EU accession negotiations of his country. He took office as EU commissioner in November 2004 with the energy portfolio, as successor to Loyola de Palacio. Dimas and Piebalgs agreed to put in place the instruments required to achieve the 20-20-20 targets for 2020:[21] a 20 per cent reduction in energy consumption, a 20 per cent decrease in CO_2 emissions from 1990 levels, and a 20 per cent increase in renewables in end-use energy consumption.

---

21   These targets were approved by the EU Council in March 2007.

As a result, the 2020 Climate and Energy Package included the second Renewable Energy Directive, a revision of the directive governing the EU carbon market, a decision on burden-sharing by member states to cut emissions in sectors not covered by the EU carbon market, a directive on geological storage of CO_2, another on fuel quality and a regulation on CO_2 emissions by passenger cars. The instruments making it possible to achieve the 20 per cent energy efficiency target in view of 2020 forecasts – the only non-binding target – were to arrive a little later, with the revision of directives covering energy labelling, eco-design, and building energy performance, along with a new energy efficiency framework directive.

Renewable energy work: just in time

The Renewable Energy Directive was one of the flagship measures in the Climate and Energy Package negotiated during the French presidency of the EU. A few days before that crucial European Council meeting, I had finalised the negotiations on the Renewable Energy Directive, for which I was rapporteur in the European Parliament. It was vital for this work to be concluded ahead of the European Council meeting, as otherwise we ran the risk of opening up sensitive issues and tying the fate of this key legislation to the outcome of haggling between EU leaders, from whom unanimity was required. It would certainly have been weaker as a result. The completed preparations allowed the directive to be incorporated directly into the Climate and Energy Package adopted in December 2008, with not a single change to the version on which the Parliament and the Council had agreed a few days beforehand. This was a relief, to put it mildly. We had succeeded in outmanoeuvring Silvio Berlusconi, who wanted to exercise his veto at the Council to require a review clause. This would undoubtedly have weakened the impact of the legislation.

In actual fact, the development of this directive was the fruit of remarkable mutual understanding on the part of the European Parliament and the presidency of the Council of Ministers. Jean-Louis Borloo, Minister for Ecology under Nicolas Sarkozy, put it this way to me: 'Turmes, you make a run for it; I'll cover you!' He supported me pushing Europe's ambitions as far as possible when it came to green energy. By encouraging renewables from the vantage point of Brussels, EU provisions could be imposed in France. He was well aware that in France, where both the left and right wings of the establishment are pro-nuclear, he would not have obtained as much in favour of renewables.

The British, meanwhile, did not want a nationally binding target for renewable energy – the key issue at stake in this legislation – and so obstructed negotiations. But the circumstances allowed this opposition to be overcome: after some domestic reorganisation, a new ministry was set up in the UK, the Department of Energy and Climate Change (DECC), aimed at bringing energy policy and climate policy closer together, and the young Ed Miliband was placed at its head. He helped us reach a compromise: it was agreed that the huge Severn estuary barrage, for which an investment decision had to be made before the expiry of the directive on 31 December 2020 but whose completion would fall after the deadline, could be counted in the UK's 2020 targets. In exchange, he gave his consent to a binding target, against the views of his own administration.

The nuclear lobby makes a play

This part of the story began in March 2006, on the eve of Commissioner Andris Piebalgs's publication of his Green Paper on energy, when his deputy chief of staff Christopher Jones replaced overnight the concept of 'renewable energies' with 'low-carbon technologies' in the text. This was nonsense systemically, and a tweak that would have placed nuclear power on the same footing as renewables. I therefore leapt into the breach to explain that having low-carbon technology targets in the electricity sector could not possibly suffice when it came to combating climate change. It would be better to have an across-the-board target for cutting greenhouse gas emissions, in addition to a specific target for the development of renewables. Over the following months, we managed to persuade Commissioners Piebalgs and

Dimas of the need for specific targets and legislation for the climate, renewables and energy efficiency – the celebrated '20-20-20' for 2020.

However, the nuclear lobby did not disarm. Ahead of the European Council meeting of 8–9 March 2007, held under the German presidency of the EU and dealing with the roadmap for renewable energy published by the Commission in January, Jacques Chirac suddenly became the nuclear industry's chief lobbyist. He wanted nuclear power to be considered a renewable source due to its low greenhouse gas emissions. And so he made the following play: 'France has insisted on renewable energy being placed in the broader framework of low-carbon energy, including clean coal, which still requires a certain amount of investment, and nuclear power.' In response, Angela Merkel clarified the issue, stating that nuclear power is not a renewable. 'We have fought long and hard for that; it is important for renewable energy to mean renewable energy, and nothing else,' thundered the German Chancellor.[22] And so it was that the Council instructed the European Commission to submit a directive devoted to renewable energy alone, and not low-carbon energy.

Guarantees of origin in exchange for cooperation mechanisms
One year later, on 23 January 2008, the Commission presented its draft directive. One major piece of progress worth noting is a binding national target for each member state determined mostly on the basis of GDP, but also taking into account each country's starting point and potential. Less encouragingly, the draft also saw the return of an old idea from the late-1990s that had previously been killed off by de Palacio. This was the harmonisation of support systems across the EU, this time concealed in a maze of technobabble known as 'tradable guarantees of origin'. I have never believed in this costly and volatile system.[23] Within the Parliament's negotiation mandate, the MEPs were swayed by my arguments and threw out this measure.

To win over the co-legislator (the Council of Energy Ministers),

---

22   Reported by Corinne Lepage in *La Vérité sur le nucléaire: le choix interdit*, Albin Michel, 2011.
23   See Chapter 9, p. 123.

I reached out to the German and Spanish governments, who at that time were championing renewables by means of their guaranteed price support schemes: EEG in Germany and a floating bonus in Spain. I met them with the Commission, since the latter was seeking to impose total harmonisation via tradable guarantees of origin market. At this informal meeting, we also won over the UK and Polish representatives who wanted to retain control of their territory and the organisation of their system. Thanks to their support, the majority went for the compromise put forward by the French presidency and Jean-Louis Borloo. The favoured line was that of binding national targets and the authorisation of national financial support schemes.

To nurture flexibility and optimise the deployment of renewables according to each country's potential, I made an additional proposal: 'cooperation mechanisms'. In the end, three of these were adopted:

- Joint support schemes, a system that was later to be used by Sweden and Norway; as a country belonging to the European Economic Area, the latter took on the EU legislation even though it is not part of the EU itself.
- Joint projects, with the idea that two or more countries could invest in major projects and split both the costs and the contributions to their respective national targets.
- Statistical transfers, allowing a member state that had exceeded its targets to 'sell' its surplus to any other member state that required it in order to achieve its own national targets.

It was this third scheme that gave rise to the most difficulties during negotiations. In July, the Council's working party dealing with energy reached an agreement on schemes allowing member states to carry out statistical transfers between underperforming countries and countries exceeding their targets. But at the very last minute, I discovered that two member states had other plans. The UK wanted to be able to include renewable projects anywhere in the world, for instance in Canada, India and China, which made a nonsense of the idea. Italy, meanwhile, was purportedly aiming to develop power lines to third countries – that is, countries outside the EU – invest in renewable energy there and repatriate green electricity. But the real aim of Italian firms Enel and Terna, with the backing of the Berlusconi administration, was to build large coal-fired power plants in Tunisia, Montenegro and Albania, thereby evading European carbon market requirements. So at the end of negotiations, we discreetly added a few technical conditions to restrict cooperation schemes to within the EU, and thereby close the loopholes that certain governments thought they had opened up. The Renewable Energy Directive thus dealt with the problem of imports from third countries.

Other sticking points: priority dispatch and biofuels
Two other problems still had to be dealt with: priority access of renewables to the grid and priority dispatch, as well as the question of biofuels.

Priority access and dispatch are a key part of the Renewable Energy Directive. These concepts refer to the legal obligation for electricity transmission system operators (TSOs), who are responsible for the system's balance, to draw firstly on renewable energy sources and only secondarily on conventional sources. This measure was harshly attacked by the European electricity oligopoly lobby, represented by the Eurelectric association. Very quickly, however, due largely to the Commission but also to certain member states, a balance was achieved that is still in place today: renewable energy benefits from priority access and dispatch provided that it does not compromise the balance of the electricity system. If excessive stress on the system is likely, grid operators are allowed to engage in restrictions (this is known as curtailment). In such cases, they are required to compensate renewable producers for the shortfall the latter incur. This compromise resulted in a very broad consensus in the European Parliament and the Council. In practice, it can be seen with hindsight that unfortunately, it is often misused under pressure from the nuclear and coal lobbies. In addition, the European Commission has not insisted strongly enough on member states applying it on the ground; the rules governing curtailment and compensation are not harmonised and national regulators are sometimes very indulgent in this respect. Inevitably, attacks by the oligopolies are continuing and even increasing, henceforth supported by the European association of transmission system operators (ENTSO-E), which, in October 2016, did not hesitate to take an opposing stand by calling to 'abolish priority dispatch for renewables'. Unexpectedly, in May 2017, ACER joined ENTSO-E in calling for a removal of priority dispatch. This is a crucial issue in the negotiations around the recast of the Renewable Energy Directive proposed by the Commission in November 2016 and is currently under examination in the Council and in the Parliament.

As to biofuels, I fought against the 10 per cent target. I did not score an outright victory – it was too important for France and its farming lobby – but we did achieve two significant improvements: an opening for electric mobility designed to deliver green electricity to power trains and vehicles, even if it took the 2016 diesel scandals to put an end to 'dieselmania' in Europe; and the introduction of ILUC, a binding method of calculating biofuels' carbon balance.

An ambitious scheme

And so it was that on 9 December 2008, three days before the European Council meeting, we finalised the agreement on the Renewable Energy Directive at the Council of Energy Ministers, a body that takes decision following the rule of qualified majority voting. Looking back at the last-minute haggling, including a great many concessions to Poland and the capitulation of the Parliament on the question of sectors not covered by the EU carbon market, I know I was right to make every effort to bring negotiations to a conclusion and not simply rely on the European Council, a body that takes decision following the rule of unanimity. My success owed much to the help of Hélène Pelosse, Jean-Louis Borloo's chief negotiator, and Urban Rid, who at that time was heading up negotiations on behalf of the German environment ministry.

We obtained a binding target of 20 per cent for the EU, shared out between member states on the basis of binding national targets. This was of utmost importance, because it immediately triggered huge investments in renewables. Even today, in its progress report the

Commission acknowledges the vital contribution of this ambitious governance mechanism on the development of the sector: 'a binding target has been the key driver for renewable energy capacity development in those member states that were previously less striving to develop their renewable energy potential.' Indeed, my involvement was not so much for the benefit of Germany, Denmark or Portugal, where energy transition has already commenced and is unstoppable; it was directed more at Poland, the UK, Romania, Bulgaria and other member states reluctant to make a stronger commitment in this direction.

A recovery programme for energy

In 2008, Europe was in the grips of economic crisis; there needed to be a response that supported both demand and consumption. In the US, President Barack Obama was able to engage a powerful, impactful stimulus policy because he controlled a federal budget equivalent to one quarter of the United States' GDP. In Europe, however, the problem was that the EU's budget accounts for only 1 per cent of Europe's wealth: not enough to make much of a difference when it came to kick-starting the economy and helping countries in difficulty.

Nevertheless, a number of measures were taken at the EU level. For instance, in December 2008, the European Council approved an increase in interventions by the European Investment Bank to the tune of €30 billion in 2009/2010, in particular to support renewable energy and clean transport and to benefit the automotive industry. It also approved the setting up of the 2020 European Fund for Energy, Climate Change and Infrastructure (the 'Marguerite fund'), in partnership with national sponsor banks, such as France's Caisse des Dépôts.

Investing in infrastructure

In addition, following a proposal by the European Commission, the heads of state and government approved a recovery programme devoted to energy worth some €4 billion, funded by the EU budget (with funds from the latter's unused portion). This programme was also used as a bargaining chip during negotiations on the Climate and Energy Package, with funds being preallocated to projects in various countries. At the end of the day, for the very first time, the Commission was providing direct funding for electricity and gas infrastructure works, which makes a lot of sense. With respect to gas, it was important to respond to the crisis between Russia and Ukraine, which led to supply problems in Eastern European countries. Historically, gas has flowed from east to west through a number of pipelines, but in one direction only. Investment in transmission capacity in the opposite direction ('reverse flow') was therefore urgent. This relatively inexpensive investment will enable gas to be transported in both directions, supplying Eastern European countries if necessary.

The recovery programme ended up working well for electricity and gas infrastructures, giving rise to the infrastructures package and the Connecting Europe Facility funding mechanism. It was also to work well for offshore wind power despite a few hiccups, such as Kriegers Flak, a project between Denmark, Germany and Sweden which had a bumpy ride due to a lack of support from the Swedish conservative government in charge at the time. The situation improved and the Kriegers Flak project is now progressing well.

As for electricity, the establishment of the European electricity market required interconnections over and above minimum mutual assistance between the various systems: the raison d'être of UCTE, the predecessor of ENTSO-E. Indeed, in the post-war years Europe's electricity grid was built to ensure that each neighbouring country could compensate for the shutdown of a large power station (1,500MW). Today, this degree of interconnection is not enough to deliver optimised electricity transfers between countries. Consumption spikes have to be smoothed and, in addition, electricity produced using solar and wind power from a plethora of decentralised sources has to be distributed across the entire system.

CCS discussions

In actual fact, the tug-of-war over the priorities for this €4 billion fund was between energy efficiency (in particular, thermal renovation of buildings) and the CCS (carbon capture and storage) systems with which lignite- and coal-fired power stations could be equipped. One of the problems with CCS is that the projects are not yet mature and are liable to create only a few dozen generously paid positions for consultants rather than thousands of jobs, as could be the case in the construction industry. I therefore fought to secure €1.5 billion of funding for energy efficiency in view of the renegotiation of the Building Energy Performance Directive in 2009. We drew on the analysis of a great many economists who were predicting a decline in the construction of new buildings due to the crisis. Building renovation is an immediate source of job creation, which is vital to the success of a counter-cycle investment of public money to kick-start and support economic activity.

The problem was that José Manuel Barroso, at that time president of the European Commission, was being wooed by the coal lobby, who were seeking compensation for the Climate and Energy Package measures. From 2006 onwards, the coal men launched an intense lobbying campaign in favour of CCS, targeting the European Commission and the International Energy Agency (IEA) as well as Chris Davies, a UK MEP and the rapporteur of legislation designed to facilitate the deployment of CCS in Europe with the benefit of a simplified regulatory framework. The partisans of CCS highlighted the fact that major technology breakthroughs were to be expected and the IEA radically changed its CCS forecasts from one year to the next. The *World Energy Outlook*, the IEA's annual report, is the energy world's forecasting bible. In 2006, it saw CCS as a non-established technology still to be implemented, hence 'not taken into account in the Alternative Policy Scenario', which was better than the baseline scenario in climate terms. Just one year later, it forecast a very optimistic figure of 310GW of CCS installed in the electricity sector by 2030 as part of one of its modelling exercises known as 'scenario 450'. By 2008, it had boosted this figure to 363GW – a whopping 17 per cent increase. One observation says it all: the term 'CCS' appears thirty-one times in the 2006 edition of the *World Energy Outlook*, sixty-nine times in 2007, eighty-nine times in 2008 and 206 times in 2009, with a roughly proportionate amount of text devoted to it each time. What happened in such a short time? It wasn't a technological breakthrough. It was well-organised lobbying.

At the end of the day I did not succeed and CCS got €1.5 billion, backed by the UK as well as Dutch and French governments. The latter supported an industrial CO_2 capture and storage project at the Florange steelworks. However, the CCS funding was not put to good use; to date, no CCS project has been implemented. The Commission's progress report brooks no contradiction: out of the six projects commenced, three were abandoned prematurely, two have run into major difficulties, and only one is struggling on. The French project never saw the light of day at Florange as ArcelorMittal took the view that it was 'not technically or economically viable'. What a waste of EU money!

The European Parliament did, however, manage to secure €125 million for a European Energy Efficiency Fund. This was better than nothing, even if it was not enough to be much of a game-changer. Today the fund is working very well, as emphasised by the European Commission: 'the fund has progressively established a solid track record of profitable investments and will actively look for additional senior investors to leverage the EU contribution further.' This experience also inspired me recently to put forward a proposal to ring-fence some EU guarantees from the Juncker plan able to leverage up to €50 billion investment for energy efficiency.

Transport: a huge source of leverage

The transport sector is responsible for a huge quantity of greenhouse gas emissions. At present, it relies mostly on oil imported from the Middle East, Russia, Norway and Algeria. The Commission had fully understood the fundamental importance of decarbonising transport to combat climate change, which is why the 2020 Climate and Energy Package included three initiatives relating to transport and energy: regulations cutting passenger vehicle emissions, a revised fuel quality directive, and a binding target of 10 per cent biofuels as part of the Renewable Energy Directive.

Fuel quality

The revised Fuel Quality Directive was adopted thanks to a favourable set of circumstances. Initially, the directive was to deal only with the impacts of fuel combustion on air quality and the related SOx and NOx particle emissions. But in 2005, a seminar devoted to the revision of this directive suggested extending its scope to include greenhouse gas emissions. This drew inspiration from California, where there was already a low-carbon standard for fuel. The European target began to take shape: in Europe, CO_2 emissions from fuel would have to be reduced by 10 per cent.

Strangely enough, the oil and gas industry did not immediately oppose this project. It has to be said that it already had quite a lot on its plate defending itself against the EU regulations on engine emissions. So the Commission's proposal was published in January 2007 without too much difficulty, despite a rather botched impact study. Negotiations on this directive were tied to the Climate and Energy Package, and so it was officially adopted in April 2009. During the negotiations, the emissions reduction target was brought down to 6 per cent by 2020 but the directive included implementation measures for biofuels, thanks to which the European People's Party (EPP), the traditional party of farmers, lent its support.

It also introduced a requirement to reduce the carbon content of fuel, designed to eliminate Canadian tar sands from European imports. While the directive itself was on the progressive side, the industry got its own back at the level of the implementation measures: it fought to obtain a 'health check' on refining in Europe and to sabotage the European environmental legislation. Worst of all, European bosses threw their efforts into ensuring that the legislation in force did not require fuel suppliers to report the carbon footprint of their petrol and diesel imports, despite this clause being recommended by Article 7a of the directive, which was also fiercely contested by the refining industry, with plenty of support from Canada. Canada has not yet given up the fight, hoping that the conclusion of a free trade agreement with the EU (the CETA treaty, partly modelled after the TTIP with the United

States) would enable it to evade this type of environmental requirement. What will become of this treaty? Just as it appeared to be in the
bag, Paul Magnette and the parliament of Wallonia stepped in, and its
entry is now subject to examination of its accounting under EU law by
the European Court of Justice.

Vehicle emissions

As far as vehicle emissions go, the story began in 1995. Held in check
by Germany and its automotive industry promoted by Angela Merkel,
the environment minister at the time, the Commission abandoned its
designs on binding legislation in favour of a strategy intended to cut
passenger cars' CO_2 emissions due to a voluntary agreement with the
automotive sector. After this failed to materialise, the Commission
turned up the heat a little and adopted two papers in parallel in February 2007: the first presented the results of a fresh examination of EU
strategy for reducing CO_2 emissions from cars and light commercial
vehicles; the second, 'Cars 21', dealt with a competitive regulatory
framework for the automotive industry in the twenty-first century.

These two papers highlighted the fact that the target of 120g CO_2/km
set out in the 1995 voluntary agreement could not be achieved by 2012
without the adoption of additional measures. Consequently, in December
2007 the Commission proposed a regulation designed to restrict average engine emissions for new cars in the EU to 130g CO_2/km by 2012.
The legislative framework enshrined an integrated approach that still
applies today: this figure must be supplemented by an additional reduction of 10g CO_2/km achieved by means of other technical improvements
and the increased use of biofuels. The compromise achieved during
the European Council meeting of December 2008 opened the way for
the regulation to be officially adopted on 23 April 2009. But here again, the
devil was in the detail of the implementation text, which allowed the
automotive industry to cheat when it came to actual emissions, a sub-
terfuge that emerged at the same time as 'Dieselgate'.[24]

---

24   See Chapter 14, p. 181.

And so to biofuels

Biofuels are a highly political subject – and a highly divisive one. At first sight, they appear to be a powerful instrument to decarbonise transport, particularly road transport. But it is vital to consider the impact on the climate of indirect changes in land use due to biofuels, and thus to measure their total carbon footprint. According to estimates, the carbon footprint of some biofuels may be disastrous, with greenhouse gas emissions that may amount to as much as 80 per cent of the fossil fuels they are supposed to be replacing. The challenge is therefore to promote only those biofuels that do not enter into competition with food production, by focusing on specific crops which do not encourage deforestation and are based on agricultural residues: in short, sustainable biofuels.

During negotiations on the Renewable Energy Directive, Paul Hodson, the head of unit with responsibility for the biofuel question at the European Commission's Directorate-General for Energy (DG Ener), fought long and hard against the carbon footprint of biofuels being taken into account, after having won an internal victory over the Directorate-General for the Environment (DG ENV). How could he be overcome? In addition to support from experts and some NGOs, the help of Anders Wijkman,[25] rapporteur for the directive in the Parliament's Environment Committee, proved decisive. During the last two hours of negotiations in late November 2008, we finally secured a compromise that opened the door to a future introduction of the measurement of indirect land use change (ILUC) due to biofuels. Based on this success, a 7 per cent cap on first-generation biofuels was achieved in 2014, along with a preference for second-generation biofuels using waste from forestry, the paper industry and the food industry. Henceforth, I think that sustainable biofuels must come from bio-refineries or from closely monitored supplies of more sophisticated products such as enzymes.

---

25   Anders Wijkman is a Swedish conservative politician, a long-standing pro-climate activist and co-president of the Club of Rome. His Johnny Weissmuller-looking haircut was very much present in the corridors of the European Parliament between 1999 and 2009.

By developing ILUC, Europe has a method to apply to changes in land use for crops destined for energy, as well as a method for calculating the carbon footprint of all types of farming. At the time, the battle was mostly against importers from Brazil, Malaysia and Indonesia who had organised ferocious lobbying via their respective embassies. However, biofuels only account for 1 per cent of the greenhouse gas emissions entailed by changes in land use compared to farming as a whole. In other words, combating biofuels is important, but not the whole story. The real battle for farming with only a minimal impact on climate has only just begun. It will be even more difficult to fight, because it will involve addressing the issue of overconsumption of meat, and policy supporting intensive livestock farming, which is destroying the climate.

The 2010 Energy Performance of Buildings Directive: near-zero-energy buildings

If energy waste in Europe is to be avoided, it is vital to ensure that our buildings are not leaking energy in all directions. Astoundingly, the Climate and Energy Package of December 2008 did not include any new legislation on energy efficiency. This arrived later, with the second Energy Performance of Buildings Directive adopted in 2010, and the Energy Efficiency Directive adopted in 2012.

A step further

The first Energy Performance of Buildings Directive, adopted in 2002, was a watershed. The EU established transparency in building operating costs using the A to G labelling: the now-famous energy performance certificates, made mandatory for each sale, disposal or letting of a home, and accompanied by recommendations as to the best way of improving the efficiency of the home in question.

But the challenge of climate change called for further steps to be taken. The idea was to incite member states to do more to encourage the owners of houses and flats to renovate their homes. However, I rapidly ran into a major political problem. In December 2009, during the final negotiations on the Energy Performance of Buildings Directive, under the Swedish presidency, the Eastern European countries opposed any stringent measures on the grounds that there was no money on the table to fund the thermal renovation of existing buildings. We had nothing more than the €125 million in the Energy Efficiency Fund from the recovery programme, well below the sums actually required.

I quickly understood that aside from a few improvements, in particular as to the methods used to calculate the energy performance of buildings, we would not be able to gain much when it came to renovation. So I concentrated on new builds during negotiations. Sweden was very attached to its strict standards in this field, in place since the 1980s.

The Darmstadt pioneer

I knew that a major step forward in quality was possible for new builds as I had been following progress in this area since the early 1990s, when I organised a study trip to Darmstadt near Frankfurt. This city is the cradle of the energy revolution in the construction industry; indeed, the first four 'passive houses' were built there in 1991 by Professor Wolfgang Feist. Passive houses bring together all the ingredients of tomorrow's housing: orientation, so as to make the most of sunlight; thick insulation, using environmentally friendly materials; automatic ventilation; and – a little-known but vital detail to achieve zero-energy buildings – the elimination of all thermal bridges at all points. The result is a building that cuts energy requirements for heating by 90 per cent. The study trip made a great impact on me, as did Professor Feist's pioneering spirit. But I was even more impressed by his visionary character and his energy, obstinacy even, in the face of frontal attacks from the oil and gas lobby, as well as from a great many architects.

Today, the four passive houses in Darmstadt have given birth to a great many descendants and there are now tens of thousands of them across Europe. The dream has come true! This has made me immune to the accusation that it is technically impossible to achieve such a thing through EU legislation. In April 2016, I returned to the city to celebrate the twentieth anniversary of the Passivhaus Institut. It was an opportunity to take the measure of the phenomenal progress that has been accomplished in the space of two decades. Today, the institute has a worldwide reach, with a branch in Canada, another in the United States, one on its way in Morocco and, most importantly, one in China. There were over a thousand people in attendance for the twenty-fifth anniversary of the first passive house in Darmstadt, over 150 of whom were Chinese. It was there that I learned a new phrase in Mandarin: *bèidòngshì fángwū*, which means 'passive house'.

Winning minds

There was nothing in the Commission's draft directive about new builds. The Swedish government, which held the rotating presidency of the Council at that time, was originally championing 'low-energy buildings', a concept which other governments could accept, but the Commission had not prepared a precise definition to match in its text, so I thought we might as well go for 'near zero-energy'! I proposed a deal to the presidency, for which achieving agreement on this issue was a must; we could reach an agreement if the EU Council of Ministers accepted a clause on near-zero-energy buildings. My amendment was approved by the Parliament, and then by the governments. It was the last point of negotiations and, thanks to the political courage of the Swedish presidency, we thereby inaugurated a new regime for construction in Europe which will apply to all new builds from 1 January 2021. What is more, since 'near-zero-energy' is more restrictive than 'low-energy', it is to be hoped that there will be no cheating on the part of member states when it comes to measuring the energy performance of their buildings.

Once the directive had been adopted, we realised that we had achieved a paradigm shift: near-zero-energy buildings had become the standard for real estate developers, architects and engineers. It has been one of my greatest victories to date as an MEP. The leap is not only symbolic; it also aims to create an innovative home market allowing the EU industry to gain experience, offering them comparative advantage on the global market competition. The transition period (until 2021) leaves enough time for adaptation. The attitude of the gas lobby in this respect is worth noting: residential and tertiary heating accounted for 41 per cent of all gas use in Europe in 2014, compared to 23 per cent for electricity generation and 33 per cent for industry. Renovating buildings therefore has a direct impact on gas consumption. In the space of just one year, between 2014 and 2015, there was a 16 per cent drop in gas destined for residential and tertiary heating! While some of this drop can be attributed to weather conditions, in particular a milder winter, the rest is without doubt the consequence of the energy efficiency policies rolled out across Europe. In view of the decrease in the size of this pie, the gas industry has therefore set up ad hoc lobbies (GasNaturally and E-Gas) to prevent any ambitious energy efficiency targets seeing the light of day for 2030.

The 2012 Energy Efficiency Directive

Today, there are no end of conclusions from the Council of Energy Ministers and indeed from the European Council, in which energy efficiency is declared to rank highly in the EU's legislative and regulatory priorities. Politicians on all sides agree that it allows progress to be made on all fronts: security of supply, industrial competitiveness, cutting greenhouse gas emissions, innovation and, best of all, jobs. The fact remains, however, that achieving results when it comes to EU legislation has been quite a battle since EU leaders do not always walk the talk. Two years on from the Energy Performance of Buildings Directive, the adoption of the Energy Efficiency Directive was the theatre for a battle of epic proportions between the Parliament and the Council. This directive is twofold in nature: on the one hand, it establishes a general framework for all of the EU's efforts in this respect, including standards for household appliances, cars, trucks and other vehicles and buildings; on the other, it is also a directive that imposes measures, in other words a plethora of obligations and instruments to be implemented by governments to cut waste.

To begin with, we clashed about the target: should it be relative or absolute? Measured in which units? On the basis of primary or end use? We achieved a victory on one point: each country now has to convert its national target for primary energy into an absolute figure of energy savings, expressed in megajoules. However, we lost on another: member states remain free to set their own economy savings levels, making the European target of 20 per cent indicative only, and not binding.

Either way, with a stated aim of improving its energy efficiency by 20 per cent, the continent of Europe has set a transformation in motion. For the first time since the Second World War, economic growth and energy de-growth will be going hand in hand. By 2020, the EU's primary energy use should have decreased to 1,474Mtoe (or 1,078Mtoe of final energy): that's 368Mtoe – 20 per cent – lower than the baseline scenario forecast. How will it go about achieving such a result?

The main measure in the directive is the obligation for energy suppliers to ensure their clients achieve savings (Article 7). This requires anyone selling electricity, gas or oil to invest in the field. This in turn encourages energy providers to refocus on the business lines and industries of the future, such as energy services – a business that is both lucrative and virtuous for society as a whole. Despite this, some electricity companies have adopted a schizophrenic position. For instance, E.ON offers a wide range of energy services as part of its obligations in the UK, whereas in Germany, it fiercely fought to stop the government establishing an energy efficiency market and instead have it introduce some derogation. To offset the absence of such a market, Germany therefore finds itself having to put in place some fifty individual measures to achieve a similar result, adding considerably to the red tape. In an irony of history, some German MEPs are now attacking Brussels bureaucracy, despite the fact that their own government has largely contributed to its existence in this respect.

The directive also cements the marriage between industrial firms, with their huge potential for energy savings but short return on investment periods of some eighteen months, and the electricity companies, which normally have longer depreciation periods.

In Denmark, over 50 per cent of energy savings derive from

projects in industry and SMEs. This is a real asset for enterprise competitiveness that I would like to see transposed right across Europe.

Long-term strategies

40 per cent of energy demand in terms of heating and electricity comes from buildings. It is impossible to take up this challenge without having a long-term strategy. The statistics speak for themselves: almost 80 per cent of the buildings that will make up all real estate in 2050 are already in existence. The gains achieved with near-zero-energy buildings apply only to the other 20 per cent. This meant that major action on existing buildings is called for. As a result, during negotiations, we drafted an entirely new article: Article 4, which requires member states to develop a genuine long-term strategy. They must rank buildings and develop an appropriate strategy for various types of building: pre-war buildings must be distinguished from post-war buildings, blocks of flats from office blocks and so on.

This idea occurred to me after reading a study by German expert Karsten Neuhoff of the Climate Policy Initiative in Berlin. Published in September 2011, this paper explains that we need to go both faster (shifting up from an annual renovation rate of 1 per cent today to at least 3 per cent) and deeper, as the name of the concept, 'deep renovation', implies, by piggybacking on works scheduled for reasons of safety, comfort and aesthetics: 'Energy efficiency improvements in the residential building stock can be maximised if deep thermal retrofits are linked to general building retrofits that are pursued for other reasons, like the improvement of building appearance.' Indeed, major renovation works are generally carried out twice during a home's life cycle: once when a young family is building its nest, and for a second time when facilities are improved ahead of retirement and the twilight years. If renovation at these times is suboptimal – for instance, 10cm insulation instead of 25–30cm – a golden opportunity is lost for several decades. The authorities must do more not only to increase the number of renovations, but also to improve their quality.

In addition, Article 8 of the Directive also created an instrument to help industrial companies carry out audits in order to be able to identify where energy reduction potential lies. Unfortunately, here again the Council succeeded in reducing the scope of this article by exempting certain companies from these auditing obligations, albeit solely on the basis of their size and not that of energy use. Small firms may use a lot of energy but, if they are properly advised, they can also achieve major reductions in energy bills. I hope that the revision of the directive will allow for the extension of energy audit obligations and most importantly, since no stick works without a carrot, provide financial assistance to firms seeking to implement recommendations expressed by auditors. This would be a win-win situation: companies would slash their energy bills and improve competitiveness; service provider compensation could be partially pegged to the amount of savings achieved; and the climate would benefit from having fewer greenhouse gas emissions.

Articles 9–12, meanwhile, require energy firms to provide consumers with reliable means of knowing how much energy they are using, keeping them regularly informed, as well as giving them the possibility of individual metering. This provides consumers with information that was previously hidden from them.

Lastly, Article 15 marks the first appearance of load management (or demand-side management) in EU legislation, in the form of deferred or cancelled electricity use.[26] This has provided an opportunity for debating a holistic vision of the electrical system that includes demand, rather than focusing solely on the means of production. Henceforth, member states are required not to penalise load management when participating in the balancing market (which provides last-minute adjustment between electricity demand and supply), thus assigning a value to load management. In any event, this is the cheapest way of making a market flexible and capable of adjusting to the domination of renewables in electricity production.

---

26   For more details, see Part Two, Chapter 21 on the electricity sector, p. 289.

Unlikely alliances

During the negotiations on this legislation, we did not have the support of our traditional German ally. The rising star of the German Liberal party, Philipp Rösler, was in the driving seat at their economy ministry at that time. Rösler was very close to the interests of the large energy firms, very liberal ideologically, and less pro-European than his predecessors; he sought to retain control of domestic energy policy. As rapporteur for this directive, I benefited greatly from a happy coincidence: the negotiations were largely conducted under the Danish presidency during the first half of 2012. Denmark is a real leader in energy efficiency, in particular thanks to Svend Auken, its legendary environment and energy minister, whose two-metre frame towered over the Council of Ministers between 1993 and 2001. Martin Lidegaard was his worthy successor. He held firm in the face of the assaults launched by certain member states against Article 7, the heart of the directive. And in the absence of any leadership from Germany, the UK found itself in the position of being able to tip the scales either way. Thanks to the Liberal Democrat duo consisting of government minister Ed Davey in London and Euro-MP Fiona Hall in Brussels, we managed to overcome the misgivings of the UK administration.

The battle was equally harsh in the Parliament. The conservatives were represented at the negotiating table by German Christian Democrat Markus Pieper. In an alliance with the UK Tories and the communists, he was potentially in a position to form a majority against the alliance of greens, social democrats and liberals. A stroke of luck rendered him unable to do so: the surprise defection of the Italian nationalists. Led by Fiorello Provera, the mayor of a small town in northern Italy whose public buildings he was proud to have had renovated, the Northern League MEPs suddenly decided to support the directive's aims with regard to energy efficiency – and provide the text with a slim majority.

So, in the end, daring won the day. The Climate and Energy Package bore fruit, over and above all initial expectations. Based on bold legislative proposals from commissioners Piebalgs and Dimas under the efficient leadership of Jean-Louis Borloo for the French presidency, and thanks to an alliance of progressive national governments, the EU established one of the most ambitious legal frameworks to fight climate change. This victory was obtained against powerful conservative forces. At the same time, another package of European legislation on the internal market for electricity was another front on which the energy companies were to take up arms.

CHAPTER 4

DEREGULATION, REGULATION AND REFORM OF THE INTERNAL ENERGY MARKET

At the turn of the millennium, the electricity market was like something straight out of the Wild West. Inspired by hard-core neoliberals, the deregulation that began with the first EU directive on the subject in 1996 established a situation of completely open competition. The EU set up cross-border markets without any consideration as to oversight or regulation.

This state of affairs triggered a full-scale 'gold rush', as electricity firms scrambled to achieve the critical mass required to prevent them from being the target of predators. An unprecedented wave of mergers and acquisitions resulted in concentration of the sector in Europe. Suez bought out Electrabel then merged with GDF to produce GDF-Suez, which went on to become Engie. Scarcely had E.ON been created out of the merger of Bayernwerk and PreussenElektra than it merged in turn with Ruhrgas to become E.ON/Ruhrgas. EDF, meanwhile, bought out London Electricity followed much later by British Energy. E.ON and RWE (Innogy) subsequently followed EDF into the UK market. Vattenfall and EDF also set up operations in Germany while EDF became involved in Italy, taking out a stake in Edison. E.ON and ACS engaged in a battle of epic proportions to acquire Endesa, which ended up belonging to Enel ... and so it went on.

Unbridled deregulation in the wake of the first 1996 package

As a newly minted MEP in 1999, I was keen to establish something akin to order in this Wild West. On 13 March 2001, the Commission published a draft directive to alter the organisation of the internal market – a text for which I was to become rapporteur to the European Parliament a few months later. As I explained in my report, the anarchical deregulation of the market had led to distortions in competition in the energy sector: 'The ten largest companies control over 50 per cent of the EU's market; other mergers are planned, and within a few years, the market is likely to be dominated by between five and eight firms.' In view of this, I wrote, 'it is especially important to avoid any situation in which there is market domination, given that electricity cannot be stored and that the possibility of exercising market power in this sector is therefore greater than in the case of other commodities'.

To illustrate the contradiction between enhanced competition and the formation of oligopolies, I asked a German expert from the Öko-Institut, Felix Matthes, to conduct research into the degree of market concentration on the basis of a method well known to M&A experts: the Herfindahl Hirschman index. His findings were that most domestic markets were so concentrated that EDF, E.ON, RWE, Iberdrola, Endesa or Electrabel were in an oligopolistic position. These organisations therefore needed to be broken up and split into smaller firms. I quickly understood that the European Commission saw things very differently: rather than splitting up these companies, it wanted to incite more competition between them by having cross-border markets with better interconnection. This led to the idea of separating the management, and indeed the ownership, of transmission and distribution networks from the business of producing electricity. The Commission also wanted to establish national regulators; although they were independent from their respective governments, the latter were very often shareholders in their 'national champion', and thus both judge and jury.

As part of these negotiations, I had the following illustration published. As things turned out, it made a lot more of a splash than I had dared hope for.

Big fish, small pond © CLAUDE TURMES

The market concentrated still further, with bigger fish swallowing smaller fish until only EDF and E.ON were left. A few months after its publication, one of the big fish whose disappearance I had anticipated, British Energy, went bankrupt, a victim of this infernal machination.

2003 and the 'second package': a first step towards reregulation

The new directive adopted in 2003, after two years of negotiations, represented a first attempt at reregulation with a view to correcting the excessive deregulation of 1996. It introduced greater transparency in the information supplied to consumers, notably with the introduction of detailed bills that had to specify the carbon footprint of the electricity used and its origin (gas, coal, nuclear power or renewables). It also established the organisational separation of integrated companies. Lastly, it introduced genuinely independent national regulators, whereas the 1996 directive had simply specified 'appropriate and efficient mechanisms for regulation', a relatively vague turn of phrase.

During the negotiations, I received support from two European Parliament heavyweights: German Social Democrat Rolf Linkohr, something of a godfather to energy between 1984 and 2004, and the

British Liberal Democrat Nick Clegg, who later entered the Cameron government as Deputy Prime Minister in the coalition. The European Parliament was thus able to throw its full weight into the negotiations. As a result, thanks to the European Commission and government support from the UK and Scandinavian countries, we overcame the misgivings of the German government and its economy minister, Wolfgang Clement, who was bitterly opposed to any independent regulation, as well as those of the French government, determined to preserve EDF's monopoly at all costs.

Local authorities ruled offside

At that time, a majority of MEPs and member states were of the opinion that the supposed benefits of deregulation should not be restricted to the wholesale market, but also serve to open up the retail market. I was not convinced of this. Rather, I was keen to establish a genuinely competitive wholesale market before taking things any further. And let's face it; individual clients are incapable of having an impact such that they can negotiate rates with their supplier. The outcome of this was the emergence of the idea of giving local authorities the power to negotiate the supply of energy on behalf of their territory to obtain better prices and services. For instance, Sheffield (a city dear to Nick Clegg's heart) would be able to negotiate on behalf of its 500,000 inhabitants. Similarly, Sipperec (a district authority for municipalities immediately around Paris) would be able to negotiate on behalf of 10 million inhabitants in the Ile-de-France region.

When it came to the ITRE Committee vote, we lost this amendment by a mere two votes. Throughout my entire parliamentary career, I had never seen so many French MEPs in the chamber as I did that day. That was when I first became aware of the lobbying abilities of EDF and GDF, who were of course keen to have a market divided into individual clients without any bargaining power. In the end, the text of the directive included a vaguely defined option of individual clients grouping together – a measure that did not produce the hoped-for results.

Nuclear money

I also suffered another defeat during the negotiations for this directive; this time relating to decommissioning funds. To my mind, the real question in view of the consolidation in the sector was the following: where was the money for the mergers coming from? How could utilities have built up the huge war chest required to take part in this massive game of Monopoly? The answer was not a welcome one: the billions of euros needed had in part been plundered from nuclear decommissioning funds. In other words, the money the companies were supposed to be adding to each electricity bill to fund the decommissioning of nuclear power plants was in fact being used to satisfy their expansionary policies. The nuclear piggybank was being invested in assets rather than being placed to one side and managed responsibly, as taxpayers were entitled to expect. To make matters worse, the larger an operator's decommissioning fund was, the greater their scope for buying out competitors.

During the final negotiations on this directive, I suggested an amendment that would require operators to set up funds specifically dedicated to nuclear decommissioning separately to their other commercial activities. This proposal was taken up by the European Parliament. However, François Lamoureux, the European Commission's director-general for Energy, was against the idea: 'It can't be done: this complex problem cannot be resolved by means of a single paragraph in a directive.' Backed by the French, the Germans and the British, the Council also rejected the proposal. Negotiations therefore ended with a victory for the nuclear lobby, at least in that respect.

The Commission contented itself with producing a non-binding written declaration, appended to the Electricity Directive, in which it undertook to address the issue. I had been outmanoeuvred by François Lamoureux and the pro-nuclear wing of the Commission, from the UK, France and even Germany, where Jürgen Trittin, the Green minister with responsibility for the environment and nuclear safety, was bound by the terms of the agreement to abandon nuclear power that had been negotiated at the national level. Fifteen years on, the Commission is still refusing to implement this written commitment.

Where has the money for decommissioning gone?

The problem for nuclear operators is one of cash. They do not have enough resources to decommission their power plants, as was expressly acknowledged in the most recent 'PINC'[27] report, published by the European Commission in April 2016. As things stand, Europe's nuclear power plants are on average 64 per cent of the way through their life cycle, but only 52 per cent of the funding theoretically required to pay for their decommissioning and waste management has been set aside.[28] Worse still, this European average includes the specific case of the United Kingdom, which lays claim to 100 per cent available funding for the nuclear piggybank (due to the fact that British taxpayers will be footing the bill). Without the UK, the average across Europe for available funding would be just 45 per cent.

As we have seen, to date these funds have been deliberately neglected and run down, and operators have resorted to an unacceptable form of blackmail: according to them, the only way of wiping this huge slate clean is to extend the lifespan of nuclear power plants in order to bring in more cash.

Given this state of affairs, the question arose as to what would happen if a company were to go bankrupt. Would taxpayers end up paying for decommissioning? As things turned out, the answer came sooner rather than later. In 2004, UK electricity firm British Energy went bankrupt. It became apparent that the decommissioning funds had disappeared, and with them, billions of pounds that had been levied on UK taxpayers' electricity bills. Today, these same taxpayers are paying all over again. Fifteen years of stonewalling later, it's worth taking a closer look at the budget of the UK's Department of Energy and Climate Change: in 2013/2014, 95.8 per cent of it was earmarked for funding the national decommissioning authority in order to pay off the nuclear debt, a staggering £7.5 billion for that

---

27   The Nuclear Illustrative Programme (PINC) is a document published at regular intervals by the European Commission pursuant to the Euratom treaty. It reports on nuclear power investments in Europe.

28   'EU expects large nuclear new-build programme despite escalating costs', 19 April 2016, energypost.eu.

year alone.[29] What is more, the independent UK authority responsible for decommissioning has estimated the total cost of decommissioning the Sellafield plant (of which the French equivalent is the La Hague reprocessing plant) at some £83 billion, with most of this bill to be footed by the taxpayer.

In a functioning market system, the funds for nuclear decommissioning should be set aside as is the case in Belgium, which achieved this in 2003 thanks to the political courage of ecologist Olivier Deleuze. During his time as Secretary of State for Energy, he set up an independent body responsible for managing these funds.

Germany, meanwhile, will be closing its last nuclear power stations in 2022. However, there are doubts about the capacity of electricity firms to honour their debt. To defuse the political time bomb ticking away in this affair, Chancellor Angela Merkel went so far as to make an appeal to her worst enemy, Jürgen Trittin; she needed the help of the German anti-nuclear movement's figurehead to establish a political consensus. The Trittin Commission's proposal, which will most likely be adopted by the government, upholds that operators should take on responsibility for decommissioning nuclear power stations and the related funding. However, intermediate and final waste storage, at a cost currently estimated at €50 billion, will be handled by a state fund to which electricity firms must pay in a total of €23 billion.

The situation in France is far more serious, because decommissioning costs are systematically underestimated there. Indeed, the cost disparities are clear in the Commission's most recent 'PINC' report. France has the lowest estimate in Europe – €300 million per reactor – as compared to €1.1 billion per reactor in Germany. In all, according to EDF estimates France puts the total cost of decommissioning its nuclear fleet at €22.6 billion, whereas it could be as high as €75 billion or more. What is more, France has unfortunately not given any official estimate of the cost of dismantling other complex nuclear sites managed by Areva or its Atomic Energy Commission (CEA), such as

---

29   'Analysis: How DECC spends its annual budget', 13 May 2015, www.carbonbrief.org.

the La Hague reprocessing plant, the Marcoule industrial site or the Pierrelatte enrichment facility. Have Areva and CEA been as reckless as EDF when it comes to decommissioning funds? That is a question to which we would dearly love to know the answer.

In Sweden, there is a commission with responsibility for estimating the costs of decommissioning and waste management. Today, Swedish operators must pay into a fund to the tune of €4/MWh following a decision taken by the Swedish government in 2014. This contribution is set to be increased, so as to ensure that enough cash is on hand when the time comes. The increase will most probably be offset by a decrease in Sweden's specific nuclear tax, in force for several years now, although it will be pegged to installed capacity rather than output. I support this approach, since it is more respectful of taxpayers and implements the 'polluter pays' principle.

Within the EU, each operator ought to be required to supply the necessary funds throughout the planned operational lifetime of power plants; in other words, during the forty-year lifespan of a reactor. This is one of the criteria if the European electricity market is to stop offering preferential treatment to nuclear power.

2009: the 'third package' and the separation of network assets

In 2009, the new review of the electricity market directive continued to redress the balance between deregulation and regulation. Negotiated under the French presidency at the same time as the Climate and Energy Package, this third package, covering the internal market, contained a 'Gazprom clause' designed to prevent the Russian giant from dominating the European market through the systematic acquisition of gas network assets.

In the electricity sector, the battle focused on separating the activities of production and grid management. This had already been at the heart of the debate on the 2003 directive, and the tone had not improved since. The struggle between vertically integrated companies, supported by their respective governments, and the majority of MEPs in favour of asset-based separation (so-called 'ownership unbundling'), was finally resolved by a heavy-handed intervention on the part of the Directorate-General for Competition (DG Comp). A few days before negotiations were finalised at the European Council meeting in December 2008, a communiqué from DG Comp came like a bolt from the blue: in exchange for dropping the inquiry underway into a possible abuse of dominant position on the German electricity market, E.ON would agree to hive off 5GW of production capacity and, more importantly, its electricity transmission network. The reaction in Brussels was one of astonishment, while in Berlin, consternation reigned supreme. The German government felt betrayed by its own energy firms.

In fact, this unexpected announcement had been orchestrated by a duo of cunning tacticians: Neelie Kroes, Commissioner for Competition, who later gained notoriety in the Panama Papers affair, and her director-general, Philip Lowe. Their backroom strong-arming forced E.ON to divest some of its assets in order to avoid proceedings that threatened to result in an extremely heavy fine. This was the first in a series of asset disposals on the German market. One year later, in November 2009, E.ON made good on its promise, selling the 10,000km or so of high-tension lines it owned to Dutch grid operator TenneT. The result was the emergence of the first cross-border grid operator, linking the North Sea to the Alps. A few months later, in March 2010, Vattenfall sold its network to the Belgian firm Elia. Despite having been fiercely resisted by the Germans, the separation of assets was underway – as was the Europeanisation of network operators. This was further encouraged by the establishment of two cooperative organisations for the latter, ENTSO-E for electricity and ENTSO-G for gas. Indeed, cross-border transfers were increasing as the market became Europeanised, and with them, cross-border conflicts. The regulators therefore needed to adjust to this new state of affairs.

Brunetta versus Meroni
As part of this third package for the internal market, the Commission suggested the creation of an EU-wide regulator, akin to other

European agencies responsible for regulating sectors such as telecoms, shipping, rail transport and so on. The Parliament was also in favour of this decidedly Europhile idea defended by rapporteur Renato Brunetta, a dyed-in-the-wool Berlusconi partisan. The major hurdle was the European Court of Justice's Meroni Ruling, a leftover piece of legislation that set a precedent for how EU institutions may delegate their powers to another entity. The Court found that any such delegation was legal only if it pertained to 'strictly limited powers of enforcement' and not 'a discretionary power implying a wide margin of discretion'. It was not the strongest of legal arguments, but member states, France and Germany to the fore, brandished this ruling to conceal their political opposition behind a veneer of law. The Parliament and the Council eventually agreed on an honourable compromise and resolved to establish the Agency for the Cooperation of Energy Regulators (ACER), headquartered in Ljubljana.

Under pressure from the City, the UK leapt into the breach once again in 2012, disputing the EU regulation that established a European Securities and Markets Authority, set up by the EU as one of its responses to the financial crisis of 2008. In a 2014 ruling, the European Court of Justice threw out the UK government's case and clarified the Meroni ruling, opening up the way for EU regulatory authorities to be set up, provided that their remit was precisely defined and open to appeal.

The choice of director for ACER was once again the theatre of a bitter tug-of-war between the European Parliament and the Council. The member states were keen to have a director without technical strengths and close to national interests. They therefore backed the candidacy of a former MEP, Bulgarian Atanas Paparizov. The latter having been largely discredited due to his pro-Gazprom political stance, however, the Parliament objected and eventually achieved the appointment of Italian Alberto Pototschnig, one of Europe's leading experts in the field, with twenty years' worth of experience in the sector. ACER gradually made a place for itself in the world of European energy, in particular through the establishment of network codes designed to harmonise the internal electricity and gas markets. The Commission is even recommending broadening its powers as part of the forthcoming review of its status.

While harmonisation of the entire electricity market is constantly improving, its physical integration remains a challenge. The high-tension lines between various member states built in the wake of the Second World War were not designed to facilitate commercial transfers. Rather, they were intended solely to ensure emergency supplies in the event of a major incident affecting a power plant in a neighbouring country. The EU therefore embarked on an ambitious programme to extend interconnections for electricity and gas. The challenge was taken up by Günther Oettinger, by dint of transforming the programme for trans-European energy infrastructures into the Connecting Europe Facility (CEF), an instrument set up in December 2013 with €5.8 billion of funding for 2014–2020. I clearly recall the first time I met him, in the office of MEP Rainer Wieland. Oettinger hailed from the same city as Wieland, Stuttgart, and also from the same political family. Wieland had put his office at Oettinger's disposal to help him establish contacts after his surprise appointment as European commissioner. The newcomer and I were from opposite ends of the political spectrum, but I had put some thought into finding a topic on which we could agree: supply networks! With this in mind, I came to the meeting with a fairly visionary brochure on interconnections of the future for Europe, encompassing connections to offshore wind farms. I turned out to have hit the mark. His eyes lit up. And at the end of the meeting, he was happy to pocket the brochure.

Twilight falls

Despite a market that was only half-regulated and the ongoing market distortions, by 2012 the EU had a legal arsenal to push for energy transition in Europe. The large number of instruments directed at energy efficiency opened up the possibility of decoupling economic growth from energy use. Renewables could gradually come to replace Europe's legacy nuclear and coal-fired power plants. The ETS, meanwhile, was designed to accelerate the decline of coal and promote electricity generated by more flexible gas turbines, in addition to solar and wind power. Despite distortions such as the non-internalisation of the full costs of nuclear power, the electricity market began to stabilise. A big step had indeed been taken towards a new energy model in Europe. But were these victories complete? Following their defeat in the Climate and Energy Package, would the gas, coal and nuclear lobbies embrace the winds of change, or prepare their revenge?

The following years were to be characterised by a climate that was far less favourable to energy transition against a backdrop of economic crisis, the resounding failure of the Copenhagen climate conference in 2009, and a major nuclear accident in Fukushima in 2011. And so it was that the 'Enlightenment' years gave way to the 'Dark Ages', characterised by reduced ambitions for renewables and energy efficiency, and by a tendency towards the renationalisation of energy policy, as promoted by certain member states.

CHAPTER 5

FROM COPENHAGEN TO FUKUSHIMA: ENERGY TRANSITION ADRIFT

On 18 December 2009, in the diminutive Arne Jacobsen room at the Bella conference centre in Copenhagen, twenty-five world leaders met in an attempt to reach a decision to continue fighting climate change. The Europeans were out in force, including Angela Merkel, Nicolas Sarkozy, Gordon Brown, Fredrik Reinfeldt and Jens Stoltenberg from Sweden and Norway respectively, the Danish president of the COP15 conference, Lars Løkke Rasmussen, and European Commission president José Manuel Barroso. Also in attendance at this 'mini twenty-five-nation summit' were US President Barack Obama and Indian Prime Minister Manmohan Singh, but not the Chinese Premier, Wen Jiabao, who snubbed the meeting, choosing rather to send his foreign affairs minister He Yafei, with whom he stayed in touch by phone.

Upon their arrival, the leaders of the 190 countries party to the United Nations Framework Convention on Climate Change (UNFCCC) had discovered the (rather rotten) fruit of ten days' worth of technical negotiations: a confused, 200-page document in which there were no specific targets, no deadlines, no extension of the Kyoto protocol and, most critically of all, no mention of verification of emissions reduction commitments. As a result, the COP15 negotiations got off to an unsteady start, with the Danish presidency out of its depth and incapable of asserting leadership.

Der Spiegel obtained access to the recordings of the proceedings, revealing just how these last-ditch attempts to boil down the final COP15 document to a few key pages played out. The Europeans were pushing for a commitment to reduce worldwide emissions by 2050 to half those of 1990 in order to limit the forecast increase in air temperatures to 2°C. But in truth, the meeting was an attempt to achieve the impossible: a commitment from developing countries, first and foremost China and India, to reduce their greenhouse gas emissions in parallel with industrialised nations. This suggestion was met with a categorical refusal.

Copenhagen, December 2009: world leaders trying to find a way out at COP15
© STEFFEN KUGLER / BUNDESREGIERUNG / AFP

Any commitment by the industrialised nations, meanwhile, would involve the United States having to do their bit; but Obama, bogged down in the adoption of his flagship reform of healthcare, was opposed by Congress on matters of climate. The hopes of European leaders were therefore dashed: in view of the refusals on the part of India and China, the US President sidestepped the issue, suggesting instead that consultations should continue in a different setting. The Chinese negotiator requested that proceedings be suspended.

After that, the mini-summit never resumed. India had already booked another meeting room, where the American, Chinese, Indian, Brazilian and South African leaders met to conclude an agreement behind the Europeans' back. The latter had no option but to sign this text, which did little more than acknowledge the powerlessness of the countries in question to agree on the issue of combating climate change. The best the agreement could come up with was a statement of principle that asserted the need to restrict the rise in temperatures to no more than 2°C by the end of the century. However, it did not give any details of how to achieve this, and postponed any adoption of a treaty on the issue.

Hardly a surprise

Expectations had nevertheless been extremely high for Copenhagen if the events surrounding the COP15 conference and the mobilisation of NGOs were anything to go by. In particular, the well-known report published by Nicholas Stern[30] in 2006 was still at the forefront of people's minds. The report put a price on failure to act with regard to the climate, giving figures for the economic and environmental costs of climate change amounting to 5–20 per cent of GDP. The price of combating global warming came to 1 per cent of GDP. In other words, each tonne of CO_2 would 'cost' \$85 worth of damage, but could be avoided with an investment of \$25. Based on this observation, Nicholas Stern suggested three avenues of action: carbon pricing, encouraging technical innovation and developing energy efficiency.

In 2009, politicians from all over the world still had to hand the IPCC's fourth complete report, AR4, published in 2007: 130 authors, with contributions from over 800 scientists, reviewed by thousands of others. The report highlighted the negative impact of climate change for the coming century, estimating that ice melt in the Arctic and Greenland could result in a one-metre rise in sea levels by the year 2100. This could lead to massive migration, accompanied by the inevitable humanitarian disasters. Even if all CO_2 emissions were to cease overnight,

---

30   'Stern Review: the economics of climate change', 2006.

temperatures would in any case continue to rise by 0.1°C every ten years. More seriously still, if we continue to emit as much CO_2 as we do today, the atmosphere will be 5.8°C warmer by the end of the century.

But at the end of 2009, resolving the global financial and economic crisis was more important in the eyes of world leaders than triggering a virtuous cycle to combat climate change and generate profits, estimated by Nicholas Stern to be of the order of $2,000 billion per year for the second half of the century. High-emissions countries – the USA, China and India foremost among them – were not of a mind to allow their hands to be tied by cutting their greenhouse gas emissions. Europe, divided and powerless, confined itself to the role of spectator to a pseudo-agreement concluded behind its back. And yet none of this really came as a surprise.

The three mistakes at Copenhagen

I believe that Europe's leaders made three mistakes at the COP15 conference. Firstly, they talked too much in terms of climate problems, and not enough about solutions. In actual fact, the EU had already implemented a multi-instrument policy in the form of its first Climate and Energy Package, adopted one year previously. When European leaders arrived in Copenhagen, it was as though they found themselves faced with a river; since they did not know how deep it was, they did not dare to cross it.

They did, however, have three stepping stones which they could have used to reach the other side: energy efficiency, renewables and interconnections and information and communications technology. But they failed to acknowledge that the solutions to climate change also produce other related benefits, such as energy independence, job creation, and less air pollution. The position of the EU revolved solely around the carbon market, perceived at that time as a punitive instrument, whereas Europe had in fact progressed a lot further than that. When it came to preparing the COP21 conference, the French presidency had learned its lesson; indeed, the Lima–Paris Action Agenda (LPAA) focused on developing an agenda of solutions.

The second mistake resided in the fact that the EU was weakened by internal divisions, in particular due to Poland and its obstinacy in peddling its 'hot air'.[31] In return for changing the baseline year for emissions reduction calculations, the Commission had agreed with the Eastern European countries that the targets for sectors not covered by the ETS and for renewables should be relatively low, and based on GDP rather than potential. The EU had also set up a financial transfer instrument within the ETS, by means of which 12 per cent of the revenue from the scheme within the fifteen countries of the EU prior to its expansion in 2004 would be transferred to Eastern European countries. As a result of this, following the Climate and Energy Package agreement in late December 2008, the Eastern European countries received a cheque for several hundred million euros.

However, no sooner had 2009 begun than the tables were turned: Poland wanted the 'hot air' to be on the agenda in international negotiations. The issue was to poison discussions for the next four years, right through until the COP18 conference in Doha. Basically, the Poles attempted to obtain on the global stage what they had failed to achieve in European negotiations. The squabble made it very difficult for the EU to develop an internal strategy for Copenhagen, since it deliberately undermined Europe's consensus as represented by the Climate and Energy Package; it was nothing less than a betrayal. The upshot of all this was that the EU could not present a united front in Copenhagen. The epilogue was to take place in 2012 in Doha, where the EU rolled over and agreed to the inclusion of most of the 'hot air' as part of post-Kyoto negotiations. And in 2015, ahead of the COP21 conference, Russia took up the baton, allowing Vladimir Putin a

---

31   When the EU expanded in 2004, the Eastern European countries were incorporated within the scope of the EU targets for greenhouse gas emissions. However, declining emissions in these countries were the mechanical result of a steep drop in industrial output after 1990 due to the collapse of the Soviet system: the emissions avoided thus were what became known as 'hot air'. The ETS emissions reduction target for 2020 was, however, based on 1990 emissions. During preparations for the Climate and Energy Package, a solution to this paradox needed to be found. If 1990 was kept as a baseline year, there would be so much 'hot air' in the system that a 20 per cent drop in emissions would be meaningless. As a result, the European Commission changed the baseline year from 1990 to 2005, thereby automatically eliminating this 'hot air' from calculations.

moment of self-congratulation for an achievement that was in fact nothing of the sort.[32]

The third mistake was to have been overoptimistic about the possibility of an alliance between the EU and United States. The Europeans' strategy for winning, at a time at which they were in the throes of Obamamania, was largely based on a transatlantic alliance, despite the fact that the US President did not have a majority in Congress to sign off on an international agreement. To make matters worse, one month before the start of the COP15 conference the Danish presidency had its own moment of internal strife, when the Danish Prime Minister dismissed Thomas Becker, adviser to the Danish environment minister Connie Hedegaard, who was to preside over the COP15 conference. This weakened the Euro-Danish strategy and destabilised Connie Hedegaard just a few days ahead of the summit. Indeed, she herself was replaced just before the end of the COP15 conference, on Wednesday 16 December 2009, by the Danish Prime Minister. The latter concluded the summit with a very poor performance that in effect opened the door to formal opposition on the part of at least four Latin American countries: Venezuela, Bolivia, Cuba and Nicaragua. Connie Hedegaard's detractors went on to use the Copenhagen fiasco to defy her authority during her mandate as EU Climate Commissioner in the Barroso Commission between 2010 and 2014.

The tipping point

In the wake of Copenhagen, pro-planet activists' morale plummeted, focused as they were on international negotiations. According to Wendel Trio, who heads up Climate Action Network Europe, this disenchantment resulted in fewer human and financial resources being devoted to monitoring and influencing international negotiations, to the benefit of other forms of advocacy and mobilisation in favour of more practical and local solutions. Away from international negotiations, a new dynamic therefore emerged in society as a whole:

---

32   'Cop 21: Poutine vante les "efforts" (inexistants) de la Russie', 3 December 2015.

alliances between local powers, with initiatives such as the Covenant of Mayors, the C40 network, and so on; climate compacts for companies; the development of energy efficiency technology; and fresh enthusiasm for renewables.

I myself was disaffected by the inability of the international community to gain anything from these annual bunfights and stopped attending COP conferences until COP21, held in Paris in late 2015. In the meantime, I continued to devote my energies to solutions such as renewables, energy efficiency and smart grids as well as grassroots mobilisation.

It was around then that we reached a tipping point in the fight against climate change in Europe. The balance of power between the advocates of ambitious climate policy on the one hand and high-emission industries (such as manufacturing-sector and energy firms) on the other shifted in favour of the latter. After years of enthusiasm from 2006 to 2009, this was a rude awakening. And those parties whose short-term economic interests had been disrupted – the oligopolies, industry, in other words, the world's polluters – lost no time in returning to the fray.

The industrial lobby made the most of post-Copenhagen blues to hammer home two falsehoods designed to weaken Europe's climate and energy policy: firstly, that if the EU were to go it alone in implementing pro-climate policy, this would penalise European firms by sapping their competitiveness, resulting in loss of market share to the benefit of China and the United States (this came to be known as 'carbon leakage'); secondly, that EU policy on renewables would increase the price of electricity and therefore be a further incitement to offshore on a massive scale.

The Copenhagen failure was to have a long-term psychological impact, and it was to be several years before a positive dynamic could be rebuilt. Against the backdrop of economic crisis, this was to be the start of the Dark Ages as far as energy transition in Europe was concerned. Not only that, the period was to witness the consequences of a major nuclear accident.

The trauma of Fukushima

On 11 March 2011, an earthquake with a magnitude of 9 on the Richter scale struck 130km off the north-eastern coast of the Japanese island of Honshu. Reactors 1 and 3 of the Fukushima Daiichi nuclear power plant were damaged, and radioactive materials began to leak out. The backup systems did not function as expected. Then, at precisely 3.30 p.m., a tsunami some fifteen metres high hit the power station, short-circuiting the core cooling system for the first three reactors, which were shut down. As a result, they suffered a virtually total meltdown, resulting in holes in the bottom of the pressure vessel. The power plant technicians, dispatched in haste to the site, injected thousands of litres of water to cool the reactors, and had to allow radioactive gases to escape in order to relieve the pressure. Thousands of square kilometres were contaminated by radioactive pollution, resulting in streams of refugees; while both the government and Tepco, the power plant's operator, were completely overwhelmed by the scale of the catastrophe. The health and environmental impacts of Fukushima have now been well documented, making it possible to take stock of the disaster that unfolded in 2011 in this region of Japan.

In Europe, home to no fewer than 129 reactors, the response was one of consternation. As it happened, on that day the Eurozone heads of state were meeting in Brussels to discuss the situation in Greece. German Chancellor Angela Merkel was informed of the disaster during her flight from Berlin to Brussels and spent most of the day following the situation live. A physicist by training and until then a devout believer in nuclear power, she had left Berlin with certainties, only to return from Brussels with doubts. The torchbearers of the mighty atom could plead Soviet technical approximations to explain away the Chernobyl disaster, but a nuclear accident at the very heart of the country that epitomised the best in technology gave a voice to the anti-nuclear lobby.

Merkel did not take long to bow to popular pressure and make a U-turn on the issue of nuclear power. Her liberal right-wing coalition government had voted to 'abandon abandonment' of nuclear power and extend the life of existing power plants, in a gesture to the four leading electricity groups that had been hard for public opinion to swallow. But in the wake of Fukushima, she ordered a safety audit of all German nuclear power stations, and immediately took the six oldest offline.

On 27 March regional elections in the Baden-Württemberg *Land*, of which EU Energy Commissioner Günther Oettinger had formerly been minister president, threw out the CDU, replacing it by a government led by the Greens, who captured 24.2 per cent of the vote. This electoral landslide was echoed in the traditional Easter peace demonstrations, with all the related anti-nuclear connotations. Perceived as having betrayed the national interest by having done a deal with the energy firms, Angela Merkel threw in the towel on 9 June, deciding to abandon nuclear power. By 2022, the seventeen nuclear reactors still in service in Germany were to be closed down. She describes the Fukushima disaster as a 'decisive factor' in this respect, explaining that 'the risks of nuclear power are uncontrollable; once that has been realised, one must reassess one's position'.

It is worth noting in this respect that it would not have been so easy for Germany to unplug its nuclear power plants without the separation of electricity production and transmission that had been enshrined in the 2009 EU Directive. The crucial clause in question automatically ensures transparency, by doing away with the major electricity-producing firms' monopoly on production capacity information. This structural change allowed Germany to take a decision based on independent opinions by German transmission system operators (TSOs) and the national regulator, whose independence is also guaranteed by the EU directives promulgated in the wake of the second internal market package. Admittedly, the TSOs were relatively sceptical initially, but their position shifted over time – something that could not be said of the negative attitude of the electricity firms. This separation of assets opened up the way for them to consider the issue autonomously.

Japan also shut down all of its nuclear reactors after Fukushima.

Following a change in government, it is currently attempting to return some to service. But for the first time in over forty-five years, Japan found itself without nuclear electricity for over four years – and the lights stayed on.

In any event, nothing has been the same since Fukushima. Formerly, nuclear power was presented as being competitive, clean and safe by its champions; they have been pulled up short. My view is that without the huge privileges from which nuclear power has benefited, it would have been put to one side a long time ago. Given the speed of energy transition, nuclear power will no longer be competitive if it has to bear all its costs. And that is before the question of power plant safety is considered – a matter buried by the Juncker Commission in the wake of a public consultation with no follow-up in 2013, in breach of the promises of Commissioner Oettinger after Fukushima.

Nuclear power plants should therefore be closed, including those in France. Despite this, EDF's strategy is to extend the lifespan of these power plants to as much as fifty or sixty years. Doing so not only hinders the development of renewables in France, it also extends the nuclear risk for everyone.

Nuclear power's over-optimistic forecasts

The fact is that despite initial enthusiasm for the technology in the 1960s and 1970s, the growth forecast for this industry has never materialised. In the 1980s, the International Atomic Energy Agency (IAEA) forecast 740–1,075GWe of installed capacity; this is two or three times more than the 356GWe actually in service – and between ten and fourteen times less than it had forecast in 1973–1974.

Despite the overwhelming evidence of results from the field, the nuclear industry remains optimistic; indeed, blindly so. The European Commission's most recent 'PINC' report demonstrates as much: thanks to overly generous estimation of the average price per kWe of €3.80–5.40 (the estimate for Hinkley Point C was as high as €6.80/kWe), the Commission's experts are predicting the construction of two or three reactors per year in Europe between now and 2050. This is madness. Today in Europe, the rate is more like two or three new reactors per decade. And indeed, it takes a decade to build a nuclear reactor, as the fiasco of the new PWRs still under construction in Olkiluoto, Finland and Flamanville, France demonstrates. Rather than the three billion euros initially planned, the actual costs of the Flamanville EPR will exceed ten billion euros.

TEAM ATOMIC JUNCKER GOES NUCLEAR

The 'PINC' document, a poisoned chalice for Juncker and his team © PETER DREDGE

How could new investments be justified after such mishandlings? Especially if governments should pay for gigantic support schemes up to €100/MWh as in the case of Hinkley Point C, while onshore wind and even now offshore wind can be built for twice cheaper? This economic failure is going hand in hand with nothing short of an industrial disaster. Meanwhile, Europe's nuclear industry is desperately clinging to the prospect of the development of the Chinese nuclear power programme – even as the country is moving towards 100 per cent Chinese reactors. These unremittingly optimistic forecasts offer a blatant contrast to the forecasts for the development of renewables; the latter are systematically underestimated in all scenarios put forward by the European Commission and the IEA.

On 15 June 2011, the European nuclear industry lobby Foratom published its outlook for 2050, and not a single mention was made of the Fukushima nuclear disaster, despite it having struck only three months previously. This silence was finally broken on 6 December with the publication of revised forecasts, just when climate negotiations were in full swing at the COP17 conference in Durban. People were expecting serious reconsideration, but the new forecasts barely mentioned Fukushima at all: 'The long-term consequences of Fukushima on nuclear power, i.e. to 2050, are impossible to predict' was the lobby's explanation. The report barely went further than acknowledging that the disaster would have 'some effect on the costs and lead times for new builds' of nuclear power plants. Could this be the understatement of the year?

Foratom ploughed on regardless, claiming that many EU member states would be continuing with nuclear power 'even if carbon capture and storage is becoming commercially available', because 'they will not find the installation of large quantities of renewables to be worthwhile either economically or operationally'. It did, however, acknowledge a long list of vital criteria for its nuclear-friendly predictions to come true: acceptance by the general public, political support, solutions for storing hazardous radioactive waste for thousands of years, increased safety, post-Fukushima standards compliance and of course funding. And it is with respect to funding that the nuclear lobby really runs into problems. In a deregulated market, there are hardly any banks or investors left willing to finance the adventure of nuclear power. After having wooed politicians and the general public with the argument of cheap energy, the lobby has had to change its tune: henceforth, salvation comes at the cost of huge public subsidies, as is the case for the Hinkley Point C project.[33]

And let it not be said that Germany has imperilled its security of supply by abandoning nuclear power. In 2010, the last full year before its change in policy, Germany had a net electricity export surplus of

---

33   See Chapter 10, pp. 128–139.

17.7TWh. And despite abandoning nuclear power, in 2011 it still had a positive net export surplus of 60TWh. This surplus increased still further in subsequent years: 23TWh in 2012, 33TWh in 2013, and 49TWh in 2015 – bringing in over €2 billion of revenue. Germany is not short of electricity. Anything but: the collapse of the ETS has pushed gas out of the electricity mix to the benefit of coal, which has become abundant and extremely cheap on a world market suffering from overcapacity. The fact is that if it had not abandoned nuclear power, Germany would be producing and exporting even more electricity today. The consequence of this would be even lower market prices and considerable economic damage for gas-fired power plants, even more of which would have been put off-stream.

What about smaller nuclear power plants?

Over and above operators' financial difficulties, another problem with nuclear power is rigidity of production; this is incompatible with the new, decentralised, flexible electricity market. The largest nuclear power plants, with outputs of 900–1,600MW, are struggling to keep in step with load-following requirements.[34] Admittedly, many reactors, particularly in France and Germany, attempt to operate with rapid changes in reactor power of 30–40 per cent. However, this is nowhere near the complete flexibility offered by renewables. And while such procedures are possible, there are a great many technical considerations and most importantly, the implications for nuclear safety have not been adequately explored. Indeed, there are physical limits to load-following, due to variations in temperature and pressure, which lead to increased material fatigue. As a result, the US regulator has prohibited this practice for reactors in the United States.

Is the nuclear lobby aware of this problem? It clearly is, because otherwise there would be no sense in it promoting research and development into small modular reactors (SMR), a field to which the UK has just allocated £250 million of funding. This is clear evidence

---

34   Load-following consists in adjusting the operating power of a power station upwards or downwards very quickly in order to respond to variations in demand.

that the sector has realised the limits of a system based exclusively on large PWR-type reactors. In France, defeated conservative candidate for the presidential election François Fillon was on the same ticket. In the energy part of his electoral programme, he proposes to develop a broad range of SMR 'to satisfy the needs of large cities or those of regions with small population density'. There are doubts as to whether this miniaturised technology would be competitive with respect to larger facilities, let alone the issue of acceptance by local populations; indeed, it is hard to believe in the deployment of hundreds or thousands of mini-nuclear reactors in a world in which security issues are a major concern. This opinion is also shared by EU Commissioner for Research and Innovation Carlos Moedas. While some EU civil servants attempted to open the door for public subsidies to 'baby-nukes', the commissioner reaffirmed that the energy transition rather calls for more renewables, smart grids and storage systems.[35]

In any event, after the failure of Copenhagen and the Fukushima disaster, the EU's position drifted still further. And matters were not improved by the failure of the keystone of its climate policy: the carbon market.

---

35   'Angriff der Atom-Zwerge', Spiegel Online, 21 May 2016.

CHAPTER 6

THE ETS AND ITS BROKEN PROMISES

When the 2008 crisis hit, the price per tonne of CO_2 collapsed from €30 to €10. The traders' explanation was straightforward: in a recession, there is less industrial demand and activity, and thus fewer CO_2 emissions. However, in actual fact the system was poorly calibrated from the outset; it was bound to derail at some point. The gap between emissions caps and actual emissions widened: the surplus of CO_2 allowances on the market had already been clearly established and ended up never being absorbed – anything but. Demand slumped, while the supply of credits actually went on to increase. As Femke de Jong, director of EU policy for Carbon Market Watch, confided in me, 'There is a lack of confidence in there being any scarcity.' However did things come to this?

The ETS – a cunning institutional plan

Initially, the ETS came about as a way of overturning a historic defeat suffered by the EU-twelve in 1991, ahead of the Earth Summit in Rio de Janeiro. The EU's Environment Commissioner at the time, the Italian Carlo Ripa di Meana, put forward the idea of a carbon tax, the revenues from which were to be used to modernise industry, by investing them in energy efficiency and production processes. He based his idea on a win-win model that had been implemented, notably in Denmark, in the 1980s. But it was not to be. He aroused the ire of heavy industry, with the latter managing to secure the support of the UK's ultra-liberal Margaret Thatcher, together with that of the governments of France and Germany. As a result, the Commission's proposal was rejected. Ripa di Meana remained true to his convictions, resigning from the Delors II Commission in order to avoid having to represent Europe at the Earth Summit in early June 1992. The EU presidency was represented at the event by the Portuguese minister of the environment of the day, none other than a certain José Manuel Barroso, who thus ended up going to Rio empty handed.

THE EUROPEAN CARBON MARKET DOESN'T DELIVER

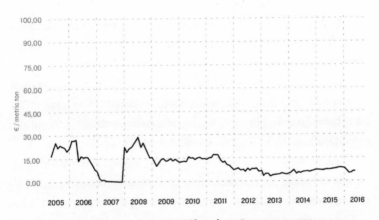

Source: ICE Futures Europe / Bloomberg © REVOLVE MEDIA

It became obvious that the EU could not hope to achieve any progress in terms of taxation so long as the latter was subject to a unanimous vote of the Council. During work on the constitution in the 2000s, the Greens therefore headed up an attempt to make environmental taxation subject to a qualified majority, in line with the resolutely pro-European stance instigated by Joschka Fischer. The German foreign affairs minister never made any secret of his federalist convictions, as exemplified by his legendary speech in Berlin on 12 May 2000. However, these daring proposals did not survive the work done on the Convention on the Future of Europe, with the final draft of the EU constitution maintaining the requirement of unanimity in the Council for all decisions pertaining to taxation.

A way therefore had to be found to escape this unhelpful mechanism – a constant hindrance to progress. After all, if twelve member states could not manage to agree on the issue of CO_2 taxation, how could fifteen, twenty-seven, or twenty-eight possibly be expected to do so? And so the ETS was born: a cunning plan to disguise CO_2 taxation as a market instrument. This made it possible to adopt a legal foundation that did not qualify the scheme as taxation, i.e. that of the environment and the internal market – and in doing so make use of an adoption process that had some chance of succeeding thanks to qualified majority voting.

The ETS is a cap and trade system featuring a total emissions cap coupled with a system of emission allowance trading. It established maximum greenhouse gas emission levels; a worthwhile measure. Initially, the creators of the ETS thought that a high CO_2 price of €40–€60/t would result in a complete reorientation of investment decisions. Simply put, at the time of implementation in 2005, the champions of the ETS made the following promises:

- The ETS will remove coal from the electricity market by internalising external costs.
- The ETS will generate investments in renewables and energy efficiency, so there is no need for specific targets in these areas.
- The ETS will address the issue of climate change, which relates to emissions, by fixing caps at levels that will combat climate change effectively.
- The ETS will generate new revenue streams for public finance that could be reinvested in greenhouse gas emissions mitigation projects.

Jos Delbeke, father of the ETS and currently director-general DG Clima (the Directorate-General for Climate Action), was also behind the attempted carbon tax of 1991. The ETS was his baby, and he was ready to do anything it took for it to become a leading instrument in Europe's climate policy. He was to go as far as to derail other instruments he saw as competitors, such as measures pertaining to renewable energy and energy efficiency. However, markets are much harder to calibrate than taxes, and the complexity of the legislation was to open the way for frantic lobbying on the part of industry.

Original sin

The ETS adventure featured its very own 'original sin': an overestimation of the number of allowances to be attributed to industries. This resulted in the ETS experiencing an initial crash in the first phase (2005–2008), at the end of April 2006: the emissions measured in five countries (the Netherlands, the Czech Republic, Belgium, France and Spain) were lower than their emissions allowance – a sign of oversupply. The market lost no time in reacting to the announcement of these figures, falling 54 per cent within the space of a week between 24 and 28 April, from €29 to €13/tCO$_2$. In May 2006, the Commission confirmed that verified emissions were 4 per cent lower (i.e. 80 million tonnes less) than the number of allowances distributed to facilities covered by the ETS in 2005.

Despite this, governments failed to learn their lesson. During phase II (2009–2012), industry continued to lead states merrily up the garden path, since the latter had no precise statistics for each facility. Industrial players were in a position of strength, and were thus able to systematically inflate the figures concerning their actual emissions. As a result, they were able to engineer a substantial overallocation from the very beginning, thus bringing prices down.

Worse still, during the negotiations about phase III (2013–2020) which took place in 2008 and 2009, the wrong calibration was extended! The 20 per cent reduction in greenhouse gases as part of the 20-20-20 package for 2020 was in fact a combination of 10 per cent consisting of domestic reductions and 10 per cent from creative accounting involving the purchase of international carbon credits – even though the Commission had sounded a warning about this in its impact study[36] published to accompany the legislative proposals in January 2008. According to its calculations, the EU should commit to an unconditional 20 per cent reduction in domestic greenhouse gas emissions, without the benefit of international credits. The model constructed by the Commission in summer 2006, 'high renewables and high efficiency', even demonstrated that if the EU could achieve its 20 per cent targets for renewables and energy efficiency, greenhouse gas emissions would in turn automatically come down by 20 per cent. The only way of achieving a meaningful price signal on the carbon market would therefore have involved raising the 2020 domestic target to 30 per cent. On the basis of these figures, the Greens and NGOs actively combating climate change therefore requested a target of 40 per cent: 30 per cent domestic plus an additional 10 per cent as part of a possible international COP15 agreement in Copenhagen.

However, under pressure from industrial lobbies and certain governments, the Commission ignored its own impact study, despite the latter being dazzlingly clear as to the future of the ETS in the event of poor calibration:

> Under a 20 per cent GHG reduction scenario where only the EU would be in demand for CDM credits and with limitless access to such credits, carbon prices are projected to be potentially as low as of 4 €/tonne and EU emissions would be reduced only marginally. This would imply that no significant changes in our energy system would be achieved.

This prophecy has been fulfilled in its entirety.

As good as dead

At the end of 2009, Europe was plunged into paralysis after the failure of COP15 negotiations in Copenhagen. The hypothesis to increase the greenhouse gas emission reduction objective to 30 per cent in case

---

36   'Impact Assessment', 23 January 2008, ec.europa.eu.

of an international agreement crisis vanished away. All that with the economic crisis in the background. And because misfortunes never come singly, the revelation in a Commission report of January 2010 that the Greek debt figures had been fudged further torpedoed any prospect of recovery.

On 15 March 2010, the EU's environment ministers attempted to respond. Gathered in Brussels, they confirmed the EU's conditional offer of 'increasing the target for reduction of these emissions to 30 per cent of 1990 levels by 2020' provided that an overall global agreement for the post-2012 phase was achieved as part of the UNFCCC. The EU Council confirmed this proposal at its spring summit on 25–26 March 2010. However, despite the twenty-six other EU member states agreeing, Poland opposed the proposal at an environment ministers' council meeting in Luxembourg on 15 June 2011. And one year later, on the eve of another meeting, Poland drove another stake into the heart of this review (which nobody was taking seriously anyway by this time), vetoing a 25 per cent reduction in EU emissions by 2020 which was nevertheless weaker than the 30 per cent initially envisaged. Carbon traders lost all confidence.

Industry itself waded in, making a bad situation even worse. From 2010 onwards, European industries covered by the ETS (electricity firms and major industrial players) bought international carbon credits by the truckload. This manoeuvre, permissible under ETS regulations, was performed on the spurious grounds that since climate change was a global problem, reducing emissions outside the EU was just as important as any domestic objective. This was nonsense, given that a robust ETS relied on a carbon budget within Europe, failing which the system was doomed to failure – as events were to prove.

How on earth did such an absurdity survive for so long? When the EU established the rules for phase II of the ETS (2009–2012) and coupled it to international efforts to cut greenhouse gas emissions enshrined in the Kyoto protocol, the major electricity firms and the European bosses' lobby BusinessEurope (known as Unice at that time) pleaded for a safety valve, in the form of international credit purchasing, to be used in the event of spiralling CO_2 prices threatening their competitiveness. The industrial players had no scruples about invoking this clause even when prices were low. Even as the ETS was barely alive, leading industrial firms such as Mittal and BASF, together with electricity companies including RWE and E.ON, sprang into the breach, buying huge quantities of international credits at bargain-basement prices (lower than €1/tonne of CO_2) – themselves the result of the uncertainty surrounding the extension of the Kyoto protocol.

These international credits (clean development mechanisms, or CDMs) were very often cheaper than emissions allowances within Europe but had the same value, since they could be traded on the European market in the same way as any other emissions certificate. In 2010, European industry bought 137 million of them in total, then 254 million in 2011 and no fewer than 504 million in 2012 – one third of all authorised credits for the entire phase. They flooded the market, thereby increasing the allowance surplus still further, even as the ETS was fading fast. This surplus shows no signs of abating, since domestic and international ETS credits acquired by companies that were not used during phase II do not expire: they are still valid for phase III, which began in 2013. This is yet another gaping hole in the system. According to Emil Dimantchev, senior carbon market analyst for Thomson Reuters, 'there was no hope of any more ambitious target, and therefore no stricter emissions cap. There were too many allowances on the market, so those who had them sold them, since they were not likely to need them.'

The result was inevitable: the price of CO_2 collapsed below €8/tonne in 2012. The European carbon market, the world's first and largest, had in effect breathed its last.

The Institute for Climate Economics (Institut d'économie du climat, I4CE), part of Caisse des Dépôts, established a very eloquent analysis of the causes of this collapse. According to a study published in November 2015, international credits account for 1,437MtCO$_2$ – a whopping 70 per cent of the 2,066MtCO$_2$ surplus observed in 2014. Only 30MtCO$_2$ – a mere 1.5 per cent of the surplus – can actually be attributed to energy efficiency and renewable energy targets being achieved. The destructive effects of international credits on the ETS was acknowledged by the Commission itself in its 2012 report on the carbon market: 'The marked reduction of prices in the second half of 2011 to levels below €10 coincides with the accelerated build-up of a surplus in allowances and international credits.' So I must admit to a rather cynical chuckle when certain DG Clima civil servants attempt to blame the failure of the ETS on competition from energy efficiency and renewables. The ETS was rendered toothless because it was poorly calibrated at the outset, and due to the influx of international credits. At the end of the day, also according to I4CE, this alleged pillar of the EU climate policy accounted for reductions of all of 0–1 per cent in greenhouse gas emissions between 2005 and 2011: not exactly a dazzling success.

Challenging climate policy: industry sees attack as the best form of defence

Despite its textbook sabotage by industrial players, the latter continued to claim that the ETS was the root of all evil, and blamed the decline of industrial employment on the 2008 Climate and Energy Package. This was a blatant lie, as proved by the statistics for Europe's steel imports and exports. In 2009/2010, after the collapse of Lehman Brothers, demand for steel in the EU fell, but despite the crisis, worldwide demand remained strong. During this phase, Europe continued to be a net exporter of steel and, according to Syndex, even increased its exports until 2014. Clearly, exports signify competitiveness; the EU was therefore still competitive in this respect. Moreover, many studies challenged the existence of the risk of 'carbon leakage'.[37]

The reasons for the decline in heavy industry in Europe were to be found elsewhere: the austerity policies imposed by the Merkel/Sarkozy duo and the right-wing parties in power across the EU,

---

37   In 2013, the CE Delft research organisation argued that the method chosen by the Commission to identify sectors that could be susceptible to 'carbon leakage' and therefore qualify for a number of free ETS credits (contrary to the auction principle) was biased. In the final analysis, it argued, the number of free allocations should be restricted to a maximum of 10 per cent of all emissions.

sapping investment in infrastructures such as buildings, bridges, tunnels and railway lines, and thus the demand for cement and steel.[38] In addition, there was a problem of overcapacity in China: from 2013 onwards, its GDP grew more slowly, which is why steel consumption fell dramatically from 735Mt in 2013 to 672Mt in 2015. This trend is likely to increase, leaving Chinese industry with a huge amount of excess production capacity to be got rid of abroad.

So what is the relationship between the decline of heavy industry and EU climate policy? The answer is none whatsoever. Instead of relentlessly attacking EU climate policy on the basis of a patent lie, industry should join forces with the Greens and the European left to replace austerity measures with a fully fledged recovery programme, accompanied by trade defence measures to counter Chinese dumping. This would allow us to break free from the naive vision of deregulated international trade. Even the European Commission admits as much about these sectors: 'Their future depends on their ability to embrace modernisation and implement innovations.' European steelmakers should therefore invest, and they have the resources to do so – thanks to the revenues generated by the ETS!

But European bosses decided to lie. BusinessEurope is dominated by four large industrial groups: ArcelorMittal, BASF, ThyssenKrupp and Voestalpine. Some of these companies are constantly flirting with climate change sceptics of all stripes, and do not hesitate to fund the most conservative of US senators.[39] They enjoy very close relationships with Bjørn Lomborg, a well-known and highly controversial climate change sceptic, invited to speak by BASF at a company managers' training course. Similarly, the boss of Voestalpine, the Austrian Wolfgang Eder (who at one time also headed up the European steel lobby Eurofer, and who now presides over WorldSteel, the world steel industry federation), systematically opposes EU climate policy,

---

38   Steel consumption in Europe plummeted by 40 per cent between 2007 and 2009. Today, it is still 25 per cent lower than 2007 levels.

39   'Tea Party climate change deniers funded by BP and other major polluters', *The Guardian*, 24 October 2010.

referring to it as 'ideological'[40] and prophesying an apocalypse: twenty million jobs lost, the end of the steel industry, the car-making industry and so on.

In one of history's ironies, between 2010 and 2014, €441 million of the money in ArcelorMittal's coffers came from ETS profits. Lakshmi Mittal, an astute businessman, has earned a lot of money through the ETS. His actions are just one example of the industry's dodgy practices. Mittal mothballed one of its steelworks, at Schifflange in Luxembourg, for three years, in order to benefit from allowances based on historic emissions, at a time when the factory was no longer producing a single tonne of steel. Journalist Élise Lucet has done an excellent job of exposing similar practices engaged in by the Lafarge group's French cement works.[41] In the UK, Tata Steel alone has earned €870 million thanks to the ETS. Talk about abuse of the system. The free distribution of allowances, which is supposed to preserve competitiveness, is in fact an incitement not to produce. I propose to stop this scam: the EU should stop handing out free allowances and instead, adopt a carbon tax at its borders, in order to protect European industry from climate dumping on the part of other regions of the world. It is a proposal from MEP Édouard Martin, former union leader at ArcelorMittal in Florange and now a progressive ally in the European Parliament.

Electricity prices and energy poverty: the industrial lobby's new angles of attack

Shortly after the adoption of the Climate and Energy Package, during the negotiation of the directives on energy efficiency and the energy performance of buildings, I took part in a meeting on energy transition at the Swiss embassy. In this meeting, the representative of Shell bemoaned the fate of hapless EU citizens: not only were they suffering the effects of the crisis, he said; they were also having to endure rising energy prices. He launched into a moving speech on energy poverty within the EU, attributing increases in energy prices to the Climate

---

40   'Steel's battle to survive in the face of spiralling environmental costs', *The Telegraph*, 22 April 2016.
41   '"Cash Investigation". Climate: le grand bluff des multinationales', France 2, 24 May 2016.

and Energy Package. I could scarcely believe my ears: how could a representative of Shell have so much sympathy for the poor?! At the time, the price of oil was over $100 a barrel. Gas contracts, which are pegged to oil prices, were highly lucrative. This was therefore a phase during which Shell was doing extremely well for itself. It took me a few days to realise just how cynical he had been.

Not only is it misleading to draw a connection between oil and gas prices and EU climate policy, there is also a good reason why electricity bills for households and small businesses are increasing. These parties are the only ones to be contributing to the necessary modernisation of the European system currently dominated by old assets. Electro-intensive industries form a large part of the electricity consumed in the EU but benefit from outstanding privileges. Indeed, in addition to massive exemptions from the ETS, electricity-intensive firms are exempt from grid charges and the payment of contributions to renewables. They really are stowaways. In Germany for instance, electricity-intensive industries win all ways round: they buy electricity at wholesale prices that has diminished since 2008, and do not contribute to the growth of renewables, thanks to huge exemptions – which in turn lead to higher prices for households and small businesses. Indeed, the German StromNEV regulation of 25 July 2005 exempts German industrial firms from contributing to the costs entailed by their use of the electricity grid. Another German directive of 30 January 2013 also grants industrial firms indirect carbon cost compensation, of around €5/MWh. Lastly, the German law of 20 July 2014 on renewable energy grants these firms almost complete exemption from taxes and contributions collected to support the development of renewable energy.

At the end of the day, while German households pay extremely high prices for electricity, industrial firms get theirs at more or less the same price as the wholesale market. This price is 'significantly lower than in the rest of Europe, with the exception of Scandinavia', as stated in a report by the Öko-Institut in January 2016. This therefore constitutes a huge cross-subsidy; a kind of electricity dumping, validated by the European Commission in November 2014, and then extended to other member states, which may be summarised by the following equation: EU citizens pay and industry reaps in the cash.

This ongoing lie is made possible only by means of a complete lack of transparency on industry's electricity bills. The fact is that the major industrial firms are not required to supply figures for their electricity supply contracts to Eurostat. The same Öko-Institut report highlights this lack of transparency: 'The fundamental problem of price comparisons based on the official statistics supplied by Eurostat is that a large number of particularities applied to electricity-intensive industrial sectors are not taken into account in the official calculation of electricity prices.' In other words, the huge exemptions from which industrial companies benefit are concealed in their entirety. Industrial firms hide behind the fig-leaf of trade secrecy in order not divulge their actual energy costs. Each time they complain about prices, the appropriate response is therefore to ask them to show their invoices. The European Commission was lucid enough to acknowledge this in a paper on steelmaking published in March 2016: 'Wholesale energy prices, the proxy for energy prices paid by energy intensive industries, are now at historically low levels.' However, the Commission's new proposal to improve energy statistics collection maintains this state of affairs, including all type of consumers in a single category, hence making comparisons impossible.

Eurelectric, the electricity oligopoly lobby, and the Magritte Group have joined forces with electricity-intensive firms in their battle for exemptions. At first sight, this appears ridiculous: electricity firms are not impacted by these taxes and withholdings on top of electricity prices, which are paid by end users. So what is the point of such a campaign? The consequence of these exemptions is that only households and small businesses contribute to funding renewables and the welfare state. For instance, households in Germany and Denmark are subject to the highest taxes in Europe, because finite resources are taxed. This revenue brings down labour costs and provides funding for pensions, education, healthcare, welfare and so on. The message of

Eurelectric, meanwhile, is 'say no to taxes'. The question is, to which ones? They cannot be referring to taxes that allow social protection to be funded by income sources other than taxation of labour; the only other possible target is the contribution destined to fund renewables. And voilà: the electricity firms' strategy is a feat of pure genius. By joining forces with their clients, they are seeking to create a negative stereotype of taxpayers having to fund renewables and in doing so, are pushing governments to slow down energy transition. The cynicism of this move can scarcely be exaggerated.

Fortunately, consumer organisations have never fallen into the trap, largely thanks to the initiatives spurred on by the director-general of the European Consumers' Union (BEUC), Monique Goyens. One such example is the following recommendation in a 2012 report by the association: 'It is essential that policy focuses on the most long-term and cost-effective solutions to solve energy poverty, namely the radical improvement to the energy efficiency standards of housing.' The report also states that 'adequate financial support for energy efficiency in buildings is therefore essential to enable all European consumers to be more energy efficient, but also in order to tackle energy poverty.'[42] BEUC has grasped the fact that the issue of rising electricity, gas and oil costs must be addressed, not by attacking energy transition but by seeking to achieve measures whereby the most vulnerable households can reduce their energy consumption, notably thanks to eco-design and energy labelling. This is the noblest solution to the conundrum of how to modernise production and grid facilities while keeping costs stable.

The real problem is Europe's high gas prices

If there is an energy price problem for Europe's industries lately, it is the price of gas. In North America, the boom in locally produced shale gas has brought prices down. The decrease has been considerable, but its extent is still less than the increase of gas prices in Europe. Why is this? When it comes to long-term agreements, most gas prices are

---

42   'Financial support for energy efficiency in buildings', BEUC, 9 July 2012.

indexed to oil prices. And those stayed at a relatively low level (between 80 and 100 dollars per barrel between 2009 and 2015) despite the economic crisis, hence affecting the business case of gas-fired electricity generation assets. Indexation is largely due to historic reasons, as gas was formerly a direct alternative product to oil. The price therefore has nothing to do with the EU's climate and energy policy. In the 1970s, one response to the OPEC boycott was to promote gas as an alternative to oil for heating; indexing it to oil prices was a way of making it slightly cheaper. But when gas started to be used to produce electricity, it came into competition with coal, nuclear power, solar power and wind power. Gazprom has naturally sought to preserve its margins. However, if gas is no longer being used just for heating but also to produce electricity, both sale prices and margins should decrease. Despite this, Gazprom has steadfastly refused to implement any such reduction, so the EU had to react. In some countries such as France, increasing numbers of long-term contracts are now indexed to market prices – 26 per cent compared to 10 per cent previously. Within the EU, some 50 per cent of gas used is still indexed to oil prices. However, many of these contracts are to expire relatively soon. This is a unique opportunity. More transparency in the conclusion of international gas deals would allow member states to form common approaches when negotiating with suppliers, thereby hindering Gazprom's strategy, which consists in imposing prices that are politically rather than commercially motivated: the Poles pay more than the Germans. The Russian power plays at work here could not be more evident.

It was hoped that with the CO_2 market, gas would replace coal on the electricity market. This, however, has not worked for two reasons additional to oil indexation: firstly, the failure of the ETS has meant that gas has not achieved any significant advantage over coal, even if it produces far fewer greenhouse gas emissions; secondly, world coal prices are currently declining sharply. Less coal is being used in the US due to it being replaced by shale gas, and less is being used in China due to the economic downturn. The 'clean/dark spread', as the competitiveness of gas compared to coal is known, is increasingly in favour of coal. In addition, the spread of solar power in Europe and its falling costs have allowed it to replace gas when coping with midday demand spikes, since its output is highest at precisely this time of day, when the sun is strongest.

Could the ETS halt the rise of coal? Yes – provided that the price of CO_2 is high enough: in other words, more than €30/t, the threshold above which coal is expensive enough to fall beneath gas in the electricity market's merit order. For lignite, which is even cheaper and more polluting, the threshold is around €70–80/tCO_2. In the second half of 2008, a large number of combined cycle gas turbines (CCGT) power plants were working flat out rather than coal-fired power stations, because ETS prices were at around €25–30/tCO_2. Since then, the collapse of ETS prices has poured cold water on any hope of pushing coal out of the market.

The combination of all these factors has meant that many gas-fired power plants have been shut down or turned off-grid. Even if the objective in the medium term is to do without all of these fossil fuels, including gas, this is a catastrophic state of affairs in the short term – all the more so in that gas firms' inability to rival coal has led to them ramping up their anti-renewables rhetoric.

2010–2016: record years for European coal

What was bad for gas turned good for coal and lignite. Failed ETS offers a great opportunity to the dirtiest power plants. While a rapid decrease in coal and lignite consumption could be expected as of 2008, these energy sources are reaching record high levels. Hence the impact of ETS on the EU power market is obvious. Take Germany, for instance. The dash for coal is not the consequence of the nuclear phase-out but the consequence of a depressed carbon market. Weak carbon price did not only kill gas-fired power plants in Germany, but also those located beyond borders in the Netherlands, Belgium, Luxembourg, Austria, France … When a 50km-long high-voltage transmission line became operational between Germany and Austria in 2015, transmission capacity between Germany and Italy (via

Austria) increased. As a result, many modern gas-fired power plants shut down in northern Italy. Even worse, the failure of ETS is putting at risk the likelihood to see Germany meeting its 2020 climate target of 40 per cent. To alleviate the consequences of a weak ETS, Germany unilaterally decided to establish a special tax on the oldest and dirtiest power plants. In 2015, its economy minister engaged in a ferocious battle with operators RWE and Vattenfall, the latter benefiting from the backing of their in-house trade unions. This lobby managed to see off the idea of this special tax on legacy coal-fired power stations and force the government to make a U-turn: operators would receive financial compensation for a period of four years, placing the cost of closing its power plants squarely on the shoulders of German taxpayers. This is nonsense that could be described as the 'polluter gets paid' principle. This institutionalised racketeering totalling €1.6 billion was approved by the European Commission on 27 May 2016, with the Directorate-General for Competition taking the view that it was logical for Germany to compensate operators for the shortfall they were suffering: 'The Commission found that the remuneration is primarily based on the forgone profits that the operators of the eight plants would have earned, had they continued operating in the electricity market for four more years, which is less than the average expected lifetime of the plants.'

It is clear that coal has no future in Europe – or anywhere else in the world for that matter. There is simply no way that we can continue to engage in the race against climate change without abandoning coal. Today, the challenge is to identify the best additional instruments to be used in EU climate policy. The principle of emission performance standards (EPS) was one such instrument proposed by the European Parliament three years ago – unsuccessfully. An option is to create a carbon floor price. Another important ingredient would be withdrawing emission certificates from the ETS market as coal-fired power plants close, on a pro rata basis.

Lastly, managing the end of the coal life cycle raises two additional questions. Firstly, the huge costs relating to the closure of lignite mines (restoration of land, groundwater protection and so on) need to be anticipated. This involves levying a tax on lignite mining companies to constitute a fund designed to cover these costs; failing this, taxpayers will once again be footing the bill. Secondly, the social aspect of this transition must be taken into account. In 2018, twelve years after the initially planned deadline, state aid for the coal industry will at last be prohibited, and the loss-making mines in Poland, Spain and Romania will have to close. There is no future for coal in certain regions as a result, so financial assistance to help deal with professional retraining of workers must be provided for.

Assessing the ETS

Eight years on, what assessment can be made of the ETS in view of its initial promises? Coal is as prevalent as ever in the European energy mix. The promise of investment being redirected by means of carbon prices has not been fulfilled either: the price of a tonne of CO_2 was less than €10 in 2009; no investment in wind power, solar power, or CCS has been made on this basis, and none ever will. Instead, green investment has been triggered by specific legislation, such as the directives devoted to renewables and energy efficiency. Today, the ETS could form a safety net, with a level of greenhouse gas emissions not to be exceeded: a sort of red line. However, this would involve the EU setting an ambitious target in this respect. Lastly, the ETS has allowed some money to be brought in thanks to the auctioning of certificates, but only extremely small amounts (given the extent to which CO_2 prices have collapsed), while free allowance allocations have endured. Unfortunately, the funds collected in this way have also been used to plug various gaps in public finances, rather than funding the investments required to combat climate change.

Not one of the attempts to restore the glory of the ETS has succeeded. The European Council has not achieved a majority to raise the 2020 target to more than 20 per cent – already achieved by 2015 – and the half-measures designed to correct the lopsided way the scheme works will not do anything to improve matters. Both the market stability reserve adopted in 2015 and the temporary withdrawal (backloading) of some of the emission certificates are the equivalent of putting sticking plaster on a wooden leg; the result of their implementation on carbon prices has been precisely zero. Former European Commission director Jørgen Henningsen (who became a consultant for the EPC think-tank on his retirement in 2006) was right when he predicted in 2010 the failure of the ETS. He has also confided in me that the recent attempts to reform the ETS were not taken seriously: 'The market does not believe in the virtues of the market stability reserve.'

Even the proposed reform for the fourth phase from 2020 to 2030 remains woefully inadequate. Apparently, neither traders nor financial analysts have been very impressed with the text put forward in July 2015 by Commissioner Miguel Arias Cañete. Experts forecast that the surplus will not be absorbed before 2030, and may even reach the lofty heights of four billion certificates on occasion. The only good news is that the EU has decided on a purely domestic target for 2030. This will prevent the arrival of new international credits on the market. However, care should be taken to ensure that no new flaw is introduced into an already weak system, for instance by coupling the European carbon markets with those implemented in Brazil, China or elsewhere. In view of the purchasing power disparities and of other local specificities, carbon prices in a tied-in system would constitute a terrible weakness. On 5 February 2016, to celebrate the first anniversary of the Energy Union, the Commission's vice president Maroš Šefčovič made a foray into this territory: 'We must support other countries such as China and South Korea in establishing a carbon market, and work to link these together worldwide.' He should think twice before talking in those terms to industrial players in Europe.

One thing is for sure: the ETS will never be a panacea. However, we should not throw the baby out with the bathwater. I am not in favour of abolishing the ETS, since it is a useful system when it comes to having a safety net and generating revenue. However, there needs to be realism as to what it can and cannot achieve. Investments in favour of renewable energy and energy efficiency will only occur as a result of legislation tailored to these fields. In the meantime, the fact is that while it may be dead in the water, the ETS is set to remain the spearhead of EU climate policy. It will be backed by industry – the very same constituency that weakened it – and by energy oligopolies who support a weak market to ambitious sectorial policies on renewables and energy efficiency. Indeed, preparation of the Climate and Energy Package for 2030 turned out to be a demonstration of just how strong these lobbies against energy transition are.

CHAPTER 7

PREPARING CLIMATE AND ENERGY TARGETS FOR 2030

On 22 January 2014, during the presentation of the climate and energy strategy for 2030 to the press, EC president José Barroso, flanked by his commissioners Connie Hedegaard (Climate) and Günther Oettinger (Energy), set the tone from the outset: 'We are well beyond the debate in which you had to be either a Green, or a defender of industry. We believe that these two positions are not contradictory, but can go perfectly well together if they are treated with common sense.' Translation: we have bent over backwards to please industry and painted it green. For my part, I saw red that day, and had good reason to do so.

Without missing a beat, Barroso went on to accept reduced targets for 2030, targets he himself described as 'ambitious and achievable'. In other words, as low as possible: a 40 per cent reduction in greenhouse gas emissions, accompanied by a target of 27 per cent for renewables (a decrease compared to previous years): this set the bar very low, and heads of state cannot be relied upon to raise it. It also placed the bar for energy efficiency very low, with a working target of 25 per cent.

It was no accident that on the very same day, Commissioner for Industry Antonio Tajani presented his paper on an industrial renaissance in Europe. He even went so far as to tacitly acknowledge his colleagues' 2030 package, inviting member states to 'take issues of competitiveness into account more systematically in every area of action', echoing the rhetoric of the European industry lobby. The fact that these two initiatives on the part of the Commission were announced at the same time speaks volumes about its mind-set when it comes to energy transition.

Concerted action on the part of lobbies

Preparation of the 2030 Climate and Energy Package, a flagship project towards the end of the Barroso II Commission's mandate, was the theatre of a major offensive against energy transition. This was to be the time in which those frustrated by the 2020 Climate and Energy Package – BusinessEurope, Eurelectric, the Magritte Group, the conservative governments of the UK, Poland and Spain, the ultra-liberals at the Commission and their ilk – were avenged for 2008.

Throughout 2013, the industry hammered home the same message: 'We support the ETS', even as they drove further nails into the coffin of the carbon market on a daily basis. 2013 was also the year when the Magritte Group established itself and came out with outlandish demands. By mid-2013, these stakeholders had agreed on one clear position: 'ETS-only': upholding the ETS as the only instrument; a flagship instrument; a key instrument; in fact, the sole instrument of Europe's climate and energy policy. This became their mantra. The EU, they chanted, should have just one climate and energy target for 2030 and nothing else – nothing about renewables, and nothing about energy efficiency. The arguments being that support for renewables would destroy competitiveness in Europe, energy efficiency was pointless, and the miracle of the ETS market would solve any and every issue of climate, energy and competitiveness.

This mantra was accompanied by lobbying at the highest levels. Gérard Mestrallet, the CEO of GDF-Suez (later to become Engie), made no secret of it. At his press conference in Brussels on 11 October 2013, he said the following:

> It is up to heads of state to decide, together with the European Commission. So we have decided to visit them all: we've seen President

Hollande; we've had meetings with the Dutch Prime Minister; Mr Cameron has agreed to the principle, as has Angela Merkel and Messrs. Rajoy, Di Rupo, and Letta. Dialogue is ongoing.

The major oligopolies were thus using their economic strength – and their personal networks – to influence policy at the highest level, not only within the Commission and the European Parliament, but also with national political leaders and directly with heads of state and government. One representative of the Magritte Group met President Barroso in autumn 2013, just when the latter was drafting his January 2014 paper on climate and energy policy orientations for 2030. Barroso came away from the meeting firmly convinced that scaling back targets for 2020–2030 was important to ensure the competitiveness of Europe's energy oligopolies.

Bosses provide backup

Gérard Mestrallet and representatives of the Magritte Group were not alone in their campaign. In addition to the large energy firms, European bosses were active from June 2013 onwards, with the publication of a report by BusinessEurope on the 2030 Climate and Energy Package. This shot down all support for renewables: 'The energy prices impact of current support schemes is not viable for the EU's economy.'

Historically, BusinessEurope has always taken a negative stance on the ETS in order to protect electricity-intensive firms. But what explains this attack on renewables and energy efficiency? It appears contradictory, because major users of energy can buy their electricity directly on the wholesale market. In doing so, they have benefited from falling prices, due in part to the collapse of the carbon market and partly to the massive rollout of renewables, while at the same time being largely exempt from the additional taxes and contributions used to fund the modernisation of the grid and support schemes for renewables. Why bother attacking a system which ensures they get cheap electricity? My theory is that BusinessEurope and the Magritte Group have come to an understanding and agreed to a certain division of labour. The electricity-intensive companies are supporting the energy firms in combating renewables, in exchange for which the latter are supporting industry in their attempts to secure exemptions. Indeed, there was some explicit back-scratching a little later, during negotiations on guidelines for state aid.[43]

This has resulted in BusinessEurope receiving support from the gas lobby. In 2008–2009, the gas companies believed they would increase market share to the detriment of coal due to a stronger carbon market, and this opened the way for the Climate and Energy Package to be adopted. As soon as it became clear that the battle against coal was to be lost, however, the gas companies changed their strategy, having understood that they needed to hobble renewables and combat any further directives liable to be as ambitious and binding. Indeed, gas could lose out in the longer term as a result of energy efficiency and renewables: while energy transition called for a number of highly flexible gas-fired power plants, capable of adjusting their output in a matter of minutes, the total volumes involved remained very low. Moreover, since almost half of all gas in Europe is used for heating and a further 20 per cent is used in industry, building renovation and improved industrial processes would lead to a decrease in gas consumption. It is a fact that this has been the case for several years now.

Studies biased against renewable energy

The Commission itself had been contaminated, in the person of Energy Commissioner Günther Oettinger. His cosiness with the business world, more specifically electricity firms EnBW and RWE, has been amply demonstrated. He has never made any secret of his dislike for re-newables, and indeed was proud of the fact that Baden-Württemberg, the *Land* of which he had long been minister president, did not have a single wind farm. It was therefore only natural for him to start

---

43   See Chapter 9, pp. 120–127.

working against renewables as soon as he was appointed, and to carry out a series of attacks against their expansion.

The political context in Germany at the time needs to be kept in mind. In 2009, Angela Merkel's CDU party chose Rösler's liberal FDP party in preference to the SPD Social Democrats, forming a coalition that was less focused on environmental issues. In 2009, the Merkel–Rösler government made a deal with the electricity companies to extend the life of nuclear power and repeal the EEG law on guaranteed feed-in tariffs for renewables. However, the Bavarian CSU opposed halting support for renewables, the latter having brought in substantial revenue for farmers in that *Land* who had gone in for biogas. As a result, the Merkel–Rösler government did not have a majority on this question. After the failure of this offensive at the national level, the hopes of the anti-renewables camp were therefore pinned on Oettinger, a conservative hardliner, doing the dirty work in Brussels instead.

The first shots were fired in April 2010 in the form of a paper from the EWI research institute which strongly condemned the 2009 Renewable Energy Directive.[44] Headed by Professor Marc Oliver Bett-züge, EWI receives financial backing from a large number of energy firms, including Engie, E.ON and EnBW. The study, which made quite a splash, concluded that guaranteed national tariff schemes – one of the pillars of the Renewable Energy Directive – should be halted as a matter of urgency. It suggested that a fully harmonised system of support for renewables across the entire European Union would result in savings of €118–174 billion for the 2008–2020 period, compared to the sum total of national support schemes. That kind of figure was bound to gain attention. However, right at the end of the study, it was conceded that 'this harmonisation gain in RES-E generation may be counteracted by additional costs of e.g. grid enhancements due to higher concentration of intermitting RES-E in certain regions resulting from harmonized support', while also stating that these additional costs 'are not considered in this study'.

---

44   'European RES-E policy analysis', EWI, April 2010, www.ewi.uni-koeln.de.

Academics quickly realised that the study parameters were biased. Mario Ragwitz from the Fraunhofer Institute and Gustav Resch from Vienna University of Technology mounted a counter-analysis.[45] This systematically took apart the EWI team's assumptions. To reach its conclusions, EWI had assumed the failure of European policy by starting with a baseline scenario well below the 20 per cent target for renewables in 2020; it had not included learning curves and decreasing costs for renewables; and to cap it all, it had banked on the unrealistic expansion of electricity networks to transport electricity from certain high-potential locations. For instance, it estimated that the share of renewables in Ireland would skyrocket from 9 per cent to 92 per cent between 2007 and 2020, while those in Estonia would climb from 1 per cent to 79 per cent for the same period. This is cloud cuckoo-land. The conclusion brooks no contradiction: 'Harmonisation of RE support based on simplistic policy options offering uniform support e.g. via a uniform RE certificate trading cannot be recommended.'

EWI conceded some flaws and would publish balanced studies in late 2011 and 2012. They concede that the solution does not necessarily involve the harmonisation of national support schemes, but rather better coordination between member states, opening the door to a moderate expansion of the electricity network. However, this academic victory was not to count for much.

In spring 2010, doubtless inspired by this well-timed study by EWI, Oettinger embarked on the perilous exercise of defining the road map for his mandate as commissioner, drafting a strategic document entitled 'Energy 2020'. The first drafts of this document were a disaster, due largely to the commissioner's unbridled efforts to defend the harmonisation of European support schemes. It is only natural for a new incumbent to seek to make their mark on European energy policy, but it is unacceptable for a commissioner with responsibility for overseeing a directive that had only just been adopted by the European Parliament and the Council to take the liberty of calling it into

---

45   'Quo(ta) vadis, Europe?', RE-Shaping (a project funded by the Intelligent Energy Europe programme), November 2010, www.reshaping-res-policy.eu.

question by viciously attacking its central component: national support schemes. Fortunately, Oettinger did not succeed in imposing his views, and the definitive version of the document adopted in November 2010 is less aggressive, even if it goes astray in justifying a certain degree of convergence and harmonisation between national schemes, stating that 'the market for renewables is moving from a local to a cross-border supply'.

Enter the pro-nuclear lobby

This account would not be complete without mentioning the role of Dieter Helm,[46] the man behind the informal EU summit at Hampton Court into 2005 which put climate on the agenda of EU leaders in 2006 at the request of Tony Blair. In the working document he presented just before the summit, Dieter Helm suggested a 'single low-carbon target' – a demand that states and pro-nuclear lobbies repeat as often as they can. Later to become Oettinger's special adviser, in 2011 the European Commission director-general for Energy, Philip Lowe, appointed Helm to head up the Advisory Group on the Energy Roadmap 2050. Helm relentlessly attacked renewables: 'Offshore wind power is pretty much the most expensive technology that could be deployed to reduce emissions.' Such a wrong forecast in light of the spectacular cost reduction achieved by the sector! A further sample: 'The reality is that many countries will in any case miss their target for renewables (including, almost certainly, the UK), so it would be better to suggest an appropriate strategy for dealing with this, rather than rushing headlong to build wind farms.' In 2012, at the invitation of the Bruegel think-tank, Helm once again held forth against the European Union's 20-20-20 strategies, 'a failure', and against renewables, 'expensive and making very little contribution' to combating climate change. According to him, the alternative solution consists in nuclear

---

46   Dieter Helm is a professor at Oxford University. He has held a large number of strategic consultancy positions within the UK government, including for the Department of Trade and Industry, the environment ministry, and the Prime Minister's office, as well as for the European Commission and the Polish government.

power and carbon capture and storage. The very same Dieter Helm was also the adviser to the Polish government, one of the most polluting countries in the world.

In January 2014, alongside Professor Bettzüge, we find Dieter Helm invited by France Stratégie, to give his opinion on the Energy Union. Like his counterpart Bettzüge, Helm did not mince words in his criticisms of both Germany ('the highly polluting path chosen by Germany is better described as brown rather than green') and EU targets:

> Current renewable energy has a negligible impact on global emissions [of greenhouse gases] and by pushing European energy prices upwards, encourages deindustrialisation. It is also incredibly expensive. What possible reason could there be to repeat this madness for 2030? The answer depends above all on the lobbying carried out by all the beneficiaries of subsidies, and campaigns conducted by environmental groups. The aim with respect to energy efficiency is too poorly defined to be coherent in any way ... The 27–27 components are especially worthless.[47]

Meanwhile Professor Bettzüge, a hard-core liberal, was to be wheeled out again on several occasions, most recently in a study by France Stratégie.[48] He attacked the EU measures pertaining to renewables and energy efficiency, taking the view that 'none of these measures can have a significant impact on emissions levels in the sectors at which the EU ETS is directed'. He went on to criticise 'the micromanagement of specific targets, for reasons of dogma rather than strategy'. According to him, the EU's 'public responses (investment in renewable energy and energy efficiency) are not as efficient as is generally claimed'. Indeed, he condemned this policy, based on distinct targets, likening it to 'a belief in a Holy Grail that has acquired the status of dogma in EU debate'.

This textbook obfuscation resulted in the French government taking a wishy-washy position during the European Council meeting in October 2014 at which the 2030 framework was discussed. Why did

---

47   Ibid.
48   'L'Union de l'énergie', France Stratégie, August 2015, www.strategie.gouv.fr.

decision makers at France Stratégie picked such disputed experts to advise President Hollande?

Renewable bubbles

One of the major criticisms of renewables at this time was that renewable support schemes created a windfall effect, which in turn created bubbles by artificially inflating investors' margins due to poorly calibrated feed-in tariffs. Some used these bubbles as a pretext to condemn the expansion of renewables by claiming that the Renewable Energy Directive resulted in high costs for end users. However, some countries, such as Denmark, Sweden and Portugal, have progressed well towards their targets, despite their pro-renewables policy being relatively cheap compared to others. Blame for the poor calibration that can be observed in Spain, the Czech Republic, Belgium and Germany cannot be laid at the feet of Brussels and the EU Renewable Energy Directive – these decisions were taken domestically.

Moreover, the bubbles that renewables are said to have generated actually relate solely to the photovoltaic sector. Their origin is due to a phenomenon nobody could foresee in Europe: the will of China to become world leader in this sector. From 2008 onwards, China decided to invest in its production capacity for photovoltaic cells and modules in order to capture the growth of the sector in Europe, particularly in Germany. Accompanied by state banks, the Chinese government practised large-scale dumping, subsidising production capacity and spurring competition between Chinese regions. Rather less well known is the fact that China's dominance is largely founded on machine tools produced by Swiss and German manufacturers. The latter have exported billions of euros' worth of machine tools over the years, thereby contributing to China's newly found strike power. To cut a long story short, thanks to the resources brought to bear, Chinese factories quickly came to account for an increasing share of world photovoltaic production capacity. The dizzying fall of solar panel prices on the global market that ensued sounded the death knell for European producers, who could not hope to rival their Chinese competitors when it came to production costs. Today, seven of the ten largest players in the market worldwide are based in China[49] (two others are in Japan, and one is in the United States).

However, the politicians took too long to respond to this new state of affairs, and to adjust their guaranteed buy-back tariffs in view of the changes in the global market. The profit margins of solar project developers were initially reasonable, but quickly became far too large following the collapse of the price of solar panels: this is what led to the appearance of speculative bubbles. The authorities obviously had to respond: Germany, for instance, drastically cut its solar power subsidies, although it did not penalise the whole of the renewable sector by imposing retrospective changes. Today, the country has a huge installed solar power capacity totalling 40GW, and this is set to increase still further.

The pain in Spain

Meanwhile, other governments made the most of this temporary instability to launch a full-scale attack on the entire renewables sector including wind power, despite it being entirely unrelated to the matter in hand. Spain is a case in point in this respect. It had accumulated a long-standing tariff deficit in its electricity system for years and this deficit ballooned under the Aznar government ahead of the 2004 elections, with the latter freezing electricity prices at artificially low levels in a purely politically motivated decision. Zapatero's socialist government, which came to power in 2004, did not dare abolish such a measure, increasing the deficit still further. To make matters worse still, there was also a 3–4GW bubble forming itself in parallel, a consequence of the 2008 subprime crisis in the US. In late 2008 and early 2009, Spain had experienced a huge influx of funds from the US directed at solar power – viewed as a blue-chip market in which analysts discerned opportunities for cash investments.

Spain had seen a huge increase in its electricity consumption in the 2000s, and had equipped itself with capacity in renewables and

---

49   'Trina Solar prend la tête du classement des fournisseurs de panneaux PV', *L'Écho du solaire*, 30 April 2015, www.lechodusolaire.fr.

gas, particularly by means of new gas pipelines, LNG terminals and a whole string of new gas/steam turbines based on 'take-or-pay' gas supply contracts. Then came the combination of the economic crisis and the advent of energy efficiency; electricity demand flat-lined and the country found itself with overcapacity. As a result, renewables entered into competition with conventional sources of energy.

A choice therefore presented itself: shutting down legacy power plants to make way for renewables, or halting renewables to protect the historic power stations. Iberdrola, Endesa and GasNatural (which had just bought the coal-related assets of Unión Fenosa) jumped at the opportunity. Dismayed by the prospect of a German scenario in which solar power would be democratised by being placed in the hands of citizens, the electricity companies elected to kill two birds – absorbing the tariff deficit, and getting rid of renewables once and for all (including citizens' investment) – with one stone. The Rajoy government (in which the current Climate and Energy Commissioner, Miguel Arias Cañete, was Agriculture and Environment Minister) implemented retrospective changes, accusing the renewables sector of being the sole party responsible for the huge tariff deficit while creating new subsidy regimes for fossil fuels.

Spain thus chose the worst possible remedy. Retroactive regulatory changes affect the attractiveness of a sector deemed too unpredictable. Access to credit subsequently deteriorated. In actual fact, the tariff deficit argument is invalid. A 2014 study demonstrated that Spain's cumulative tariff deficit of some €40 billion would have been higher still without the benefit of renewables, which generated some €7 billion of savings through lower electricity prices.[50] At the end of the day, Spain has placed itself in the most ironic of situations: by slamming the brakes on renewables, the former champion of wind power is in grave danger of not attaining its 20 per cent target in 2020. Another knock-on effect has been that wholesale electricity prices have inevitably risen. This of course is to the liking of the historic operators, who

---

50   'Study of the macroeconomic impact of renewable energies in Spain', Asociación de empresas de energia renovables, 2014.

can rely on the lack of electricity interconnection with neighbouring countries to prolong this favourable (for them) state of affairs and ensure that wholesale prices do not converge downwards with the rest of Europe, despite tear-jerking accounts by politicians of the isolation of the Iberian Peninsula. An important victory for Iberdrola, Endesa and GasNatural Fenosa.

Bubble benefits

Who remembers the bursting of the dotcom bubble in 2000? Admittedly considerable financial damage was done, but there was not so much as a dent in the growth of the Internet. It was little more than a childhood illness as a swiftly growing market came of age. When it comes to solar power, the overheating witnessed in Germany was not entirely fruitless: without the German market, the Chinese would never have invested so massively in the production of solar panels, and so there would never have been such low prices. Solar power relies on semiconductor technology: this is the preserve of the digital world, which experiences extremely short innovation cycles; wind power, on the other hand, is tied to mechanical engineering, in which innovation cycles are longer. As a result, the price of solar panels is coming down faster than that of wind turbines.

In any case, bubbles on certain domestic markets have been used to put feed-in tariffs for renewables into question. As a result, a large number of member states have shifted to a system of awarding allowances on the basis of auctions; this also allows regulation to be pegged to quantity rather than price. This shift has also come about with the blessings of DG Comp. The traditional market players could not be more delighted: the change has slowed the growth of renewables. The massive administrative complexity entailed by this type of scheme is more favourable to large, well-established corporations than grassroots initiatives.

The genuine but limited existence of bubbles in the solar power sector thus provided an ideal pretext to impose sweeping changes impacting all renewables, shifting away from guaranteed tariffs to auctioned feed-in premiums.

Scenarios under starter's orders

At the beginning of 2010, everybody was aware that the European Commission was preparing its own scenarios for 2030 and 2050 and so rushed to put forward their own particular forecast in an attempt to influence these. When it came to the outlook for renewable energy in Europe, the key contenders included the following:

- Eurelectric's scenario, 'Power Choices', devised in 2011 by Professor Pantelis Capros, and his PRIMES model, developed by the University of Athens. This naturally gave pride of place to nuclear power, whose share of Europe's electricity production pie was predicted to increase to 28 per cent by 2050, and CCS, with fossil fuels accounting for 31 per cent.
- The European Climate Foundation's November 2011 forecast, based on a low-carbon scenario in 2050 for the electricity sector, with more realistic figures for renewables. However, it did not provide for the abandonment of nuclear power, and was optimistic as regards CCS. Furthermore, it anticipated a great many new high-tension lines and overestimated the deployment of large, centralised renewable projects to the detriment of broader citizens' participation.
- The Green Vision scenario, developed by Felix Matthes' Öko-Institut and published in January 2011, set out a path towards complete 'decarbonation' of the European electricity system by 2050, thanks to renewable energy (90 per cent of the energy mix) and a proactive policy in favour of energy efficiency and grid modernisation.
- The proposals of the European Renewable Energy Council, EREC, aimed to reach 96 per cent renewables in 2050 (100 per cent in the power sector) with an intermediate step of 43 per cent in 2030.

Adopted in December 2011, Günther Oettinger's energy roadmap to 2050 ended up being based on Capros' model. This roadmap does have the advantage of offering a whole range of scenarios based on highly variable proportions of renewables, energy efficiency, nuclear power and CCS. The 'high renewables' scenario appears to be the most virtuous in the document when it comes to bringing down energy bills and dependence, for systemic costs that are very close to the baseline scenario. However, some of the parameters used are open to debate: the method used to calculate the 'high-efficiency' scenario make this option extremely expensive, due to the discount rates used in the model. Another area of uncertainty is the 'low nuclear scenario'.

Despite a range of scenarios demonstrating the possibility of aiming for 30–35 per cent renewable energy by 2030, the Commission decided to suggest a lower target of 27 per cent. How can this lack of ambition be explained? Instead of basing their proposals on credible scenarios, Barroso and Oettinger made the arbitrary call that Poland would never accept more than 40 per cent of greenhouse gas emission reductions. However, scenarios demonstrate that any target of more than 27 per cent for renewables would automatically involve this 40 per cent target being exceeded. As a result, the Commission opted for the minimalist figure of 27 per cent.

The travesty of governance

The 20-20-20 objectives for 2020 come along with robust govern-ance involving national binding targets. When Barroso announced his targets for 2030, talking in terms of a 'binding target in terms of renewable energy across the EU', this was nothing short of a huge travesty: the prospect of the Commission launching infringement proceedings against itself if this target was not achieved was simply unthinkable. Barroso was seeking to save face, but in fact he achieved nothing more than the destruction of existing governance regarding renewables (a combination of EU targets, binding national objec-tives, national financial support schemes, and cooperation mecha-nisms in place between member states) by caving into the position of the UK, which wanted nothing more to do with binding national targets. In his letter to Barroso in December 2013, David Cameron went further still, demanding the elimination of the targets for green-house gases, renewables and energy efficiency in favour of a single climate target.

The reason for national targets is simple. Renewables are physical infrastructures with an influence on a country's electrical system, the design of its grid, and its spatial planning. In the absence of any national policy, there is no infrastructure development, and no backing from governments to support projects locally. In the absence of binding national targets, there is less incentive to invest in renewables, since there is less security for investors. This uncertainty will then have to be reflected by banks in higher costs of access to capital. For capital-intensive sectors such as renewables, this is very bad news.

How can a robust instrument be capable of replacing binding national targets? Two years on from Barroso's vapid proposals, the Commission has nothing more than a few sketchy ideas. It is considering establishing a specific budget line that would allow renewables to be funded from the EU budget. But 1 per cent more renewables would be equivalent to at least €8–12 billion a year – or a massive €40–60 billion as part of the next multiannual financial framework review. What hope could there be of a political majority for such a sum? Realistically speaking, none whatsoever.

To avoid certain member states acting as stowaways without making any contribution to achieving EU targets, in spring 2016 France and Germany came up with a joint document designed to put forward their idea of a 'gap filler' mechanism being established to make up this potential shortfall. Under this proposal, countries that do not go far enough compared to national benchmarks would have to pay into an EU fund for the development of new renewable energy projects, until such time as the target fixed for the EU as a whole has been achieved. This option deserves closer examination; nevertheless, I remain convinced that the existing form of governance is the best way forward. It needs to be preserved while improving everything that can be improved, in particular by moving on from virtual cross-border cooperation and statistical trading to genuine joint projects.[51]

---

51   See Chapter 18, p. 247.

ETS-only or bust

The 2030 Climate and Energy Package deals a harsh blow to energy transition, embodying a lack of ambition. With less than a year left in their respective mandates, Barroso and Oettinger both implemented nothing less than a scorched-earth policy. It represents a complete denial of the very policy that delivered Barroso's success in terms of climate matters. Indeed, the main lesson to be learned since 2007–2008, with the launch of the 2020 climate policy, is that the EU had got the issue of 'multi-instrument' policy right.

The EU has managed to stay on track for its 2020 climate change targets thanks to investments in renewables and energy efficiency. The Ecologic institute comes to the same conclusion:

> The three targets serve different purposes, all of which are worthwhile political objectives in their own. Moreover, they are mutually support-ive of each other. And having multiple targets represents a hedging strategy against political failure in one target area.[52]

The European Commission director-general for climate Jos Delbeke acknowledged as much during a presentation at Carbon Expo on 20 May 2014, in which he explained that between 2008 and 2012, some 86 per cent of the decrease in emissions was attributable to the decrease in energy intensity combined with less carbon-intensive energy (in particular, thanks to renewables).

After those seeking to slow down or even prevent energy transition had enfeebled the ETS and the position of renewables, they moved on to target energy efficiency. In this aim, they were to benefit from crucial support within the European Commission itself.

---

52   'The next EU climate and energy package', Ecologic Institute, 15 August 2014, www.ecologic.eu.

CHAPTER 8

THE 2030 ENERGY
EFFICIENCY TARGETS

Within the space of six months in 2014, the Barroso Commission succeeded in destroying all Europe's ambitions when it came to energy efficiency. The chances of bringing down Europeans' energy bills evaporated, as did the chances of cutting Europe's gas imports, despite the acute crisis with Russia. Officially, it all began on 22 January 2014 with a presentation by the Commission of its 2030 climate and energy strategy. It was then that Commissioner Oettinger announced an evaluation of the Energy Efficiency Directive, 'looking at the progress made towards achieving the 2020 target' before proposing a target for 2030. His aim was already clear: 'The Commission's analysis shows that achieving a 40 per cent reduction in greenhouse gas emissions would require increased levels of energy savings, amounting to some 25 per cent in 2030,' he announced. What he left unsaid was that a 25 per cent target for 2030 would in fact halve present-day energy efficiency efforts. It was therefore wholly hypocritical to talk in terms of 'increased levels'.

How did this sorry state of affairs come about?

An all-out attack from industry
There is still huge potential for energy efficiency in industry, not only in terms of optimising processes but also through improved energy efficiency for pumps, valves and motors. Indeed, Swedish firms such

as steel makers SSAB have undertaken research projects designed to bring their CO_2 emissions down to zero by means of improved process performance. The Norwegian group Hydro has done something similar for aluminium. The EU's Energy Efficiency Directive enshrined the principle of energy audits in large companies, and the measures implemented have in many cases resulted in savings. Between 1990 and 2009, there was a 30 per cent drop in European industry's energy intensity.

GDP GROWTH DECOUPLED FROM ENERGY CONSUMPTION SINCE 2006

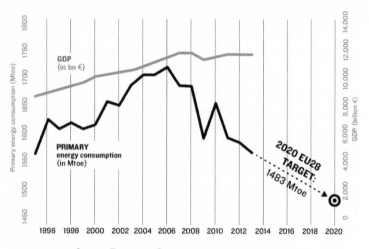

Source: European Commission © REVOLVE MEDIA

There have even been national programmes to stimulate energy efficiency in industry, such as the Swedish PFE programme, under which tax exemptions are granted to industrial companies that commit to investing in energy efficiency measures. Sadly, the system was deemed unlawful by DG Comp.

The campaign waged by lobbyists representing industrial interests in Brussels is, however, ideological in nature; energy efficiency restricts consumption and therefore, it is argued, hampers growth. Nothing could be further from the truth. The Commission's report published on 20 July 2014 shows that 'well before the crisis hit in

2008, the EU had started to decouple economic growth from energy consumption through increased energy efficiency. An increasing decoupling of economic growth and energy consumption has continued since then, driven by price signals and by a comprehensive set of energy efficiency policies.'

Despite this, BusinessEurope and BASF lobbied against the Energy Efficiency Directive, on the grounds that growth in that sector should be based on increased consumption of gas, and therefore of energy as a whole. So industrial firms complained, even though the Energy Efficiency Directive was wholly painless for them, indeed, produced positive effects by bringing down their production costs, in particular thanks to process optimisation.

Industry argued that the ETS was the best way of handling their economic optimum. The European Commission agreed with them, convinced that the ETS is 'the main tool to drive energy efficiency in industry'. This makes no sense at all: with an ETS price of less than €5/tCO$_2$ and very low electricity prices for major industrial players, there is no encouragement to invest in improved energy productivity. As a result, the Commission's 23 July report automatically exempts industries covered by the ETS from any binding measure in terms of energy efficiency: 'The regulatory framework ... is in place, with the EU Emissions Trading Scheme.' What could be simpler than that? Industry has gained yet another exemption, even though energy efficiency is the only way to remain competitive compared to the United States, which enjoys lower gas prices.

Challenging the models

The low energy efficiency target of 25 per cent is the result of a tug-of-war between different Commission departments. DG Ener was in favour of a more ambitious target, but DG Clima did absolutely nothing to progress the issue: its director-general, Jos Delbeke, is convinced that the development of energy efficiency is inversely proportional to the usefulness of the ETS in bringing down greenhouse gas emissions. As a result, DG Clima basically stabbed DG Ener in the back, on the twin grounds that 'too much energy efficiency will kill the ETS' and 'the ETS is cheaper than energy efficiency'. The reasoning is the same as that put forward to scale back renewable energy targets for 2030 as, according to Delbeke, the ETS is sufficient for the purpose. In January 2013, he declared that 'the renewable energy target was very useful in the past. Will it be as useful in the future? That's a question that needs to be examined.' Just as in the case of renewables, calculating energy efficiency targets solely on the basis of greenhouse gas emissions targets stifles EU ambitions as regards both the climate and energy.

When it came to the 2030 targets, the Commission had decided on its position before even examining the various possible scenarios. For instance, in January 2014 it was decided at the highest level of the Commission that the EU should not plan for a GHG reduction of more than 40 per cent for 2030, since Poland considered this to be the maximum acceptable level. The Commission therefore skewed its model to achieve the desired result. In order to obtain an allegedly optimal figure of 25 per cent for energy efficiency, the Commission deliberately inflated the model's discount rate for energy efficiency: how else can one explain the fact that in a world of historically low interest rates, the Commission came up with a discount rate of 17.5 per cent for thermal renovation of buildings in Europe? According to Brook Riley from Friends of the Earth Europe, a 17.5 per cent discount rate is more or less the level observed on the financial market for high-risk activities such as oil drilling in Iraq...[53] Models were run with the sole aim of artificially inflating the costs and thereby supplying grounds for a pitifully low target of 25 per cent. In this instance, modelling was carried out simply to provide support for a decision after the fact.

And in any case, which model was used? It was, of course, none other than PRIMES, a matrix developed in 1993 by Professor Pantelis Capros at the University of Athens that has since enjoyed a virtual monopoly when it comes to the Commission's modelling. From one contract to

---

53   'Battle of the Discount Rates', European Council for an Energy Efficient Economy, 1 April 2015, http://www.eceee.org/all-news/columnists/Brook-Riley/battle-of-the-discount-rates

the next, the model has acquired an increasingly predominant role in Europe's energy conversations. The fundamental problem with PRIMES is the lack of transparency about the parameters used. The secret of this infernal machine was finally revealed when the German environment minister asked Professor Capros to evaluate the European Commission's 2030 scenarios, which had been modelled by none other than Capros himself. The result came as a surprise. In Brussels, the impact assessment based on the PRIMES model concluded that 'a main target for greenhouse gas emissions reduction represents the least cost pathway to a low carbon economy which of itself should drive an increased share of renewable energy and energy savings in the Union'. In other words, focus on the ETS and everything else will follow naturally. In Berlin, however, the same model leads to a diametrically opposed conclusion:

> The PRIMES-based projections confirm that there exists a workable combination of ambitious greenhouse gases target and high shares of renewable energy sources and energy efficiency ... Clearly the combined trio-target and Market Stability Reserve scenario has merits regarding policy implementation, reduction of uncertainty and stability/predictability of price signals for investors thereby reducing costs of capital.

So what is the explanation for the mysterious fact that PRIMES-Berlin contradicts PRIMES-Brussels? The answer is quite simply the discount rates used by the model. In his German study, Professor Capros stated that the PRIMES model was identical to the one used in Brussels, with just one exception: 'Within the area of renewable energy and energy efficiency lower financial risks, which lead to lower cost of capital, were assumed.' This demonstrates the limits of using a model; by tweaking its parameters, you can obtain any result you wish, in much the same way as a jukebox: drop in a coin and it will play any song you like.

On 21 October 2015, I challenged him at the European Parliament about this ridiculous state of affairs. Visibly irritated, he retorted that his academic references were 'irreproachable'. That aside, the question is whether or not proper professional practice was observed. Should the Commission not have a more transparent model, similar to the open-source model used by the US Department of Energy, rather than a black box such as PRIMES? The American system is based on free access to the model. In return, when signing the agreement, users undertake to provide complete transparency as to the parameters they use, such as the estimated costs of new nuclear power plants, lifespans, the cost of wind power and so on. I would like to see a similar model in Europe in order to impose greater transparency on lobbies, NGOs and the Commission itself. Everyone should use the same model and be fully transparent about the parameters they use in order for the debate to be truly democratic.

An attempt in this direction is currently underway. When Dominique Ristori became director-general for Energy, he launched research into a new model, Potencia, developed in-house by the Commission's Joint Research Centre. Four years on, the model has still not seen the light of day, even if we are told (every year) that it is to be operational very soon. Little wonder that unofficially, EC civil servants have renamed the project 'Patientia'! The Commission is working on it, but cannot seem to calibrate it. Instead of working in isolation, it should have put together a consortium comprising several European model-builders; this would have accelerated works and inspired greater confidence in the model itself.

What is for certain is that the great weakness of PRIMES is the fact that it is largely top-down, basing its forecasts on historic trends and using various econometric calculations, whereas the new model would be bottom-up; in other words, it would take production technologies, behaviours and energy uses into greater consideration. This would make it less conservative when it comes to energy efficiency and decentralised energy. There is just one drawback: it will come too late for the Commission's modelling exercise for 2030. I do, however, hope that it will be released one day and be open-source.

Hope from Juncker?

However, a response to these shenanigans began to emerge. On 17 June

2014, in a letter to the commission, no fewer than nine ministers representing seven EU countries (Germany, Belgium, the Netherlands, Greece, Ireland, Luxembourg and Portugal) appealed for a binding target for energy efficiency: 'The signatories of this letter share the conviction that the forthcoming review of the progress towards the 2020 energy efficiency target should present a proposal for a binding target for energy efficiency in 2030.'[54]

On 9 July Jean-Claude Juncker, who headed up the European People's Party list that won the May 2014 European elections and therefore qualified as a candidate for the presidency of the European Commission, met the Greens as he did the rounds canvassing support for his appointment by the Parliament in mid-July. After a discussion about the importance of energy efficiency in reducing energy dependence, cutting bills and improving enterprise competitiveness, Juncker committed to a binding target of at least 30 per cent. The Greens were appreciative, and many of them supported him during the vote on his investiture. During his investiture speech on 15 July, he said: 'I believe that a binding target of 30 per cent energy efficiency is an absolute minimum if we want to be credible and look to the future. We cannot claim to be leaders when it comes to climate change policy if we do not become better at energy efficiency.'

The following week, the Barroso II Commission was to put forward its target in this respect, so this speech by the future president created quite a stir. Panic ensued for the intervening week. José Manuel Barroso and Catherine Day wanted to stick to 25 per cent in order to save face. On Wednesday 23 July, during the meeting of the College of Commissioners, the most progressive members (Neelie Kroes, Cecilia Malmström, Martine Reicherts and Connie Hedegaard) put an ultimatum to the Commission president: 'Either we decide on 30 per cent now, or we leave the whole thing to Juncker.' The wrangling continued. Barroso had to postpone his press conference. He and Day were furious at being put in the minority, but they had no

---

54   'Call for a proposal on a binding energy efficiency target for 2030 in light of the forthcoming EED-review in July 2014', www.eceee.org.

choice but to capitulate. They were forced to raise the target from 25 per cent to 30 per cent, albeit at the expense of various concessions. The paper, approved at the very last minute, therefore concludes as follows:

> Given the increased relevance of bolstering EU energy security and reducing the Union's import dependency, the Commission considers it appropriate to propose a higher target of 30 per cent. This would increase the costs of the 2030 Framework by €20 billion per annum but would still deliver tangible economic and energy security benefits.

These words hastily added at the end of the document run counter to everything else in it. As such, they represent a victory over the wishes of Barroso and Day.

The battle is not over

The European Parliament is on a more ambitious line and has been constantly renewing its demands for a binding target of 40 per cent for energy efficiency, both in its motion ahead of the COP21 in October 2015 and in the Energy Union resolution adopted in December 2015. Most recently, the Parliament again voted in favour of the 40 per cent figure in its resolution on the progress of the Energy Efficiency Directive adopted on June 2016, despite efforts on the part of the German conservative rapporteur Markus Pieper to thwart ambitions in this respect.

The EU Parliament has also been able to force the Commission to model a range of scenarios of between 27 per cent and 40 per cent energy efficiency. In addition, in the summer of 2016 European Parliament president Martin Schulz wrote to President Juncker to advocate more objective modelling for the development of forthcoming proposals on cutting CO_2 emissions in sectors not covered by the ETS, energy efficiency and renewables. In the latest modelling, the discount rate has been reduced to 10 per cent, which is progress of a sort. A 4 per cent discount rate would be really honest, though, if the multiple benefits of energy efficiency are to be taken into account. Such a step would have quite an impact. Indeed, a study by Ecofys published by the EU's Coalition for Energy Savings shows that with a discount rate of 4 per cent, an energy efficiency target of 35–40 per cent becomes profitable. It is therefore vital for the Commission to change its tune and stop simply opting systematically for the cheapest option without taking into account the non-economic benefits of energy efficiency on air quality, energy security, jobs, the reduction of energy poverty and the like. After all, when you buy a car, do you automatically choose the least expensive one? Not necessarily – and yet this is precisely what the European Commission is doing in recommending a 25 per cent target.

The unremitting assault by those keen to dig the grave of energy efficiency has ultimately paid off. This, despite the fact that energy efficiency addresses a whole range of issues in Europe's energy policy, such as making energy efficiency cuts to household bills, increasing the competitiveness of manufacturing industry, decreasing energy dependence, helping to combat climate change and reducing air pollution. The fact is that putting this issue at the top of policymakers' agendas is a constant battle. January 2014 was to mark a setback in this respect. And with a few months left to run before the end of the Barroso II Commission, energy transition was by no means home and dry.

CHAPTER 9

GUIDELINES ON STATE AID

Around one month prior to the planned approval of the guidelines on state aid for environmental protection and energy on 9 April 2014, I got a phone call from a worried European Commission civil servant, who said: 'If there isn't a lot of external political pressure, we're going to lose everything: departments are attacking the feed-in tariffs for renewable energy!' I suddenly realised that the stakes were high and marshalled all the resources I could in an attempt to minimise the damage.

What are these guidelines on state aid? The guidelines are an instrument which, potentially, are a very practical way of reducing congestion at the Commission. They are a kind of template that member states who wish to grant public aid to certain sectors must abide by. The Commission has a whole series of them for different fields: railways, research, airports and of course energy and the environment. They are quite useful, in that they do away with the need for an ad hoc examination procedure. They allow the Commission to make quicker rulings when a member state informs it of a support scheme, such as a premium paid to renewable electricity producers or a tax exemption for industrial firms. All they have to do to make a decision is refer to the guidelines rather than having to carry out a thorough investigation of the measure, which can take months. Member states and the companies in question work to comply with the guidelines ahead of any national state subsidy being granted, in order for validation by DG Comp to be little more than a formality.

However, I'm increasingly under the impression that when it comes to energy, the guidelines are more of a political instrument than a means of cutting red tape. They are used to oppose feed-in tariffs for renewables, despite these being guaranteed by the Renewable Energy Directive adopted by the European Parliament and the Council, which represent 450 million citizens and twenty-eight EU governments respectively. Naturally, DG Comp defends their approach to the hilt, and quickly takes offence at any attempt to dispute them. It argues that the guidelines are simply an interpretation of the EU Treaty, which takes precedence over the directives and regulations adopted by lawmakers. The fact is, however, that this is an antidemocratic procedure and an abuse of power, given the degree to which a few lines in the relevant clauses of the Treaty are extrapolated into one hundred and fifty pages of guidelines.

Renewables fall under the scrutiny of DG Comp

Right from his arrival in Brussels, as a declared renewables sceptic Commissioner Oettinger went to work behind the scenes to dismantle national support schemes. In doing so, he joined forces with the major electricity firms in their fight against feed-in tariffs for renewables. Meanwhile, the ultra-liberals within DG Comp sought nothing less than the abolition of feed-in tariffs for renewables, on the grounds that they represented a distortion of competition in a pure and perfect energy market. This is ludicrous in view of the fact that fossil fuels have been the greatest beneficiaries of state subsidies for decades, and that the nuclear debt exceeds subsidies to renewables – as the Commission itself acknowledges.[55] This is yet another illustration of the principle of double standards that all too often prevails at the Commission.

Feed-in tariffs are a fundamental part of energy transition; without them, what individual would run the risk of committing their personal funds to a renewable energy project that requires a huge capital contribution? What farmer would imperil a lifetime's savings

---

55   'Subsidies and Costs of EU Energy', Ecofys, 11 November 2014.

to install a biogas installation? Feed-in tariffs are vital if electricity production is to be democratised – an outcome resulting in a new form of competition for energy firms. Both the enemies of renewables and hard-core liberals therefore wish to abolish feed-in tariffs and re-place them with calls for tender, a cumbersome process with inherent risks. Calls for tender are necessarily complicated to respond to, and they need huge bank guarantees and require contracts to be signed with turbine manufacturers.[56] Each of these aspects creates barriers to entry for SMEs, municipalities and individuals alike. The prospect of an individual seeking to set up their own solar panels being able to compete with a huge company such as EDF to win a call for tender is simply unthinkable.

Article 3 of the Renewables Directive could not be clearer when it comes to national support schemes: in order to reach the directive's targets, 'member states may, inter alia, apply the following measures: (a) support schemes; (b) measures of cooperation between different member states and with third countries'. Subsequently defining new conditions for support for renewables by revising the guidelines is an abuse of power on the part of the Commission, since it runs com-pletely contrary to a piece of legislation. Guidelines drawn up by over zealous functionaries should not take precedence over European law.

DG Comp has never concealed its hostility towards renewables, seen as the target to be brought down. Brigitta Renner-Loquenz, the head of unit for state aid for environmental protection and energy, made this clear during a conference on the subject on 12 April 2013: '[There is] pressure from intermittent renewable energy sources and the decommissioning of conventional power plants on infrastructure. Intermittent renewable energy sources causes concerns on stability of the network and generation adequacy.'

As a result of this, in 2014 part of the Commission therefore sought to overturn the definitive text of the 2009 Renewables Directive – perhaps unsurprisingly, since it was a long way from the original

---

56   These issues have been highlighted by the International Renewable Energy Agency (IRENA) in its auction handbook.

draft. Initially, the Commission wanted to establish a European green certificate market as the only support scheme for renewables, rather than national schemes: these green certificates would be tradable, exchangeable and valued on a market, with a value fluctuating with supply and demand. With the benefit of the bitter experience of the ETS, the European Parliament and the Council opposed this, since the system would have led to high price volatility and higher costs for the system as a whole. Since the value of the certificate would be calculated according to the value of the MWh generated from the most recently installed capacity, terrestrial wind power and solar power would have the same value as offshore wind power, a more recent and therefore more expensive technology, offering the former unjustly high profit margins. Green certificates could work in a highly uniform market in which the marginal costs of various technologies are pretty much equivalent in each country. This is the case in Scandinavia, where renewable targets are achievable largely due to biomass and onshore wind power, which have similar costs. However, extending this principle to the whole of the EU is a pipe dream. Why on earth should German wind power have the same value as Romanian wind power when their capital costs and operating conditions differ so widely? Renewables always include a local component. A single market for green certificates would be in denial of this obvious fact.

A study carried out by Ecofys in partnership with a great many European research institutes has analysed all European support schemes, and has reached precisely the same conclusion: a certificates market would 'mean strongly increasing price risks for plant operators' and 'tend to favour incumbent players', while 'windfall profits may occur for the lower cost technologies'. In view of this, such a system 'may be useful in countries with low differences in the generation costs of potential RES-projects'.[57] It is therefore understandable that the Renewable Energy Directive restricted itself to guarantees of origin, designed simply to trace renewable production, but did not create

---

57   'Design Features of Support Schemes for Renewable Electricity', Ecofys, 27 January 2014.

any market on which they could be traded. This was in order not to jeopardise making renewables a success story in Europe.

The myth of technology-neutral auctions

One of the only European countries to have opted for a system of technology-neutral auctions is the Netherlands. It is perhaps no co-incidence that Alexander Italianer, the current secretary-general of the Commission, who headed up DG Comp at the time along with Gert-Jan Koopman, deputy director-general with responsibility for this matter, are both Dutchmen.

And today, the Netherlands are well behind other countries when it comes to the 2020 targets. The reason for this is to be found in the Commission's 2015 progress report, which states that 'the uncertainty concerning investment incentives resulting from reforms of the sup-port schemes was the main reason why the Netherlands' renewable energy development was lagging behind'. What possible point could there be in disseminating a method that has been shown to be so counter-productive? Even the Dutch themselves have made adjust-ments since; having failed to generate sufficient investment, they have set up a dedicated auction system for offshore wind power. Limited, specific, well-designed auctions are not such a bad idea. They make sense when it comes to large-scale projects to which access is any case limited to major developers with the relevant technical and adminis-trative capabilities. Indeed, in 2016 Denmark used such a scheme to fund the Kriegers Flak offshore windfarm, at a cost of €50/MWh. But the general use of technology-neutral auctions is systemic nonsense, since the various renewable energy sources have complementary properties. Once the Dutch had extracted themselves from this ide-ological straitjacket, in July 2016 the Netherlands were also able to finance an offshore windfarm at a cost of €72/MWh. The most recent German tender was awarded in early April 2017 to a €0/MWh bidder! It means that under some very specific conditions, project developers could build offshore wind parks without public subsidies on top of wholesale market prices. However, this is far from being the truth on most markets and this approach is extremely risky as it bets on a future meaningful increase of market prices.

The only benefit of technology-specific auctions is that they are a better reflection of real costs than feed-in tariffs, which are sometimes poorly calibrated. However, they impose limits on size by restricting total installed power per year in any given country. Since forecasts and potential are very often underestimated, a generalised auction system ends up capping investments and therefore slowing down energy transition.

In spite of all this, in the final version of the guidelines on state aid adopted in June 2014, technology-specific auctions are the exception and technology-neutral auctions the rule: 'The bidding process can be limited to specific technologies where a process open to all generators would lead to a suboptimal result which cannot be addressed in the process design.' In summary, thanks to Joaquín Almunia and Oettinger, the Commission has ended up imposing a broken system on the EU.

Blackmail

For their part, France and Germany had guaranteed tariff systems that they were not about to abandon. Indeed, the two countries had committed to support schemes during negotiations on the 2008 Renewables Directive. How did the Commission manage to succeed in the face of these two governments?

Here's what happened in France. Anti-wind power associations, who had joined forces in the Vent de colère federation, attacked the state over its wind power tariffs. They won a partial victory at the European Court of Justice: in a December 2013 ruling, the latter required France to provide official notice of its support regime in order for this to be validated by the Commission – something it had omitted to do. Fortunately, the French Council of State (the Conseil d'État, the highest administrative court in the French system) did not annul the disputed order – doing so would have been disastrous for the French wind power industry. However, as a result, the French government was dependent on the goodwill of DG Comp for approval of a revised system. The Commission therefore kept the French authorities waiting while negotiations on the guidelines ran their course, so France kept a low profile in this respect, preferring to concentrate on the reform of its national support scheme.

That left Germany and its EEG law on feed-in tariffs. So the Commission decided to wage a war on two fronts, attacking both the EEG law and the tax exemptions for industry. Indeed, the German system was based on cross-subsidies, which meant that energy transition was to be paid for by small-scale consumers such as households and small businesses, on whom very high additional taxes were levied. Meanwhile industrial firms, particularly electricity-intensive companies, were exempt from these. The fact was that political support for energy transition in Germany was grounded on this balance between guaranteed feed-in tariffs and tax exemptions. For the broad CDU/SPD coalition government, the two went hand in hand. Clearly, DG Comp was keen to reduce these huge German exemptions in order to make things fairer between Germany and other EU nations. However, I remain convinced that above all this was a huge bluff on the part of the Commission. Its attack on tax exemptions for industry was in fact blackmail pure and simple, designed only to obtain a bargaining chip in the discussion on renewables. As a result, Germany's economy minister Sigmar Gabriel had to focus his energies on defending exemptions for German industry, rather than feed-in tariffs.

The Commission made the most of this to attack guaranteed feed-in tariffs for renewables – a gift to Eurelectric and the Magritte Group. At the same time, instead of cutting back overgenerous German exemptions for industry, the Commission extended them as another gift, this time for BusinessEurope's electricity-intensive firms. The big losers in this were individual citizens, since they were doomed to continue bearing the full cost of energy transition and offsetting the huge exemptions granted to industrial players.

I met Competition Commissioner Joaquín Almunia a number of times during this political battle to make him aware of the issue. I will never know just how well informed he was. He never said a word; he simply sat there smiling. It was impossible to have any discussions at all with him; he always changed the subject. He was enigmatic and hard to read. What I wanted to know was whether Almunia was party to this move against renewables (perhaps as a result of lobbying on the part of Iberdrola and Endesa) or whether Oettinger had succeeded in putting him in the minority, aided and abetted by other EPP commissioners. Whatever the truth, the outcome marked the end of feed-in tariffs for renewables, to the benefit of technology-neutral auctions, which have become the default option.

The struggle for a de minimis clause

Auctions limit quantities and hold back individuals and cooperatives. This prevents democratisation of the European energy system. And that was the only political argument that could carry any weight. It was the one I used in extremis to persuade Almunia to establish de minimis clauses which, in other words, is a certain threshold (1MW for solar power and 6MW units for wind power) beneath which small projects would be exempt from these guidelines. This was definitely Plan B, a last-ditch clause, but at least it managed to save small investors in renewables. The argument that won over the commissioner was that these guidelines would prevent the entry of new participants into the market, since renewables foster competition. That's because anybody can become a producer, following the example of the thousands of Europeans who, either individually or through cooperatives, have already started producing solar power, wind power and biogas.

However, we were far from being out of the woods when it came to state aid. After having abolished guaranteed feed-in tariffs for renewables in its new guidelines, the Commission shamelessly rolled out the red carpet for guaranteed feed-in tariffs that were twice as high for British nuclear power – for a period of thirty-five years. The green light for Hinkley Point C embodied the double standards that prevail at the Commission. And more tellingly, it was a parting gift from Barroso to Cameron before the former left Brussels.

CHAPTER 10

NUCLEAR POWER: THE UNTHINKABLE GO-AHEAD FOR HINKLEY POINT C

It is extremely rare to resort to a formal vote by the College of Commissioners for a decision, as the Commission usually works with consensus. But on Monday 6 October 2014, three weeks before the end of the Barroso II Commission, there was a sudden flurry of disquiet: the College was divided as to whether or not to grant huge state aid to the Franco-British nuclear power project at Hinkley Point C. Three days before the Commission was to meet, there was still no guarantee that the quorum for resolution to be adopted would be reached. The commissioners were on their way out, and clearly some of them did not wish for such a manoeuvre to form part of their legacy.

Time was running out: the decision absolutely had to be taken on Wednesday 8 October. Catherine Day, the Barroso Commission's loyal secretary-general whom the British could always rely on, whipped in the commissioners. Some, such as Tonio Borg from Malta, were enjoined to remain in Brussels. As things turned out, only six commissioners did not attend the 2,100th meeting of the Commission.

In the light of Günther Oettinger's declarations, it would seem obvious that he would be voting against the Hinkley Point C project. Indeed, a few months earlier, he had described the project as 'Soviet'. Not only that, he had previously ruled out the prospect of granting state aid to the nuclear industry, in public. Despite which, he ended up casting a vote in favour, as did the majority.

The Commission, which is supposed to serve as guardian of the EU's Treaties, lost credibility by accepting the Franco-British arrangement. Indeed, in doing so, it wholly betrayed the internal electricity market. With a price tag of €24 billion, this was surely the heist of the century.

Massive state aid

In its 2008 Nuclear Illustrative Programme (PINC), the Commission itself had stated the following: 'It is important to ensure in the EU that nuclear energy projects do not benefit from any state subsidy.' In taking this decision, the Commission therefore chose to ignore its own policy in terms of state aid to nuclear power. Guaranteed feed-in tariffs, known as 'Contracts for Difference' or CfD in the UK, were to be applied to the electricity generated by these new reactors. Guaranteed and indexed for a period of thirty-five years, they amount to some £92/MWh (€117/MWh), which is twice the price of electricity on the UK wholesale market, which at the time was €50–60/MWh. The cost of building this Herculean project comes to some €24 billion. The UK government's guarantee is enormous. Even Pieter Cleppe, head of the Brussels-based ultra-liberal think-tank Open Europe, was to declare that 'many people in the UK are concerned by the fact that the government has negotiated a minimum energy price that is much too high'. Worse still, if market prices fall, the gap between these prices and those paid to EDF will increase still further. This ensures that EDF will benefit from vastly overinflated repayments of stranded costs.[58]

Prior to the Commission opening an in-depth inquiry, the project's backers had had the nerve to claim that no state aid was involved! In fact, there can be no doubt at all that this subsidy regime ticks all the boxes to qualify as state aid. It benefits nuclear power production by providing a guaranteed feed-in tariff for thirty-five years; it commits state resources in the form of a guarantee underwriting the

---

58   Stranded costs refer to operating commitments or guarantees granted to a private-sector operator by public-sector authorities for a given period.

financial risks entailed; it distorts competition; and it has an effect on cross-border trade.

How on earth did EDF manage to achieve this? Well before the 2010 elections, the group had infiltrated political circles in the UK to prepare the ground and ensure that it had the support of both leading parties: the thoroughly pro-nuclear Conservative Party and Labour, more reluctant but wooed over through the recruitment of Andrew Brown, brother of the then Labour Prime Minister Gordon Brown. Andrew Brown was head of media relations for EDF Energy, the British subsidiary of EDF in London, and therefore well connected politically. As soon as the Tory government came to power, in a coalition with the minority Liberal Democrats, EDF set the wheels in motion: a guaranteed feed-in tariff, a carbon floor price and a state-backed financial guarantee. The Liberal Democrats are a relatively progressive and anti-nuclear party. We are indebted to them for many victories in the European Parliament during the time that their former leader Nick Clegg was an MEP. He supported me during negotiations on the Internal Electricity Market Directive in 2003. Fiona Hall later did the same when it came to the 2008 Renewable Energy Directive and the 2012 Energy Efficiency Directive. Their election manifesto ahead of the 2010 elections was anti-nuclear. After the coalition deal with the Conservatives, this morphed into nuclear power without state aid – a deal that allowed Nick Clegg to secure the position of Deputy Prime Minister. And after all that, the Lib Dem energy minister Ed Davey agreed to the largest ever subsidy for a nuclear power project in Europe. The party was to pay the price of these U-turns at the following elections.

In any event, there can be absolutely no doubt about the double standards when it comes to renewables versus Hinkley Point C. There is no reason whatsoever why the Commission should agree to guaranteed tariffs for this nuclear project and refuse to do so for renewables. It is dishonest, to say the least, to suggest on the one hand that support for mature renewable technologies should be cut in order to place them in direct competition with conventional technology, while simultaneously maintaining that nuclear power requires state aid just like other immature technologies, especially when it has been in commercial use for almost sixty years. Indeed, this also explains why EDF has never been part of the Magritte Group: it could not decently clobber renewable support schemes while at the same time demanding exactly the same type of support for nuclear power. Without massive public-sector support, Hinkley Point C could certainly never happen.

Brexit blackmail undoubtedly had something to do with it, too. There is no denying that the threat of the UK leaving the EU had a major influence in this respect. Pro-nuclear MEP Giles Chichester, also MP for the constituency of Hinkley, virtually said as much himself. Jean-Pol Poncelet, managing director of the European nuclear lobby Foratom, was more forthcoming: 'Should we give the Brexiteers a pretext for voting Leave in the forthcoming referendum?'[59] According to him, 'it is hardly surprising that there is a political aspect [to Hinkley Point C].' For once, I actually agreed with him. Incidentally, Jean-Pol Poncelet was one of my lecturers on climate change and energy when I was studying environmental technology in Arlon, in southern Belgium, in 1988. Oddly enough, I am indebted to him for my commitment to the climate as it was after having read the Bundestag's report on climate change for the exam he set that I became aware of the main challenge to face our generation and discovered my life's calling. I am also indebted to him for my anti-nuclear stance. During a visit he organised to Belgium's nuclear waste storage laboratory in Mol, we met a paleolinguist who calmly explained to us that he was seeking to develop signs that humans would be capable of understanding tens of thousands of years hence, getting across the message that there was a cavern in that location that should not be opened under any circumstances. The scale of the debt that we were leaving for future generations suddenly overwhelmed me.

Moving the state aid goalposts

It has been pretty much forgotten that Hinkley Point C had almost been approved previously. Going back a little, in early 2013 the UK and EDF had already planned to officially request permission from the Commission. But although they have always denied it, the project's backers knew very well that it would involve huge state subsidies, and that getting these approved by DG Comp would involve a lot of work. Indeed, there was a non-significant risk that Brussels might refuse, given the difficulty of justifying such aid, both legally and in terms of healthy competition within the internal market.

So instead, they had the idea of mounting a highly discreet but very effective lobbying campaign to make the most of the huge opportunity presented by the review of state aid for environmental protection and energy, which was underway at that time. The goal was to include nuclear power within the scope of these new guidelines, in order to avoid ad hoc examination by DG Comp being required each time a new case of nuclear investment backed by public funds arose. The advantage of the guidelines was that they provided a sort of simplified procedure. For Hinkley Point C, this would avoid all the problems of a cumbersome procedure lasting several months, delaying the final investment decision and possibly even signing the product's death warrant in the event of a negative response. In the initial project, EDF was supposed to have a 40–50 per cent stake and Areva a further 10 per cent, with other investors making up the rest.

So to minimise the risk of major changes or even a refusal under existing rules, the best solution was to change the rules. DG Comp certainly had form when it came to moving the goalposts mid-match. In July 2001, after years of fruitless discussions with the Spanish government, Competition Commissioner Mario Monti simply changed his own analysis methods overnight pertaining to state aid for stranded costs to authorise over €10 billion worth of Spanish stranded costs (*costes de transición a la competencia*). Rodrigo Rato, the then Spanish economy minister, had met him shortly beforehand.

In an irony of history, it was another Spanish commissioner, Joaquín Almunia, who allowed himself to be persuaded to include aid for the construction of new nuclear power stations within the guidelines on state aid for environmental protection and energy. But when the Commission's working document was leaked to the press in July 2013, it caused a scandal. Accused of bias in favour of nuclear power, Almunia kept a low profile and swiftly embarked on a damage limitation exercise. On 19 July 2013, in an article published in the *Financial Times*, his spokesman minimised the scope of the draft, describing it as nothing more than a preparation document. In the same article, I described this view as 'ridiculous'. Indeed, the subtitle of the article left little room for doubt: 'The EU has drawn up plans to change state aid rules to make it easier for member countries to subsidise nuclear power.' On Twitter on 23 July, the commissioner himself issued a denial: 'We are launching a consultation regarding public aid to nuclear, without taking an ex-ante position', before his spokesman once again came to the rescue in the letters column of the *Financial Times*, that same day:

> The Commission has not yet taken a position on whether or not such specific rules are needed and will launch a public consultation in the autumn to gather the views of member states and stakeholders. While no specific clause has been introduced into the guidelines, the Commission will continue to examine notifications on the basis of the treaty's general rules on state aid, developing specific criteria depending on the cases brought before it.

The problem was that this was during the third round of consultation on the guidelines, and there had been no mention whatsoever of aid for the construction of nuclear power capacity during the first two rounds. The manoeuvre was so blatant that it had manipulation written all over it. Quoted by the German papers, Energy Commissioner Günther Oettinger, who had been very closely linked to the discussions, did not shrink from entering the fray: 'The preparation of the state aid guidelines in the fields of energy and environmental protection and the decision regarding the support for nuclear energy in Europe needs a decent and intensive discussion. [...] We have received requests from member states. We cannot ignore it.'[60]

---

60   'State aid for nuclear? Are you kidding?', 26 July 2013, energypost.eu.

According to this working document from the Commission, support for investment in nuclear power was justified by Article 2(c) of the Euratom Treaty.[61] However, the introduction to Article 2 specifies that this is possible only 'as provided in this Treaty'. And Title IV, which deals with investments, specifies nothing more than exchanges of information concerning investment projects. Invoking the Euratom Treaty to justify state aid for investments allowing nuclear power to be developed is therefore a fallacious argument. The working document also specified that aid destined to cover the insurance costs of facilities over and above domestic and international requirements could be authorised. This basically amounted to a blank cheque for the nuclear sector when it came to any issues of liability in the event of a nuclear accident – a topic on which Oettinger had in fact promised to legislate.

Almunia certainly did not anticipate the opposition that his move was to entail, and found himself having to defend this explosive dossier on his own. On 8 October 2013, even the College of Commissioners turned their backs on him during an orientation debate. The official report of the proceedings shows that Oettinger did nothing whatsoever to support him and 'felt it was appropriate for each authorisation for state aid for nuclear power to be examined individually'. Almunia eventually admitted his mistake, and that was the end of that. The worst was thus avoided on that occasion: Hinkley Point C would not be approved by Brussels without a murmur. However, that was not the end of the matter. Exactly one year later on 8 October 2014, the Barroso Commission was to greenlight Hinkley Point C.

The end of nuclear power in Europe

Paradoxically, Hinkley Point C has sounded the death knell of Europe's nuclear power industry. The project is too large for Areva, which is virtually bankrupt, and for EDF, which is faced with colossal levels of debt and attempting to scale an impossibly high wall of investment in the years to come. It therefore needed much more than

---

61   Dating from 1957, this treaty was designed to facilitate investment in nuclear power in order to nurture its development.

the UK government's guarantee to see the light of day. The project's continuation depends on foreign investment. As a result, within the space of a few months, an industry that has been deemed to be strategic by every French government since the Second World War is being sold off to the Chinese.

From the outset, EDF announced that it only wanted a minority stake in Hinkley Point C in order not to wipe out its finances with this investment. So a partnership was formed with Centrica and Areva, allowing these two companies to take out a stake as well. But after having analysed the consequences of the Fukushima disaster, the UK firm backed out in early 2013. Two years later in 2015, Areva also pulled out as it had become apparent that the French firm, laden with debt, would be incapable of honouring its commitments. Instead, EDF started discussions with Saudi investors and the Chinese company CGNPC. The Saudis did not follow up, with the result that EDF was ultimately obliged to increase its stake in the project from 40 per cent to 66 per cent and include Hinkley on a balance sheet that was already not in peak form. This major change goes a long way to explaining why Thomas Piquemal, EDF chief financial officer, resigned one year later. In a hearing before the French National Assembly's economic affairs committee on 4 May 2016, he told MPs of his 'despair'. Unfortunately, this alarm signal remained largely ignored by French policymakers.

CGNPC's Chinese contingent took out no more than the remaining 33 per cent stake, and managed to obtain a significant concession in return: the terms of the agreement grant Areva's fiercest competitor technical assistance from EDF in having their own third-generation reactor (a 100 per cent Chinese copy of Areva's EPR known as Hualong) approved by the UK. This will enable them to carry off future nuclear contracts under the very noses of their European competitors. As a result, Hinkley Point C has killed off the long-term sales prospects for French-made EPRs.

Meanwhile in France, the fact that François Hollande has signed the contract for Hinkley Point C with the Chinese, followed by the possible sale of Areva, also to the Chinese, is a major geopolitical earthquake that has somehow escaped much analysis. When it comes to nuclear power, the code of silence reigns supreme and nobody has said a word. In the United Kingdom, however, the outcome has not gone down so well. When the Chinese Premier visited London in October 2015, the armed forces had something to say: 'Is this a good idea when it comes to the geopolitical and military independence of the UK?' The Labour Party in particular took up the issue of whether a Chinese presence in domestic nuclear power was opportune. Even Nick Timothy, a close adviser of the future Prime Minister Theresa May, raised the possibility of CGNPC infiltrating the UK's IT network to 'halt power production whenever they want to'. This is all far from reassuring.

French nuclear power simply doesn't add up.

Areva gets bogged down

The beginnings of the French nuclear industry's financial troubles can be traced back to 2003 in Olkiluoto, Finland. That year, Areva committed to a risky contract with utility TVO, delivering a turnkey EPR no later than 2009 at a construction cost of €3 billion. This unbridled optimism bordered on the reckless and, at the very least, bore witness to the arrogance of the French nuclear industry. Twelve years after works first started in 2005, the project has still not been completed, the bill has more than tripled and the TVO group has commenced legal proceedings against Areva. Colossal amounts of money are in play, relating to compensation for late delivery of the reactor and TVO's corresponding shortfall in earnings. This mess is an ominous sign for the French nuclear industry.[62]

At the same time, Areva persisted in its commitment alongside EDF in the construction of a second EPR, this one in France at Flamanville. But once again, the same causes produced the same effects: multiple delays, and a bill at least three times higher than forecast. Not only that,

---

62   'Dans le bourbier d'Olkiluoto, l'EPR finlandais d'Areva', Les Échos, 24 February 2016.

further clouds began to gather. The French Nuclear Safety Authority uncovered a large number of defects in certain parts destined to be fitted to PWR reactors[63] – and not minor ones either. The closure head and the base of the pressure vessel cast in its Le Creusot plant.

There was no way Areva could walk away from this disaster unscathed. Eleven years after initial ground-breaking, not a single electron had been produced by an EPR. Bankruptcy loomed: the group announced a deficit of almost €5 billion for the 2014 financial year, followed by €2 billion in 2015. Areva went up for sale, but buyers were not exactly queuing up. In 2016, EDF was therefore frogmarched by the French state, in its capacity as shareholder, to enter a bid for the group's reactor business. EDF set conditions to François Hollande, Manuel Valls and Emmanuel Macron, which stated that it would not buy debts from the Olkiluoto fiasco or from Flamanville. At the end of the day, it will therefore be down to the state to absorb Areva's colossal debts.

EDF in poor health

Leaving aside Areva, EDF itself is also beset by very serious financial difficulties. The French law on the new structure of electricity markets (known as the 'NOME Act') did away with regulated tariffs for industrial consumers as of 1 January 2016, and allows alternative energy suppliers such as Engie and Enel to engage in highly aggressive prospecting. At the same time, EDF is required to sell some of the electricity produced by its nuclear fleet to its competitors, at a rate of €42/MWh.[64] However, nobody actually wants any at that price. As a result, EDF will have to sell a large part of its nuclear electricity on the spot market at €24/MWh, the average of the prices observed on the electricity market during the first half of 2016.

In late November 2015, the French state rushed to EDF's aid by announcing a new subsidy. This took the form of forfeiting annual

---

63   'Anomalies de fabrication de la cuve de l'EPR et irrégularités détectées dans l'usine Creusot Forge d'Areva', ASN, 27 October 2016.

64   As part of regulated access to legacy nuclear electricity ('Arenh').

dividends for a three-year period and on the basis of the ten-year average, this will amount to €2 billion a year. The move came as a surprise given the state of France's public finances, not to mention the country's struggle to abide by the Stability Pact. During this period, EDF lost 8 per cent of its stock market capitalisation and was forced out of the legendary CAC 40 listing in December 2015. Despite being a shareholder, the French state chose to ignore this downward spiral and announced further recapitalisation of €3 billion in March 2016. The markets, however, were not to be so easily deceived. In May 2016, ratings agency S&P downgraded EDF's long-term score and described its outlook as 'negative'. The ratings agency also assigned EDF's debt to its 'speculative' category. Moody's soon followed suit, downgrading EDF's rating twice in May and September 2016. The ratings agencies' threats became self-fulfilling prophecies and a vicious circle began: the greater EDF's debt, the lower its ratings, the harder the company's credit terms became and the greater its debt. Since EDF has taken out several tens of billions of euros' worth of loans over 100 years, a negative rating means these loans will be included in the group's debt. Surprisingly enough, DG Comp never investigated the French part of the state aid granted to HPC but only the British part.

EDF's disastrous financial circumstances would be even more apparent if the group had not resorted to some blatant cooking of the books: by extending the lifespan of its reactors to fifty years, it has spread their depreciation over an additional ten-year period.[65] In actual fact, the reactors are planned to have an operating lifespan of forty years. Any extension could only take place with approval of the French Nuclear Safety Authority, which is far from a given. Meanwhile, the French Financial Market Authority, AMF, has opened an inquiry into the sincerity of information disclosed by EDF since 2013. But once again, DG Comp has chosen to look the other way.

EDF's board of directors met on 10 July 2016 and adopted the final investment decision. After much dithering on the part of the new UK

---

65   'La prolongation des centrales nucléaires en question', *Le Figaro*, 23 February 2016.

Prime Minister, Theresa May, EDF and CGNPC eventually signed the Hinkley Point C agreement with the UK government on 29 September 2016. However, there still remain a great many legal barriers. On 10 December 2015, the EDF trade unions invoked their whistleblowing rights on the grounds that poor strategic decisions by the management 'would inevitably lead EDF into an industrial, economic and corporate dead end'. The dispute proceedings brought by the trade unions are still underway, although they were thrown out in the first instance.

Ultimately, it will be up to the European Court of Justice to decide after a joint claim was brought before it by Austria and Luxembourg against the European Commission's decision to authorise the project. While President Juncker and Competition Commissioner Margrethe Vestager may choose to hide behind the decisions taken by their predecessors Barroso and Almunia on Hinkley Point C, they will have to step up to the plate when it comes to dealing with another, similar burning issue: the joint Russian–Hungarian project for a new nuclear power station in Paks.

But not even the infamous decision in favour of Hinkley Point C was to be the nadir of energy transition's 'Dark Ages'. In order to complete the renationalisation of European energy policy, Europe's governments still had to seize institutional power over and against the Community method – something they also achieved during this process, just a couple of weeks later.

CHAPTER 11

RENATIONALISATION OF CLIMATE AND ENERGY POLICY BY THE EUROPEAN COUNCIL

In October 2014, after the toughest of negotiations, EU heads of state and government agreed on the broad orientations of the 2030 Climate and Energy Package. I can bear witness to the fact that the atmosphere was very different from back in 2008. The awareness of the need to combat climate change was scarcely more than a distant memory. On this occasion, only one thing mattered for the heads of state: emerging from the economic crisis at all costs. There was just one glimmer of hope on the eve of this crucial meeting of the European Council, which was that Europhile Herman van Rompuy was still in the driving seat and not his Polish successor Donald Tusk, whose mandate did not officially begin until a few weeks later. It was therefore up to the man famous for his haikus to achieve a delicate compromise.

That said, this glimmer of hope was in danger of being extinguished by the chilly winds blowing from UK PM David Cameron in an alliance with the Visegrád countries (Poland, Hungary, the Czech Republic and Slovakia). Admittedly, Nicolas Sarkozy had already dealt quite a blow to the Community method by kicking some of the decisions on the 2020 Climate and Energy Package upstairs to the European Council of December 2008. But six years later, on 23–24

October 2014, the European Council upset the fundamental institutional balance. Under the regime of unanimity, it prejudged the outcome
of political negotiations that would normally take place under the
regime of qualified majority. This was by no means an insignificant
change. It marked a major shift, with the return of the 'power of veto'
granted to each member state – a move in the opposite direction to
the progress, over several decades, of the Community method.

A review of the treaties

Articles 191 and 194 of the Treaty on the Functioning of the European
Union[66] could not be clearer: decisions pertaining to climate change,
renewable energy, energy efficiency, the internal energy market,
security of supply and interconnections are to be taken pursuant to
ordinary legislative proceedings. As part of these proceedings, the
treaty establishes two co-legislators that must approve all new legislation in the same terms: the European Parliament and the Council
of the EU, often referred to as the Council of Ministers. The Parliament is made up of 751 MEPs directly elected by the citizens of the
EU. It takes its decisions on the basis of a simple majority, as is the
case in all of Europe's parliamentary assemblies. The Council, meanwhile, represents member states: each government occupies one of
the twenty-eight seats around the table. Decisions are taken on the
basis of a qualified majority: this means that any proposed legislation
must receive the support of 55 per cent of member states representing
65 per cent of the population of the EU. As a result, some countries
may be in a minority and legislation with which they disagree may be
adopted, which makes sense in terms of European democratic logic.
The extension of qualified majority voting to most policies has taken
place gradually as Europe has come together in order to break free of
purely nationalistic hobbyhorses and incite decision makers, to place
the EU's general interest above the specific interests of any given state.

---

66   The Treaty on the European Union (TEU) sets out the EU's institutions and its founding
      principles, while the Treaty on the Functioning of the European Union (TFEU) details the
      remit of the EU, its decision-making procedures, and its internal workings.

The Council of the European Union is not the same body as the European Council. The European Council is a select body that gathers heads of state and government and takes decisions on a consensus basis in order to issue general orientations and strategic direction. It is this body that upset the existing balance by getting involved in the detail of negotiations rather than restricting itself to general orientation. The conclusions of its meeting on 23–24 October 2014 are so specific that they prejudge the outcome of the legislative procedure and prevent the lawmakers from exercising their prerogatives. This has had the effect of devaluing the Council of the European Union, while making the European Parliament little more than a 'registration chamber', if not a purely consultative body.

In October 2014, the European Council thus trampled the treaty itself underfoot, thereby achieving nothing less than an institutional coup d'état, in full view of the Commission, which is the guardian of the treaties. But since the latter's president, José Manuel Barroso, was on his way out, it made little difference to him.

Upsetting the institutional balance

The heads of state and government thus started meddling in the governance of renewable energy and energy efficiency, establishing target levels and deciding that these would not be transposed into binding national targets. The conclusions of the European Council are also highly detailed when it comes to the ETS. It is all there in writing: 'The European Council will keep all the elements of the framework under review and will continue to give strategic orientations as appropriate, notably with respect to consensus on ETS, non-ETS, interconnections and energy efficiency.' Each time a member state is afraid of being put in the minority by the Council of Ministers due to the qualified majority system, this means it will be able to automatically exercise a veto by sending the issue upstairs to the heads of state and government, who rule unanimously. This is a perversion of the mandate of the European Council with respect to the co-decision procedure in place between the European Parliament and the Council. Simply put, instead of qualified majority voting which could put some member states in a minority, the UK, say, automatically has a right of veto over energy efficiency and renewables. Poland has the same right with regard to the ETS and coal and France could do the same with regard to interconnections.

What is more, when transposing the mandate of the European Council into concrete legislative proposals, the Commission ratified this coup d'état. In July 2015 during his speech before the European Parliament's ITRE committee, EU Climate and Energy Commissioner Miguel Arias Cañete had this to say:

> When we prepared the proposals on the ETS mainly, we took the decision to follow very closely the European Council conclusions of October 2014 because that was a very balanced package and very complicated. We know that everybody accepted ambitious climate targets … It is a balanced agreement and we decided, as Commission, to stick to the package and deliver a proposal that is as well-drafted as we could, but based on the package.

I had to remind him on that occasion that the European Commission was not under orders from the European Council, but ought to be respecting the wishes of the European Parliament in their entirety.

What is more, the Commission's statement was in complete contradiction with what Jean-Claude Juncker had said to the Parliament ahead of his investiture a year earlier, when he promised a Commission that would not simply be the 'Secretary-General' of the Council; a Commission that would be 'political … more political … highly political' and not 'a technical committee made up of civil servants who implement the instructions of another institution'.

In the light of this upset, how could the European Parliament possibly fulfil its role as co-legislator? These conclusions by the European Council were an affront to us as MEPs. The heads of state were attempting to tie our hands and prejudge the outcome of democratic discussions to be held in the Parliament.

The UK in the driving seat

Long before Brexit, the UK had already implemented its own reform of
the electricity market by means of Contracts for Difference, followed by
a capacity market (which incidentally was challenged in the European
Court of Justice). There was a kind of 'energy Brexit' before the real thing,
with a gradual departure of the UK from the European energy market.
Today, there is little interconnection between the UK grid and the Continent. This 'splendid isolation' comes at a price: electricity is twice as
expensive on the British wholesale market as on the Scandinavian market
Noordpool, or those of Germany or Benelux – regions that have much
better interconnections and boast a great deal of renewable capacity.
Could it be a coincidence that steelmakers TataSteel opted to close their
British factories rather than those located in the Netherlands, which
have a well-interconnected market resulting in lower electricity prices?

British Tories are also instinctively opposed to national targets,
preferring to have free rein to indulge in nuclear power and protect
the income of their large oil and gas firms such as BP, with the latter
reluctant to go much further in terms of energy efficiency. In his letter
to Barroso in December 2013, David Cameron thus openly requested
an end to EU renewables and energy efficiency policies after 2020, two
topics on which British administration ended up in a minority during
negotiations between the Parliament and the Council respectively in
2008 and 2012. With Brexit-based blackmail in the background, he
demanded a review of all three targets (for greenhouse gas emissions,
renewables and energy efficiency) in favour of a single climate target
based on the ETS – despite the latter having been on life support for
many years. This really marked a huge step backwards.

The UK had been discreetly planning such a move for some time,
under cover of the innocent-sounding Green Growth Group. Set up
in 2014 by the UK Secretary of State for Energy of the day, Ed Davey,
it brought together the most climate-friendly sates such as Sweden,
Denmark and Germany in a bid to influence the development of the
2030 Climate and Energy Package. But what was originally designed
as a coordination group between forward-looking countries was

exploited by the British, who turned it into the spearhead of reactionary policy when it came to renewable energy governance. For instance, the signatories loudly demanded 'a binding EU renewables energy target which should not be translated into binding national targets by the EU'.[67] This was both skilful and cynical: the cover of a pro-climate name (the 'Green Growth Group') salved the consciences of the other signatories, even as they were torpedoing renewables.

The ultimate weapon of Brexit, already deployed to force the Commission to cave in on Hinkley Point C, was once again brandished, enabling Cameron to win another round on that occasion. On 23–24 October 2014, against the backdrop of this Brexit blackmail, he put a gun to the heads of his opposite numbers to convince them to relax the energy efficiency target to 27 per cent and do away with mandatory national targets, the cornerstone of any ambitious policy.

How on earth did the Franco-German duo let that be passed? Angela Merkel, still reeling from the sorry episode of the review of the guidelines on state aid for renewables, was keen to retain some margin of manoeuvre to develop green energy in Germany. In exchange for this purely national freedom, she consented to sacrifice a coherent European approach. Admittedly, she had little other option. Merkel was very much alone on that occasion. France was not exactly above reproach: while the country had adopted ambitious national targets (32 per cent renewables by 2030, a lot better than nothing), it categorically refused to embed this vision in binding European scenarios on the outmoded grounds of national free choice, whereas the latter is an illusion in a Europe seeking to achieve closer cooperation between member states. Anxious not to upset its British ally in view of the nuclear partnership concluded with EDF, President Hollande abandoned Merkel by the wayside, thereby burying any forward-looking European vision.

Poland wins on coal

Analysis of the agreement at the European Council of 23 October

---

67   'Green Growth Group Ministers' statement on climate and energy framework for 2030', 3 March 2014, www.gov.uk.

2014 also confirms Poland's ability to disrupt European climate policy. During negotiations on the 2008 Climate and Energy Package, it had already wrested a huge concession. Article 10c of the ETS directive provided for EU countries with a low GDP to be able to allocate pollution rights free of charge to electricity firms, provided that the latter invested an amount equivalent to these allowances to 'modernise and diversify electricity production'.

In actual fact, these derogations served to provide massive subsidies to electricity producers using coal, as a recent report by Carbon Market Watch indicates. Poland achieved this by 'diverting' billions of euros obtained under the terms of Article 10c. A total of 680 million free allowances were awarded for the 2013–2020 phase in this way, with a total worth of billions. The amounts of allowances assigned to each country were, logically enough, related to their size. In 2013, only 10 per cent of investments funded by means of Article 10c were devoted to low-carbon technologies or diversification of the energy mix, while 90 per cent were used to modernise infrastructures used to generate power from fossil fuels.[68]

The Polish coal-fired power plant of Bełchatów,
one of the most polluting installations in the world
© BOGUSZ BILEWSKI / GREENPEACE POLSKA (CREATIVE COMMONS)

---

68   European Commission impact assessment, published in 2015.

In Poland, these investments were, for instance, used to modernise the Bełchatów power station – the largest and most polluting lignite-fired power plant in Europe. As a result of this investment, closure of Units 1 and 2, the oldest and dirtiest, was pushed back from 2015 to 2017 and 2018 respectively. A new 858MW unit has also been commissioned. European Commission data shows that following these subsidies, the Bełchatów power station actually gave off more CO_2 than previously: 37 million tonnes in 2013, compared to approximately 30 million tonnes per year between 2007 and 2010. Doing so much damage to the planet using funds earmarked to combat climate change is an achievement in a league of its own.

It beggars belief that the European Council has done nothing to halt this state of affairs. Its conclusions could not be more disappointing: 'Member states with a GDP per capita below 60 per cent of the EU average may opt to continue to give free allowances to the energy sector up to 2030.' This is a huge gift to Poland, as it can exploit this provision to encourage the generation of dirty electricity. Combating climate change will have to wait for another day. And all the rhetoric about 'the fundamental importance' of 'full implementation of an integrated European energy market' is nothing more than empty words if the power stations in Visegrád countries obtain unfair competitive advantages compared to electricity producers in other EU countries. These derogations embody the extension to 2030 of the unsound decisions taken as part of the 2020 Climate and Energy Package. While the 2008 decisions may be excused on the grounds of unforeseen consequences, the same could not be said in 2014.

Not only did Poland obtain an extension for these exemptions, it also walked away with another favour: a new Modernisation Fund would be set up in order to help Eastern European countries invest in energy transition. The Polish government was keen for member states to retain sole control of this fund. Fortunately, pro-climate governments did manage to achieve a compromise, under the terms of which the EIB would be involved in choosing which projects to support. This is encouraging in view of the EIB's sustainability criteria, which tend to militate against coal.

A few deals between friends

I am opposed to the renationalisation of energy policy. If everybody defends their national energy mix to the very last, it will be impossible to optimise the system across Europe, or even macro-regions. Lower costs will never be achieved, nor will there be any improvement in energy security, despite both of these benefiting the population as a whole. Despite this, a large number of member states, including Poland and the UK, were keen to see renationalisation, taking a stand against the move to have national targets for 2030 as had been the case for 2020. Unfortunately, they were supported by the nuclearcrat wing of the French government. Rather than ally itself with Germany, Scandinavia and Benelux to defend the Community method, in summer 2014 the latter decided to give carte blanche to the renationalisation camp. Similarly, both the authoritarian Hungarian government and the Eurosceptic government in power in Prague much preferred a national approach – since their prime ministers had a veto on EU decisions at the European Council. Germany was left pretty much alone on the other side; the support of 'small' countries such as Denmark, Portugal and Sweden was not enough.

At the end of the day, one of the big winners of this meeting of the European Council is 2,500km away: Vladimir Putin. Adopting a target of 40 per cent energy efficiency in 2030 (the oft-repeated position of the European Parliament) would allow our gas imports to be reduced by 40 per cent, which is equivalent to more than the entirety of Europe's Russian gas imports. It follows that by confining themselves to 27 per cent energy efficiency, the Europeans have shot themselves in the foot.

A new hope?

The Magritte Group and BusinessEurope had much to be happy about that evening: the European leaders had set a pathetic target for renewables on their domestic market. The real losers were, firstly, ordinary citizens, who would not see their bills go down and who would remain dependent on Russian gas; secondly, the European Parliament, whose legitimacy was trampled underfoot; and, of course, the climate.

Fortunately for European energy policy and transition in Europe, the new Commission that took over in November 2014 brought a new hope, with the arrival of Jean-Claude Juncker. He included in his political guidelines his intention to go further on energy efficiency and to make the EU world number one on renewables.

Besides, some small comfort could be taken from the conclusions of the European Council of 23 October 2014, which confirmed that the 'EU targets for greenhouse gas emission reduction, renewable energy and energy efficiency ... need to be fully met by 2020'. This offered some prospects that the efforts of the UK and Poland to wreck the existing legal framework for 2020 would come to nothing. The ambitions regarding renewables and energy efficiency would be pursued to the full, with the result that energy transition and the fight against climate change would continue in subsequent years. The basest national intentions would not get the better of the virtuous dynamic put in place by the 2008 Climate and Energy Package – indeed, they never will.

The next challenge was to put some flesh on the bones of the new 2030 Climate and Energy Package – a challenge that the new Commission suggested should be met within five years, before the next EU elections in 2019. With the dawn of this new era, the centrifugal forces of renationalisation and the centripetal forces of Europeanisation were to come increasingly into conflict. What would be the role of the Energy Union proposed by Juncker in such an environment?

CHAPTER 12

FROM TUSK TO JUNCKER: THE SHIFTING CONCEPT OF AN ENERGY UNION

In May 2014, for the first time, the European elections resulted in a fully fledged political debate across the EU, with each of the main political groups having designated a leader: Jean-Claude Juncker for the EPP, and Martin Schulz for the Social Democrats. Following a clear victory by the EPP, Juncker was thus appointed as the head of the European Commission on 27 June 2014.

At 10 a.m. on 15 July 2014, Juncker gave his investiture speech before the European Parliament in plenary session in Strasbourg, prior to his official election by a vote of MEPs at 12.30 p.m. The speech on this occasion is generally similar to one a prime minister might give before their national government, stating broad policy objectives. Juncker lost no time in outlining the need to concentrate on ten key areas. The third of these was energy. Under this heading, he announced his intention to reform and 'reorganise Europe's energy policy into a new European Energy Union'. The MEPs with expertise in the field were left aghast; was he seeking to implement the reactionary plans of Donald Tusk, the Polish PM who was about to become president of the European Council?

The Energy Union as seen by Donald Tusk
In spring 2014, Tusk was still Polish Prime Minister. His proposal, set

out in a fifteen-page document in an article in the *Financial Times* of 21 April 2014, involved six foundational pillars. It is well worth analysing, because it sheds light on the attitudes of certain Polish policymakers with respect to climate and energy.

The Tusk plan emerged shortly after the events of March 2014, when the crisis between Russia and Ukraine broke out, leading to the annexation of Crimea. This led to a battle of wits between Vladimir Putin and the EU, complicated by Europe's energy dependence on Russia – not only for gas, but also nuclear fuel, oil and coal. At the European Council's meeting that spring, the leaders therefore asked the Commission to carry out an in-depth study of the EU's energy security and present an overall plan to reduce this dependence at the summit on 26–27 June 2014.

Donald Tusk saw this as an excellent opportunity to promote his vision of energy security, which could be summarised as deeply anti-Russian and pro-coal. Indeed, he had constantly argued along these lines during his tenure as Polish Prime Minister for the previous seven years. Now, he was attempting to transpose the policy implemented in Warsaw to Brussels, under the cover of a new Energy Union combined with some advances in terms of power networks.

The first pillar on which his proposal rested was infrastructures. This did in fact mark some progress compared to the Polish approach, given the extent to which the country had fought for years against any interconnection projects.[69]

The European Council had sought to put an end to 'energy islands' in the wake of its in-depth debate on energy on 4 February 2011: 'No EU member state should remain isolated from the European gas and electricity networks after 2015 or see its energy security jeopardised by lack of the appropriate connections.' Never one to worry too much about consistency, Tusk realised that his concept of the Energy Union

---

69   Poland dragged its feet when it came to the planned LitPol gas pipeline designed to free the Baltic states from their exclusively Russian supply. The same was true when it came to electricity, with the government doing anything it could to prevent cheaper electricity from Germany and Scandinavia arriving to compete with local, Polish coal. As a consequence of this isolationist policy, Poland now has the highest electricity prices on the wholesale market.

would only go down well with other member states if it went hand in hand with an expressed wish to extend the European network of interconnections.

The second pillar involved the Polish PM stating the obvious, in the form of a few proposals on solidarity that did little more than repeat the directive that had been in place since 2010 on the security of gas supply, even though the Commission was already working on a revised directive, finally proposed in February 2016. Tusk also somehow forgot to mention that the EU budget had helped Poland to fund reverse flow projects and interconnections for gas, which already ranked highly in the EU's priorities when it came to energy infrastructures.

The third pillar, which according to Tusk was the flagship proposal for the Energy Union, called for common purchases of gas, an old idea designed to put pressure on Gazprom in order to be able to negotiate as a group and achieve more attractive prices. Under pressure from the Poles and from Tusk himself, who became president of the European Council at the end of 2014, this plan was to endure for some time as part of the Commission's and the European Council's priorities; in December 2014, the latter declared the need to 'assess options for voluntary demand aggregation mechanisms ... in compliance with EU and trade law legislation'. But analysis by the Commission's legal and competition departments showed that it would be impossible to implement such a scheme in practice.[70] It was finally put to rest on 16 February 2016, when the new legislative proposal by the Commission on the information exchange mechanism with regard to intergovernmental agreements in the field of energy referred to nothing more than the potential for 'coordination between member states' for gas purchases. Tusk's proposal was thus buried with full honours.

The fourth pillar was devoted to the 'development of Europe's indigenous resources', a euphemism for Polish coal, lignite and shale

---

70   The Commission's position was basically that it was up to industry to come up with proposals. Industry, for its part, wanted nothing to do with bulk purchases of gas: 'Non-commercial mechanisms, notably collective purchasing [...] would distort the market, could be inefficient and very costly. Such ideas should not be pursued,' argues the EU's natural gas lobby GasNaturally.

gas. Tusk was therefore suggesting that subsidies should be granted
to investments in coal. This despite the fact that according to Julia
Michalak, from Climate Action Network Europe, 'generous public
financial aid schemes for coal-based power in Poland ... have failed
to reverse this trend because the industry is simply not competitive
with foreign coal sources. Russian imports amount to 60 per cent of
Poland's total coal imports.' This analysis proved prophetic: world coal
prices have continued to fall.

Reinvesting in coal-fired electricity generation makes no sense
at all, either economically or with respect to the climate. Polish coal
simply cannot survive without state subsidies and the COP21 Agreement, secured in Paris, does not allow support for this resource to be
continued. However, the plundering of funds derived from free ETS
allowances has demonstrated that the Polish government will stop at
nothing when it comes to propping up the country's coal industry.

The fifth pillar involved diversifying Europe's energy supply by
strengthening ties with all other oil and gas producers to replace imports from Russia. Instead of organising a proper strategy for reducing
the EU's chronic dependency on imports of fossil fuels – one based
on renewables and energy efficiency – Tusk was simply suggesting a
switch to a different dealer for the supply of the black drugs (in similar
fashion to the Azeri dictator Ilham Aliyev, who rivals Putin when it
comes to his record on human rights).

The sixth and last pillar was little more than a repetition of existing
provisions on strengthening Europe's Energy Community, an international organisation that includes the western Balkan states, Moldova
and Ukraine, with a view to bringing their legal frameworks into line
with European standards.

Six pillars may sound like plenty, but they did not make for a firm
foundation. Simply put, Tusk's vision of the Energy Union amounted to a few commonplaces, a few absurdities, and the scandalous
promotion of fossil fuels. Indeed, the latter was the key issue for
Warsaw's former strongman. His approach was not solely concerned
with saving Polish coal; he was also seeking to offer a future for fossil

fuels through the promotion of two technologies in particular: the extraction of shale gas and the reuse of CO_2 captured and stored by means of hypothetical CCS installations.

The illusion of 'clean' fossil fuels

The myth of 'clean' fossil fuels is based on the promotion of shale gas, wrongfully qualified as a source of energy that is both sustainable and non-polluting, and on the sequestration and storage of CO_2 combined with its reuse for industrial processes, thereby giving coal an appearance of clean energy on the grounds that it is a source of 'recyclable' emissions.

What about shale gas?

The Poles and the British are the most ardent promoters of shale gas in Europe, seeking to imitate North America, which embarked on the adventure of shale gas several years ago now, in order to ensure some domestic production – at the cost of huge environmental crimes that are, for the most part, being brushed under the carpet. Could Donald Tusk be Europe's version of Dick Cheney? No, because Europe is not the US. Fortunately, our legal arsenal when it comes to protecting the environment means that such a highly polluting procedure cannot be so easily promoted. What is more, the geography and geology of the United States are more suitable for fracking, with large, sparsely populated expanses of land.

Unsurprisingly enough, that didn't stop Kurt Bock, CEO of German chemicals giant BASF, from coming out in favour of shale gas in 2014, declaring it to offer 'huge opportunities'[71] while also admitting that its impact on Europe's economy would be relatively slight. Hydraulic fracturing, or 'fracking', is a dream come true for the chemicals industry, which sees it as a new outlet for its nasty cocktails of products, injected into the ground during the process.

In Poland, despite the unwavering support of Tusk governments,

---

71   'BASF: shale gas offers "huge opportunities"', 23 May 2014, www.plasticsnews.com.

the leading oil and gas exploration firms have left the market. There are a number of reasons for this departure. Firstly, the specifics of Polish geology make any extraction technically complex and highly expensive. Secondly, farmers and local communities have come out strongly against fracking,[72] in particular due to the major environmental damage it causes: Poland has relatively scarce water resources, so any pollution of its rare water resource would be a major disaster. As a result, the prospect of shale gas in the country has been a flop, as I am sure will also be the case in Europe as a whole.

Today, the British have taken up the cause, lobbying in favour of shale gas with the support of Shell. The speed with which British Conservatives leap to criticise the alleged environmental consequences of wind farms is matched only by their refusal to acknowledge the dramatic impact of shale gas on the climate. The UK's DECC has even developed an incentive policy with respect to deep drilling and fracking. In its view, 'shale gas has the potential to provide the UK with greater energy security, growth and jobs'. However, there has been stiff opposition in a number of locations, with a highly effective and structured movement that has not hesitated to take the fight through the courts. This grassroots action has resulted in the government having to revise its options and prohibit drilling in certain areas of England. Scotland, for its part, decided on a full moratorium in January 2015. In France, civil society mobilisation and the efforts of my counterpart José Bové pushed the government to ban fracking.

Shale Gas Europe, a pro-shale-gas lobby to support the technology, which it describes as 'very important for the EU', first appeared in Brussels in 2012. But the NGOs responded immediately, denouncing greenwashing on the part of many companies and professional associations. In 2014, Friends of the Earth published a report entitled 'Fracking Brussels', in which the organisation identifies the supporters of fracking and reveals the extent to which they have infiltrated the ranks of policymakers. The Greens also launched an anti-fracking

---

72   It is worth noting the enormous amount of groundwork done in Poland by my honourable friend in the Greens, José Bové; he acted as a catalyst for local opposition.

campaign. At the end of the day, the supporters of shale gas have not achieved much in Europe. Many countries remain opposed to the concept, while countries initially announced as some sort of Eldorado, such as Poland and Romania, have not lived up to expectations at all. Only the UK has persisted, but I am convinced that grassroots opposition will end up prevailing there too.

'Clean coal' – really?

Poland long took the view that CO_2 capture and storage (CCS) offered a bright future for coal. I am not entirely opposed to CCS. In the Vision 2050 scenario, CCS is called for to bring down GHG emissions by 95 per cent, as the European Commission states in a report on the future of CCS in Europe, in particular 'to be able to reduce emissions in industries with process emissions that cannot be avoided' (such as cement-making, chemicals, and in blast furnaces for steel and aluminium). However, CCS is far from being a proven technology. Carbon dioxide is a solvent capable of dissolving the rock within which it is confined, creating doubts as to whether storage sites can be properly sealed, with the accompanying risk of this technology becoming a carbon time bomb. But to the technical challenge of geological sequestration of CO_2, there is also a cost issue. A coal-fired power plant equipped with CCS is losing efficiency and flexibility, hence profitability. Faced with such costs, Poland began to have second thoughts. Now, following the CCS fiasco, the Polish prefer to talk in terms of 'clean coal'. Does such a thing actually exist? It sounds like something from the 1950s or '60s.

This new technological speculation that has emerged, based on the assumption of improved efficiency on the part of coal-fired power stations, coupled with reuse of the CO_2 given off, in order to avoid storage costs, is known as carbon capture and utilisation (CCU). CO_2 is a solvent used in industrial processes, so the idea is that greenhouse gas emissions could be reused as a recyclable raw material. However, the facts and lessons of experience need to be examined more closely, as does the economic feasibility of any large-scale use of CO_2. Even the IEA, despite being an ardent proponent of CCS, admits that CCU would be little more than a drop in the bucket when it comes to greenhouse gas emissions. Indeed, in its special report published in 2013 it acknowledged that the main applications to solvents and refrigerants require relatively small quantities of less than 1 million tonnes of CO_2 per year ($MtCO_2$/year) worldwide, while the soft drinks industry needs scarcely more than $8MtCO_2$/year. The IEA's conclusion is as follows: 'Chemical uses of CO_2, which is a relatively abundant source of carbon, remain limited despite carbon being the basis for most of our goods and fuels. This is because CO_2 is unreactive and usually requires large amounts of energy to break its chemical bonds.' Europe's largest coal-fired power station in Bełchatów, Poland, emits some $37MtCO_2$/year – enough for it alone to produce four times the annual amount of Coca-Cola bubbles worldwide. This solution to climate change does not appear to be very credible.

Juncker's Energy Union: a new start?
Fortunately, in his investiture speech Juncker was quick to move away from these carbon castles in the air, setting out his understanding of the Energy Union: 'I strongly believe in the potential of green growth. I therefore want Europe's Energy Union to become the world number one in renewable energies.' He went further still: 'I would also like to significantly enhance energy efficiency beyond the 2020 objective, notably when it comes to buildings, and I am in favour of an ambitious, binding target to this end.'

In other words, Jean-Claude Juncker salvaged Tusk's initial project and transformed it into a forward-looking political instrument, lightyears away from the original proposal. This approach was enshrined by the addition of a subtitle to the Energy Union: 'with a Forward-Looking Climate Change Policy'. Juncker entrusted the vice-presidency for Energy Union to Slovakian socialist Maroš Šefčovič, an old hand at European diplomacy. He also combined the Energy and Climate portfolios, handing them over to the Spanish conservative Miguel Arias Cañete. This repartition of attribution is not the most helpful. It would have been better to have a vice president for Climate at the Commission, with responsibility for ensuring that EU action across all sectoral policies was consistent with regard to the climate. Indeed, climate is a cross-cutting issue, with implications on the environment, agriculture and transport. Juncker has become notorious for his bear hugs and back-slapping, with varying degrees of friendliness;[73] this is perhaps illustrative of how he embraced Tusk's Energy Union and promptly turned it into something completely different.

In the hands of Juncker and Šefčovič, the Energy Union took on board the climate and energy values of the 'Enlightenment' years. The document adopted by the Commission on 25 February 2015 was structured around five different aspects. Henceforth, it placed energy efficiency and demand reduction at the top of European energy policy priorities – a significant step forward that also marked a break with the Barroso years. In addition, the Energy Union went hand in hand with the emergence of a new electricity market, defined in terms of new, decentralised sources of production being placed in the hands of innumerable stakeholders.

However, the document did not go so far as to draw a line under the previous view of energy. The text begins by discussing security of gas supply, and makes a point of indulging the pro-nuclear lobby in the section devoted to research and innovation. And while the EU's desire to become the 'world number one' in renewables is a laudable goal, there is no accompanying practical strategy to achieve this aim.

At the end of the day, the Energy Union is a strategic framework that will need to be fleshed out with concrete proposals during the current and forthcoming reviews of the principal legislation in place covering renewables, energy efficiency, the internal market and the security of gas supply. Together with the European Fund for Strategic Investment (EFSI, also known as the Juncker Plan) and the COP21 Paris Agreement, it constitutes one of the three pillars on which the

---

73   The boisterous welcome by Juncker of heads of state and government at the Vilnius summit in May 2015 has gone down in history. Pictures of Juncker's 'face-slapping' went down a treat with the European press and satirical programmes such as *Le Petit Journal* in France.

EU can build in order to pursue and extend energy transition. All the tools to move forward are there. And even if the reactionary lobbies still retain all their ability to do damage, I have a few ideas as to how these tools could be used to good effect. It is to this subject that we will turn in the second part of this book.

PART TWO

THE FUTURE
OF ENERGY
TRANSITION
IN EUROPE

Once energy transition had been incorporated into EU legislation, thanks to the measures put in place under the oversight
of Loyola de Palacio and more particularly after the first Climate and
Energy Package in 2008, the oligopolies lost no time in responding to
this threat to their existence. For seven whole years, they systematically
sought to undermine these advances by every means possible, both in
Brussels and by using their privileged access to prime ministers and
ministers with responsibilities for energy. The 'Enlightenment' years
were followed by the 'Dark Ages'. What of the future?

I believe there are three factors that could combine to set Europe on
the right path again: President Juncker and his version of the Energy
Union, favourable to green technology and concerted climate action;
the European Fund for Strategic Investment (EFSI) to recover from the
economic downturn, largely based on the promotion of renewables and
energy efficiency; and thirdly, the encouraging outcome of the COP21,
which could mark a watershed in the fight against climate change.

Three new instruments: the Energy Union, the Juncker Plan and the COP21 Agreement

Today, we stand at a crossroads. The strategy details of the Energy Union promoted by the Juncker Commission have not yet been clearly defined: it will be up to lawmakers to flesh them out. In any event, it offers an amazing opportunity for energy transition, due in particular to two of its fundamental components: the principle according to which energy efficiency should take priority (known under the 'efficiency first' slogan); and Europe's stated aim of becoming (or remaining) the world number one in renewable energy.

President Juncker has also launched a major initiative to stimulate fresh investment in Europe's economy: the Juncker Plan, spearheaded by the EFSI (European Fund for Strategic Investment). This is a highly valuable instrument that takes into account Europe's greatest difficulty: a lack of investment. Cheap capital is abundantly available on the financial markets, but there is a reluctance on the part of the latter to commit to investing in the future, seen as a high-risk proposition. State funding, meanwhile, is scarce, so the Commission's proposal is to use it as a guarantee, thereby bringing down real and/or perceived risk. Naturally, such investments should be directed towards renewable energy and energy efficiency as a priority.

At the same time, the COP21 Agreement has changed the game at a global level. It has impressed on people's minds the fact that it will be impossible to keep global warming beneath 1.5°C unless we decide to abandon the use of most of the world's fossil fuel reserves. Carbon risk is therefore a very real thing, and investors will gradually be pulling out of fossil-related assets in favour of green technology. The COP21 conference was also a turning point when it came to raising awareness of the potential of renewables and energy efficiency, as well as the role that millions of stakeholders can play in this field: individuals, cooperatives, municipalities and others.

Together, these three opportunities form a springboard for the resurgence of energy transition in Europe – and fulfil the Greens' vision of energy that is both efficient and '100 per cent renewable'. The text of the COP21 Agreement reached in Paris involves greenhouse gas emissions being reduced to virtually zero. If such a process is to be implemented, our societies need to be transformed by making energy efficiency a priority (wasting less energy) and accelerating transition towards a system based wholly on renewable energy. Despite the foot-dragging on the part of the pro-nuclear lobby and the advocates of CCS, in the medium term renewables will inevitably account for 90–95 per cent of our energy use.

A turning point in geopolitics

We are at a historic moment: for the past one hundred years, energy geopolitics has revolved around the principle of strength being measured in terms of available energy resources, or having an army that can gain access to resources which are then plundered. The new shape of geopolitics is more a case of having the best environmental technologies – and thereby gaining an advantage over everyone else. In other words, those who have mastered solar and wind power, smart grids, and energy storage will be in positions of strength; anyone bringing down their imports of fossil fuels will increase their geopolitical independence.

The peace policies of the future will involve accelerating the proliferation of green technology worldwide to reduce our dependence on countries like Russia and Saudi Arabia when it comes to fossil energy resources. It is clear that abundant oil resources lead to authoritarian regimes.

This is a genuine challenge for Europe: how can ambitious policies be pursued with regard to the climate, energy and transport if the prices of coal, gas and oil are low, and electricity prices are at historically low levels? One of the challenges for European policy is that of anticipating this change, as a result of which access to resources will no longer be directly linked to geopolitical power.

'100 per cent renewables' – a target within our grasp

Today, robust and credible scenarios are emerging in Germany, France, Denmark and Sweden for a roadmap towards '100 per cent renewables', hand in hand with the reduction of our energy use in absolute terms. We will transition from energy from below to energy from above. Achieving this also entails a far greater degree of inter-connection in the system, made possible by the digital revolution that is currently underway. This is crucial in order to incorporate several million wind and solar power production facilities, compared to the several hundred facilities providing electricity from coal and nuclear energy today. Electricity production, buildings and transport will all be interconnected. All-electric heating and transport, combined with optimised data management, will allow energy to be stored on a massive scale, including in the batteries of cars connected to the grid during charging and discharging.

Transport remains the hardest sector to 'decarbonise'. At present, 90 per cent of all vehicles still use fossil fuels. The reason is simple: this type of energy is extremely dense, easy to transport and not very flammable. However, the prevalence of diesel has experienced a serious setback in Europe: Dieselgate. I am convinced that the growing awareness of the health impacts of diesel will hasten the triumph of electric mobility. At the same time, we can already start taking action by changing individual mobility in cities: fewer cars, more pedestrianised areas, bikes and green public transport. This trend is already evident in the emergence of green cities, which also encourage thermal renovation of buildings, in synergy with clean transport in eco-districts. Encouragingly, there is no shortage of ex-amples. Malmö in Sweden has a neighbourhood that is 100 per cent powered by renewable energy. Some 70 per cent of Portugal's electri city comes from renewable sources. The city of Munich is hoping to have 100 per cent green electricity by 2025. Even industry is getting in on the act: in the wake of the COP21 conference in Paris, dozens of multinationals have committed to the principle of 100 per cent renewable energy.

The choices we are making today will commit us for a long time hence. They will have an impact on our social, economic and environ-mental future. What would the consequences of a scenario combining energy efficiency and 100 per cent renewables be?

Socio-economic consequences

Such a scenario is labour-intensive. It is decidedly contemporary, encouraging the development of cutting-edge technology and creating high-quality jobs, both in the digital world and in construction. It calls for a workforce with improved skills and qualifications, involving training – this could be organised as part of Europe's social dialogue.

As to democracy, energy transition puts decision-making power back in the hands of the end user. As things stand, individuals pay for fuel and utilities without really being able to know or understand just what makes up the bill: they are treated little better than wards of court. With the decentralisation of the means of production, self-production and digitalisation together open up the possibility of consumers being at the controls (provided of course that a suitable compromise with regard to privacy issues can be found), and becoming 'consumer-actors'.

The EU has been enduring an economic crisis for eight years now and poverty is increasing. Energy poverty is one of the symptoms of poverty becoming more widespread: keeping warm could even become a luxury. As Hervé Kempf[74] has demonstrated, households pay the most for transport, heating and electricity, in that order. Our scenario would reduce vulnerability by combining public policy in favour of green transport and the thermal insulation of buildings.

Since 2008, Europe has suffered first and foremost from under-investment. The crisis runs deep in the realms of construction and infrastructures: roads, buildings, heating networks, power stations and transmission lines are all ageing. To overcome this, there needs to be reinvestment in the infrastructures of the economy of the future: rolling out solar and wind power production facilities, building renovation, transport electrification and the extension of broadband Internet. European technologies are among the best in a great many of these fields. Solar power, wind power, green cities, DC power lines and the management of significant quantities of renewable energy in power grids

---

74 *Comment les riches détruisent la planète*, Seuil, 2007.

have all been developed in Europe. The EU could reap the benefits of a market that is set to increase tenfold worldwide. This is therefore the right time to be investing in green technology, restoring optimism and creating a dynamic that will improve competitiveness on export markets. The Juncker Plan is a good start, but much more needs to be done.

In addition, there needs to be fresh investment of new tax revenues in energy transition. This revenue could be increased, for instance, by establishing a carbon floor price. Innovation involves a combination of financial instruments and social policies to stimulate cooperatives, cycle networks, car-sharing and so on. Bus drivers, academic researchers, heating engineers and farmers could become everyday climate heroes. This grassroots dimension would make a society based on 100 per cent renewable energy that much more meaningful.

Environmental consequences

Energy transition impacts climate change first and foremost, but at the same time, it also affects health, by reducing particle pollution from coal and diesel and protecting biodiversity. According to the WHO,[75] air pollution has been responsible for more than 8 million deaths over the past ten years. No climate policy, health policy or environmental policy can ignore energy transition. All three aspects are linked.

This is precisely why I am convinced that nuclear power is not a solution to climate change. It is a form of energy that runs counter to the principles of democratisation and decentralisation that we see at work today. Then, too, there is the issue of radiation: what is the point of running the risk of a major nuclear disaster in Europe when there are cheaper, safer alternatives?

Transition also has a positive impact on water policy, since it reduces the water footprint of energy production – unlike the exploitation of shale gas, which can have disastrous consequences on the potability of groundwater. Similarly, air pollution due to electricity generation and internal combustion engines is ridiculously high in the EU. All

---

75   'Preventing Disease through Healthy Environments', World Health Organization, 2016, apps. who.int.

this could be changed through popular mobilisation, as was seen with the 'Krakow Smog Alert' Facebook campaign that took place a few years ago, resulting in the council deciding to prohibit the use of coal for heating from 2018 onwards. A similar line of thinking will result in diesel being banned from city centres; Anne Hidalgo, for instance, has plans to 'eradicate diesel from Paris'.

A society based on 100 per cent renewable energy will also take better care of biomass, using it in accordance with strict rules on biodiversity, such as the sustainability criteria that form part of the directive on the promotion of renewable energy. Sustainability criteria are required for all types of biomass, including solid biomass. On a planet which will be home to between 10 and 12 billion people by the end of the century, food production must take priority over energy production. Naturally, there are limits to the quantities of biofuels that can be produced without imperilling this principle. Biofuels should therefore target sectors where they are presently the only alternative to fossil fuels, such as aviation (in combination with partial electrification for ground operations, take-off and landing).

Lastly, the impacts of wind power on biodiversity, both onshore and offshore, are now well known. They can be avoided or kept to a minimum thanks to a number of measures: environmental impact assessments, improved wind turbine blade design, site monitoring using thermal imaging cameras and so on. Indeed, many projects have actually allowed better-protected habitats for various species in the vicinity of these facilities, as is the case for the golden eagle at the Beinn an Tuirc wind farm in Scotland. Similarly, the Horns Rev windfarm offshore from Denmark has been designed to be as species-friendly as possible using new techniques: visual and acoustic monitoring using sensors and thermal imaging cameras; tagging mammals; creating new habitats for fish round the turbine mast anchor piles; and keeping seals and porpoises at a safe distance during site construction.

Converting the try
The Energy Union, the Juncker Plan and the COP21 Agreement are

all recently implemented and all of them are tremendous opportunities. For the moment, they are nothing more than instruments; they achieve nothing on their own, but are designed to be used to move things in the right direction. It is now up to the various stakeholders to convert them into powerful sources of leverage for energy transition, in each of the key sectors to which we will now turn.

CHAPTER 13

TOWARDS 100 PER CENT RENEWABLES FOR ELECTRICITY

The electricity sector is currently undergoing a staggering revolution due to a combination of several major changes. The first of these is the decreasing size of the means of production, including smaller installations for energy production using solar power, wind power and biogas. Whereas formerly the system could rely only on a limited number of large facilities in Europe, most of them using hydro power, nuclear power, coal or gas, today there are millions of these facilities. The fight against climate change and nuclear power has led to a process of decentralisation based on renewable energy. Combined with digitalisation, this phenomenon has led to profound changes in the energy system. Miniaturisation, decentralisation and digitalisation together form a triptych framing the new electricity market – and enabling millions of citizens everywhere to play an active role in it.

The changing energy system
The historic system, based on rigid output and artificially inflated consumption (for instance due to electric heating, motorway lighting and so on), was characterised by a baseload – in other words, the existence of a permanent minimum output. This will disappear as both production

and consumption become more flexible. Advances in information technology have paved the way for three new developments:

- Firstly, system operators can manage the flow of electricity across larger geographical areas, even across national boundaries. Initiatives such as Coreso and TSCNET, delivering analysis and making coordination at this scale possible, have emerged.
- Secondly, powerful computers and sophisticated algorithms optimising both grids and market operations, and organising energy flows from scattered sources dispersed across huge areas, have made it possible to manage this degree of complexity.
- Thirdly, increasingly accurate and reliable weather forecasting has allowed market players to anticipate the production of solar and wind power in real time, or at least with sufficient accuracy to take part in the electricity market; the latter is now shifting from a 'day-ahead' basis to a same-day basis.

Not only are there new technological possibilities, but a new societal dynamic is also at work. The speed at which information is exchanged is increasing to the extent that we have reached a tipping point, with the system opening up to the participation of individuals, small businesses and farmers. This is the Internet of Energy imagined by Jeremy Rifkin, also known as the 'Enernet'.

This step forward will lead to renewables accounting for over 60 per cent of electricity consumption by 2030. Could this figure realistically reach 100 per cent by 2050? Well, such has already been the case occasionally: in 2016, for several days running, Portugal had electricity that was almost 100 per cent renewable in origin, from wind power, solar power and hydroelectricity. Germany achieved something similar on 15 May 2016, as did Denmark, for a single day in 2015. We are still a long way from 100 per cent over long periods of time, but these examples show that the system is capable of dealing with such quantities of renewables. In summer 2016, Sweden reasserted at the highest level its desire to achieve this objective by no later than 2040.

Gradually overcoming obstacles

Is a 100 per cent renewable electricity system achievable? Is it technically possible? In the space of twenty years, wind turbine performance has improved by a factor of forty. In 1990, the average power of an onshore wind turbine was 0.5MW for a 40m-high installation. Today, the average height of wind turbines being installed across Europe is over 100m, with average installed power of almost 3MW. Some experiments go even further still: in 2009, the eleven most powerful onshore wind turbines ever built (7MW) were commissioned at Estinnes, Belgium, as part of a demonstration project funded by the EU. For their part, the most powerful offshore giants have installed capacity of 8MW per turbine, soon to increase to 10MW. Forthcoming technical breakthroughs, such as the huge 50MW wind turbines currently under development in the United States (featuring a completely revolutionary design of blade) are of course fascinating, but by no means indispensable to the swift penetration of renewables in their current form. Production technology is largely in place already: there is no need to wait for some theoretical great leap forward.

Cost reductions

The second oft-cited barrier relates to costs. Admittedly, all forms of renewable energy are expensive at the outset. That said, both wind and solar power costs have fallen dramatically. Take solar power, for instance: in the early 1990s, the average cost of a photovoltaic module was approximately \$8/W. By 2015, the price had come down to \$0.30/W – a 26-fold drop in twenty-five years. While it is not quite that spectacular, the learning curve for lithium batteries is nonetheless impressive, with annual cost reductions of 14 per cent between 2007 and 2014, from \$1,000/kWh to \$410/kWh. Elon Musk, the founder of Tesla, recently announced his intention of producing batteries at a price of \$250/kWh in the years to come.

One simple story suffices to illustrate this new state of affairs. Under pressure from environmentalists with regard to its wood supplies, the Ikea group decided to clean up its act by committing to a sustainability policy, including a 100 per cent renewable electricity supply, all-LED lighting and so on. The group's strategic management considered going further still, looking at whether the consumer brand should become a player in the energy market. The group examined the possibility of marketing energy kits combining solar panels and batteries. In 2011, the management asked itself a specific question: 'How much would such a kit cost?' The answer was not long in coming: 'At least as much as a car; let's forget it, it's not our business.' Five years later, the question came up again. The answer, however, was no longer the same: kits could henceforth be marketed for about the same price as a fitted kitchen. Unlike cars, fitted kitchens were very much Ikea's business! And so it was that in April 2016,[76] the group decided to embark on this adventure and start offering solar panels for sale in its ubiquitous blue and yellow stores. It is a striking demonstration of how the massive decrease in solar power costs has enabled photovoltaic panels to enter the world of retail distribution.

PHOTOVOLTAIC CELLS GOT 25 TIMES CHEAPER IN 15 YEARS

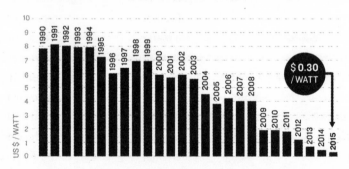

Source: Bloomberg New Energy Finance & pv.energytrend.com
© REVOLVE MEDIA

Renewables now cost less than new nuclear power, which is estimated to have a price tag of around €120/MWh for EPRs, such as that used at Hinkley Point C. Coal appears more competitive, but only because the external costs of pollution are not incorporated into the price.

---

76   'Ikea starts selling solar panels in UK stores', *The Guardian*, 25 April 2016.

Coal-fired power plants fitted with CO_2 capture and storage systems would cost far more than solar or wind power, which is why Poland finally abandoned the idea of getting involved with CCS. Put another way, renewables cost about the same as gas-fired power stations and will become comparatively cheaper as and when gas has to pay for its climate-related costs. These cost reductions are reflected in the feed-in tariffs offered for solar power installations, which have fallen by 80 per cent in 10 years, standing at €87/MWh in 2015.

Once the 'polluter pays' principle kicks in, renewables are therefore the cheapest source of electricity. However, there is still an issue of perception when it comes to their costs, linked to the very low prices on the wholesale electricity market at present. In Germany in 2008, wind-generated electricity commanded feed-in tariffs of €90–95/MWh, while wholesale prices stood at around €50–60/MWh, buoyed up by a carbon price of €20–30/tonne. This state of affairs led to a reasonable differential of €30–40/MWh, funded by a charge tacked onto consumers' electricity bills. By 2016, wind power had become much cheaper, with feed-in tariffs of around €70–75/MWh. But electricity prices had also fallen significantly, due to the low price signals coming from the European carbon market; this led to overproduction of electricity using coal and lignite in Europe (2014 and 2015 were in fact record years for this type of production). Wholesale prices therefore collapsed to around €20–30/MWh, so the differential borne by renewable support schemes was higher in 2016 than it was in 2008. However, the more the 'polluter pays' principle is applied to the electricity sector, the smaller this differential will become: in the absence of a properly functioning carbon market, this is why a CO_2 floor price would be a good thing.

Grassroots support

Some critics allege that people are generally opposed to wind and solar power, invoking the 'Not In My Back Yard' (NIMBY) principle. My personal experience is rather the opposite: if people are offered a local means of participation, they take control of renewable energy and get involved in order to attract local investment. NIMBY therefore becomes PIMBY: 'Please, In My Back Yard'! Indeed, it is no accident that the European champions of wind power, Denmark and Germany, are also the countries in which there are the most grassroots cooperatives.

It is true that few individuals make such a choice based primarily on a desire to combat climate change. But people can and do support renewable energy projects because they are local and attract revenue into the local economy. A small proportion of the population will always be opposed to wind turbines. But the true NIMBYs are in fact the so-called national champions, such as EDF in France, RWE and E.ON in Germany and Enel in Italy: their position can be summed up as 'Not In My Domestic Market'. They refrain from investing in renewables on their own markets in order not to eat into the profitability of their ageing nuclear power plants and fossil-fired power stations.[77]

Storage and security of supply

Lastly, there is the issue of whether a system largely dominated by renewables could provide adequate security of supply. What happens when there is neither wind nor sun? Various experts have come up with theoretical responses, carrying out computer simulations for a 100 per cent renewable scenario in the German, Swedish and French systems.[78] To manage a system of this kind, a number of different sources are required. In Europe, on average, solar power runs for 1,500–2,600 hours per year; onshore wind power for a further 1,600 hours; and offshore wind power for 3,000–4,500 hours. To this can be added biomass, geothermal power and, of course, hydroelectricity. The strength of renewables lies in their diversity. It is the authorities' responsibility to organise and plan this complementarity in terms of space management and network modernisation. And this is precisely why the technologically neutral auctions imposed by DG Comp are not fit for purpose: wind power is not in competition with solar power, any more than onshore

---

77   See Chapter 1, p. 6.
78   'Un mix électrique 100% renouvelable? Analyses et optimisations', Ademe, October 2015, www.ademe.fr.

wind power is in competition with offshore wind power. On the contrary, all these options complement each other.

The important thing is for installed production capacity to be able to satisfy demand at any point in time. There are two potential problems: too much and not enough production. To address this, a highly flexible system is required, with various options which the market and system operators can use on a permanent basis:[79]

- Interconnections, with networks that balance the system across larger geographical areas, increasing the probability of finding enough wind or solar power in sufficient quantities within a given region.
- Demand-side management: this is relatively cheap compared to all the other options, and allows large quantities of electricity consumption to be deferred: industry is capable of increasing, decreasing or deferring its electricity consumption, allowing it to adjust to the price signals observed on various markets. For instance, from its control centre near Chambéry, the French firm Energy Pool can defer 2,500MW of industrial consumption – the equivalent of two nuclear reactors. According to US regulator FERC, some 20 per cent of America's entire electricity consumption could be made completely flexible through demand response measures. In Europe, analysis indicates that, depending on the scenario, the net benefits for the electricity system of improved penetration of demand response mechanisms could amount to €2.5–€7.9 billion[80] by 2050, in particular through massive savings on the need to extend transport and distribution networks.
- Lastly, the EU already has huge storage capacity in the form of pumped hydraulic storage. Total installed capacity currently stands at 42GW, spread across 170 facilities. While most of this hydraulic capacity is quite old, it is on the increase due to modernisation decisions taken during the mid-2000s, at a time when the difference between the base price and the peak price of electricity was very

79   'Flexibility options in electricity systems', Ecofys, 10 March 2014, www.ecofys.com.
80   'Demand Response at the DSO Level', SEDC, April 2016, www.smartenergydemand.eu.

high, making storage that much more profitable. This differential has decreased in recent years, in particular because solar power can now meet midday consumption needs. The main hydroelectric pumping sites are currently concentrated in Scandinavia and the Alps, but the Balkans also has immense potential, as yet untapped.

Today, experts are also looking at other storage options, including batteries. Some believe that electric vehicles connected to the grid could not only be recharged from time to time, but also supply electricity to the grid at other times. Could this compelling vision actually come to fruition? It all depends on the ability of batteries to maintain their performance levels after repeated charging and discharging. It also depends on the development of attractive business models for car owners, who will doubtless be loath to see their battery being fiddled around with remotely by system operators. Other specialists are more in favour of installing large, industrial-scale batteries close to a transmission and distribution system's production and dispatch facilities. For instance, in Germany, a company called MVV has deployed batteries in some districts of the city of Mannheim, renting out their use virtually to private customers.

The problems resulting from production that varies second by second, minute by minute, hour by hour, over half a day or over a whole day can therefore already be addressed by demand response, hydroelectric storage and batteries. They could quickly replace what are known as the 'must runs': the old and highly polluting power plants that old-world stakeholders insist on keeping in the system, arguing that there is no alternative.

And what of seasonal variations, which can lead to stress on the system during certain rare occasions – particularly during winter, on days where there is less sun and no wind? This is a more serious challenge. Europe is addressing it, in particular by exploring the possibility of 'power to gas': this involves using spare renewable electricity to perform electrolysis of water, producing hydrogen, and ultimately methane, for injection into existing gas networks. Europe's electricity system would thus converge with gas infrastructures: demand in gas will decline, but the existing infrastructures could find a use during the transition to a zero-carbon world. This process is not energy-efficient, due to the significant losses during energy conversion, but it could solve the problem of seasonal shortfalls. Another, supplementary option could be to keep a number of open cycle gas turbines in operation, to serve as a top-up facility.[81]

Towards a more responsive system

In the future, we will therefore have an electricity system characterised by decentralised production, extensive networks, storage and demand-side management. The progress of digitalisation has made management of such a system possible thanks to large numbers of sensors and automated processes, as well as the constantly increasing calculation power of computers themselves. Ten years ago, wind turbines rotated simply on the basis of how hard the wind was blowing. Today, they are controlled remotely and can be adjusted on the basis of their production capacity, in addition to observed and forecast weather conditions. The same applies to solar power, with increasingly sophisticated inverters.

In addition to electricity distribution system operators (DSOs) and electricity transport system operators (TSOs), the market itself can also provide a degree of coordination in the form of the price signal conveyed to players.[82] To achieve this, the EU must change its model, currently shaped around the requirements of the old world. These consist of rather unresponsive demand, 'dumb' grids, hydro-electric-only storage and a small number of large production facilities. On the electricity exchange, the old world's baseline market is the

---

81   The reason for using open cycle turbines rather than combined cycle gas turbines, given that the latter are much more efficient, is that while combined cycle gas turbines are more sophisticated, they are also more expensive; they can scarcely pay for themselves on the basis of 200–300 annual hours' operation, the expected total for these top-up power plants in a system largely dominated by renewables.

82   TSOs manage the high-voltage electricity network, while DSOs manage the low-voltage electricity network, which distributes electricity to individual users. In France, the TSO is RTE, while the DSO is the state-owned company Enedis.

day-ahead market: every day, at 3 p.m., an auction is organised for the following day, in one-day sections. But the closer we get to real time, the more reliable offers of supply will be, allowing producers to adjust their offers to variations in wind and sunshine. The market should therefore transition towards an intra-day system, in which bids can be made virtually in real time, for fifteen-minute units. For the last few minutes, the TSOs would take over, managing network-balancing in real time and streamlining any discrepancies between the supply announced in advance by the producer and the actual production they can provide at any given time. This should stop TSOs having to constantly strive to overcome significant discrepancies.

We have the tools
The technological, economic and systemic problems with transition-ing towards 100 per cent renewable electricity simply do not exist. The obstacles are nothing more than political and are kept in place in particular by the operators of the existing fleet of conventional power plants. They are resisting this paradigm shift at all costs, since they are naturally keen to keep their assets working for as long as possible.

Why am I so optimistic as to the ability of the system to include such a large proportion of renewables? On 20 March 2015, Europe experienced a solar eclipse which constituted a full-scale test for Eu-ropean TSOs.[83] On that day, 35GW of solar power capacity abruptly went off the market, returning shortly thereafter. This was much more acute than simply a couple of clouds scudding across Europe. Despite this, the event passed off without incident, thanks to the information and communications technology that allowed this extreme degree of variability to be anticipated.

And for any remaining doubters, the threat of not having a backup in the event of any failure in renewable production is not a pressing problem in the immediate future: existing coal and gas-fired power plants will not be closing down overnight. They will still be around to

---

83   'Solar eclipse March 2015: The successful stress test of Europe's power grid', ENTSO-E, 15 July 2015, www.entsoe.eu.

help with the transition of the system, providing support as needs be over the next ten to fifteen years – the time needed to improve the use of demand response and flexibility management, bring storage technology to maturity, bring down the cost of batteries, and interconnect the network still further. That said, if the aim is to bring down CO_2 emissions 80–90 per cent by 2050, the electricity sector will have to progress towards 100 per cent renewable energy faster than others.

My proposals:

- Modelling 100 per cent renewable scenarios for all Europe's macro-regions.
- Innovation in the field of batteries and smart grids using large-scale demonstration projects, in order to test 100 per cent renewable energy electricity infrastructure in actual operating conditions.
- Continuing to diversify the renewable energy mix by optimising the complementary nature of existing sources (onshore and offshore wind power, solar power, hydropower and biomass) while also supporting the development of emerging marine technologies.
- Restoring the Intelligent Energy Europe programme in the EU budget, in order to develop exchanges of best practice, feedback from innovative projects in the fields of renewables and smart grids, and cooperation between energy transition stakeholders both locally and regionally.

CHAPTER 14

DIESELGATE: HASTENING THE TRANSITION TO CLEAN TRANSPORT

Any energy policy worthy of the name must also address transport, a sector responsible for some 31 per cent of our final energy use and 20 per cent of our greenhouse gas emissions. Not only are these proportions significant, transport is also the sector in which emissions are increasing the most: Europe's transport is belching out 20 per cent more emissions today than it was in 1990. It is the only sector which has seen its emissions rise over the period, in the face of all the discussions about climate change.

What is more, the 2020 Climate and Energy Package adopted in December 2008 established a legislative framework that made provision for transport emissions to decrease across the EU. And indeed, they have gone down slightly since 2007, thanks to a number of factors: demanding legislation, the economic crisis and high oil prices, at least up until 2014. However, the fall could have been greater still if carmakers had abided by their obligations.

For instance, consider the package's landmark measure: the EU regulation on CO_2 emissions standards for new passenger cars, which involved cutting fuel consumption. This was the spearhead of European policy regarding the climate and energy efficiency, with the ultimate aim of capping emissions at 95g CO_2/km by 2021, 40 per cent below 2007 levels (158g CO_2/km). However, it was to prove to be one of the policy's greatest disappointments.

On the one hand, there was the theory: on paper, emissions were supposed to decrease from 146g to 123g CO_2/km – a fall of 16 per cent between 2009, the date on which the regulation was adopted, and 2014. On the other hand, there was the reality: car fuel consumption decreased by less than 3 per cent according to the NGO Transport & Environment (T&E), which looked at actual emissions, not those measured on paper.[84] To achieve this pathetic result, no legislation was in fact required; even before the EU regulation was adopted, manufacturers had already achieved fuel consumption improvements of 1–1.5 per cent. The explanation of the gap between actual emissions and those measured during laboratory tests – 40 per cent, or sometimes as much as 50 per cent – is simple: the carmakers exploited every loophole in the system imaginable in order to slip through the net. Such collusion between car manufacturers, measurement laboratories, certification authorities and, in some cases, even governments, is unacceptable. It came to light in the wake of another widespread piece of fraud, this one discovered in the United States: Dieselgate.

Institutionalised cheating on a massive scale, a.k.a. Dieselgate

Dieselgate is the largest case of industrial cheating ever uncovered. The health of the inhabitants of Europe has deliberately been jeopardised. Volkswagen, together with other carmakers, knowingly manipulated their software over a period of several years. On the worst-polluting diesel engines, Fiat's depollution technology shuts down after just twenty-two minutes in operation and Renault's equivalent system shuts down when temperatures fall below 17°C. Simply put, there is no depollution throughout the winter. This type of trickery applied not only to passenger cars, but also to light goods vehicles, vans and trucks. Some fifteen motor vehicle manufacturers thereby succeeded

---

84   'How clean are Europe's cars 2015', Transport & Environment, 11 June 2015, www.transportenvironment.org.

in turning Europe into a unique continent: the only one in the world to have so much diesel. Indeed, diesel accounts for 53 per cent of new vehicle registrations in Europe, compared to less than 3 per cent of total fuel consumption in the USA, less than 2 per cent in Japan, and less than 1 per cent in China. The only other equivalent outside Europe is India, where diesel also accounts for almost half of the total vehicle fleet.

This is a health scandal on a par with smoking and reveals the same degree of heartlessness on a massive scale. According to the estimations of the European Environment Agency, 400,000 premature deaths are attributable to air pollution in the EU due to NOx alone – the particles around which most of the cheating in Dieselgate focused. This is much higher than the number of road deaths per year: 26,000 for the European Union as a whole.

In Europe, this bears witness to the monumental failure of regulation of the industry: the European Commission and member states have failed to control certification properly. Certification is national in all but name, since each entity is in competition within the EU, bringing standards ever lower: the looser they are, the more business comes in. It is high time to put a stop to this regulatory tourism. Before the scandal became public, thanks to the determination of US regulatory authorities, the Commission already had access to all the information, through its Joint Research Centre (JRC) in Ispra. This research unit, funded out of the EU budget, is one of the only active laboratories in this sector in Europe that is not dependent on orders from the automotive industry. The Commission did use the JRC to carry out tests, but it did not disclose the results – whereas in the United States, each official test is published online. Failure to do the same amounts to a law of silence, under cover of which the automotive industry in Europe has been cheating as it sees fit.

After having discovered just what was going on with test manipulations, the EU belatedly established emissions tests in real-life conditions. However, the industry managed to obtain nonsensical exemptions: instead of a conformity factor of 1.2, they have come away with a factor of 2.1 until

2025, and after that 1.5.[85] In other words, manufacturers have the right to market vehicles with emissions twice as high as the standard limit. Just imagine the outcry if the same were to apply to speed limits! The automotive lobby is highly effective. They cheated for ten years and now enjoy the benefit of an exemption to carry on as before for a further ten years. As part of the inquiry commission set up by the European Parliament to shed light on these anomalies, I took it upon myself to speak out against this 'carmorra': an obscure, Mafia-like system under the terms of which the European Commission and certain member states such as France, Germany and Italy have enslaved themselves to the automotive industry, while the alarms being sounded by their own authorities have fallen on deaf ears.

The roots of this scandal date back to the 1970s. To defend themselves against imports from Japan and South Korea, countries which were highly competitive when it came to petrol engine vehicles but lacked experience with diesel engines, the European automotive industry's strategy was to consistently favour diesel. In many countries, it succeeded in obtaining tax incentives to this end. According to T&E,[86] diesel subsidies in Europe currently amount to €27 billion a year in total, which is a world record. The only way for European carmakers to function legally and comply with increasingly stringent EU legislation on vehicle CO_2 emissions would have been to launch lower-powered cars that were lighter, or used hybrid technology. But the industry preferred to cheat and continue spreading diesel with gay abandon in order to push the performance of this fuel, which is more efficient than petrol, but also more polluting, to the maximum.

Massive use of diesel is also an aberration for refineries. Diesel is a by-product of refining petrol; in other words, diesel cannot be produced without producing petrol first. European refineries could only lose at this game: the EU has to export this petrol surplus even as it is importing diesel, in particular from Russia. As a result, it has

---

85   The conformity factor is a tolerance threshold that allows a certain degree of difference between measured emissions and the theoretical maximum values specified in law.

86   'Europe's tax deals for diesel', Transport & Environment, 23 October 2015, www.transportenvironment.org/

found itself in direct competition with the United States to get rid of its petrol surplus, in particular on the West African market, for which it was traditionally the supplier. For its part, the US has the benefit of local raw materials in the form of non-conventional oil and its domestic market is shrinking thanks to vehicle efficiency standards; their exports are thus rising. In summary, due to the intentional imbalance of taxation at the request of the carmakers, we find ourselves importing diesel – and not knowing what to do with all our petrol. Not only has this caused a health crisis, it is also a nonsense in energy terms.

By definition, there is no economic future for diesel engine cars. To comply with health standards, they need to be fitted not only with an engine but also a small automated chemical depollution plant since diesel is so much dirtier than petrol. However, this on-board mini-factory is far too expensive for small cars, and is therefore uncompetitive. To make matters worse, depollution uses a lot of energy and thus eats away at diesel's comparative advantage over petrol. On top of that, there are issues of space and comfort: diesel exhaust fluid such as 'adblue', injected to reduce NOx levels in exhaust gases, must be stored on board the vehicle. This is tricky for compact city cars, unless they can make do with smaller quantities by ensuring that the vehicle gets to pass certification tests with the help of a defeat device. To save money in the short term, the carmakers have carried on cheating – at the expense of the lives of hundreds of thousands of citizens.

There will also be economic consequences. Since manufacturers have staked their all on diesel, they are now lagging behind on hybrid and electric vehicles. Toyota is now into its fourth generation of hybrid vehicles, whereas in Europe we are still on the first generation, or second at best. What is more, most of the batteries used in European models are produced in Asia and the USA. This places Europe at a competitive disadvantage compared to Japanese cars, Chinese manufacturers such as BYD and the US firm Tesla, all of which committed to electric vehicles far sooner. Forty years after having started the mania for diesel in order to protect themselves from competition from outside Europe, carmakers are now finding out that what goes around comes around.

© ANDY SINGER

Dieselgate should be a wake-up call for us to accelerate energy transition in transport and implement powerful, ambitious EU legislation. The issue is not simply that of the climate, but also one of public health and liveable-in cities. City authorities will inevitably end up having to ban diesel, under pressure from city-dwellers and in order to abide by European air quality standards. The air in some city centres is becoming unbreathable.

Today, there are 1.2 billion cars worldwide. This number could reach 3 billion by the year 2050, which would be an absolute disaster. What is more, according to the European Commission, city journeys of just a few kilometres account for 23 per cent of all the transport sector's CO_2 emissions. Attractive mobility services, including car-sharing and car-pooling, need to be developed if the number of cars on the roads is to decrease. The good news is that current trends are also heading that way: mobility services are progressing, while individual car ownership is not perceived as being as important as it once was. This can be clearly seen in the US: between 2007 and 2011 alone, car purchases by 18–34-year-olds fell by 30 per cent. Surveys[87] interviewing households involved in car-sharing reveal that the desire to own a car evaporates once the need for mobility is satisfied by some alternative means. In short, cars are now less of a status symbol for young people. This state of affairs is an opportunity for electric cars to come to the fore; they can hasten the tendency to distinguish ownership from use, since they are expensive to buy but cheap to use. This makes them ideal for car-sharing, particularly in built-up areas, where residents prefer mobility services to car ownership, with all the latter's attendant hassle.

Trams are also making a comeback in many European cities. Dublin, Bologna, Bilbao and Tenerife are just some examples of this renaissance. The same is true in Algiers, Tunis, some cities in Brazil, and even New York. And, after twenty years of talking about it, Luxembourg has even joined these efforts at long last.

Urban planning is also a powerful source of leverage for transition. The city of Copenhagen is a model in this respect, where the morning commute sees far more people cycling to work than driving. Local government has turned Copenhagen into a user-friendly city. Denmark has put in place high taxation on cars, and has the lowest per capita car ownership of any highly industrialised European country (415 cars per thousand inhabitants).[88] Today, the Danes have the longest life expectancy in the EU and Denmark ranks among the highest-placed countries when it comes to rating overall happiness and quality of life. The country has even been engaged in genuine strategic thinking about how to create local venues devoted to leisure activities.

The dominant urban planning model after the Second World War drew inspiration from the precepts of Le Corbusier, with cities being divided up on the basis of types of activity: sleep, leisure, shopping and work all took place in different, dedicated districts, connected

---

87   Eliot Martin, Susan Shaheen, 'The Impact of Carsharing on Household Vehicle Ownership', *Access*, issue 38, 2011.

88   Romania, Hungary, Latvia, Croatia, and Slovenia do even better, but this is mostly due to financial poverty. Luxembourg, on the other hand, comes bottom of the class, with 678 cars per 1,000 inhabitants; the EU average is 498.

by road traffic networks. We need to abandon this model, cutting journey distances and increasing neighbourliness, as proposed by architect and town planner Jan Gehl.[89] Town planning determines how people travel. Today, it should encourage green mobility: walking, cycling and the use of public transport.

With this in mind, in July 2016 the International Transport Forum, affiliated with the OECD, published its first scenarios[90] for car-free cities. By doubling the capacity of surface public transportation systems such as minibuses and share taxis, the total number of private cars in a city such as Lisbon could decrease by as much as 97 per cent without journey times becoming significantly longer for local inhabitants. Cars are attractive, because you can travel virtually from your bedroom to your desk without leaving your own private bubble. Some town planners think that the best way of breaking people out of this cocoon is to do something about underground car parks in office blocks and city centres. For instance, in the Vauban eco-district of Freiburg in Germany, you have to walk past the tram stop and the bike-sharing station before reaching the car park.

Electric cars: the obvious way forward

Cars of the future will be 100 per cent electric and hybrid in the meantime. From an energy perspective, an electric motor is far more efficient than a combustion engine. Elon Musk, the founder of Tesla, is currently pushing the envelope of this technology and disrupting the automotive status quo. His influence has been such that after dismissing him out of hand in his early days, they are now all rushing to copy him.

What is needed now is public policy that promotes electric vehicles. For instance, could there be a law to require vehicle manufacturers to produce a quota of electric cars? Or a law granting a bonus on new purchases? European countries will no longer be able to subsidise

---

89   'Pour des villes à l'échelle humaine', Écosociété, 2013.
90   'Shared Mobility. Innovation for Liveable Cities', OECD, International Transport Forum, 10 May 2016, www.itf-oecd.org.

electric cars once they have conquered a significant share of the total fleet, so the best means of action is through legislation. The forthcoming regulation on passenger car CO_2 emissions should be extended to prohibit the marketing of vehicles powered by fossil fuels by 2030 at the latest. This is the only way that Europe's entire car fleet could become carbon-free by 2050.

Solutions for batteries

There is, however, one outstanding issue: what will the life cycle for batteries look like? They could be leased rather than purchased to ensure that manufacturers develop an effective processing chain for maintenance and recycling, thus avoiding the waste engendered by programmed obsolescence. Since batteries will require renewal more often than the vehicles themselves, recycling will also provide a lucrative business model: the lithium, nickel and cobalt contained in the batteries are valuable metals well worth recovering. Some US firms have already entered this segment. In Europe, the new proposed directive on batteries and accumulators should offer a robust means of tackling the issue of recycling car batteries properly.

What about charging times? There is a need to offer both slow charging in existing parking spaces at home (houses and apartment parking bays), as well as fast charging during parking for short periods, such as at supermarkets and motorway service stations. The issue of harmonising charging across Europe is another important industrial challenge: the mass deployment of electric vehicles necessarily involves standardisation. We must not repeat the mistake of mobile phones, with all the frustrations of a different charger for each model.

We also need to see vehicles within the overall context of the electricity system. Some interesting initiatives are emerging in this respect. For instance, Tesla has invented batteries that can be installed at home, and serve as an interface between the car and a photovoltaic installation. In Frankfurt and Mannheim, German utility MVV has set up battery containers: people can rent batteries and store their electricity in each neighbourhood, rather like a virtual bank account for power.

No clean transport without clean electricity

However, there's also the question of whether the electricity for cars is itself green. The challenge is to ensure that 100 per cent of the electricity each car uses comes from renewable sources. Failing this, the result would be cars using nuclear power or electricity from coal, which would be a real step back. In 2008, the Barroso Commission initially suggested a figure of 10 per cent for biofuels. The definitive text of the Climate and Energy Package was improved by MEPs, specifying 10 per cent renewable energy for transport. This opens the door not only to second-generation biofuels, but also to electric transportation.

Meanwhile, manufacturers currently benefit from preferential treatment when they market electric vehicles: under the terms of EU law, such vehicles are deemed to emit 0g CO_2/km. This piece of accounting fiction allows carmakers to decrease the average emissions of their fleet as a whole and, in doing so, indirectly allows them to market a greater number of polluting vehicles. There are two ways of combating this: the best option would be to require manufacturers to secure a renewable electricity supply for car buyers throughout the entire lifetime of the vehicle; alternatively, the authorities could assign each vehicle the average emission levels of the European electricity mix. Indeed, taking into account the actual emissions of cars is a major step towards including electric mobility within the global energy system.

The last question to be dealt with here is that of the potential stress on the system of the mass electrification of transport. The detractors of electric vehicles argue that the network would not be capable of absorbing the charging requirements of a fleet of several million electric vehicles. However, the figures deserve closer study: Bernard Laponche and Benjamin Dessus from Global Chance have estimated that a fleet of 7 million electric vehicles in France – already quite an optimistic number – each travelling 15,000km/year would consume 15TWh: this is barely 4 per cent of current French nuclear power output. There is therefore no cause for concern, especially if this figure is compared to the requirements of electric heating, which eats up some 40TWh of electricity annually in France. The upshot is that electricity use will not increase in spectacular fashion with the electrification of transport. Such a prospect is a myth, as even RTE admits. The problem is not one of volume but of network spikes: the grid needs to become more flexible.

Still on the to-do list

A number of issues have yet to be addressed: long journeys, for holidays, for instance, and the matter of public finances. Many families buy their car on the basis of the longest journey they are likely to take, even if this is a rare occurrence, such as their annual holiday. This leads to cars being too big for daily requirements. Solutions do exist. Smart, for instance, offers buyers a small car for city use and a larger vehicle to rent for holidays. Swiss railways (CFF) have offers combining a train journey with a rental car. CFF has billed itself as a mobility company, rather than simply a railway operator, for some ten years now. This type of offer addresses the problem of the 'last mile' between the nearest railway station and the final holiday destination, which is often isolated; indeed, it is hard to replace cars for this last mile. SNCF and Deutsche Bahn would do well to consider similar schemes.

Meanwhile, in a report to François Hollande, Michel Derdevet, secretary-general of the French DSO ERDF (known as Enedis since 2016), has argued in favour of innovative mobility corridors across Europe: these 'green motorways' would 'link together 70,000km of European motorways with charging stations every 80km, in both directions, for a total of 1,750 stations. The estimated cost of a major EU project of this type, benefiting all European citizens, would be some €450 million for the electrification aspect.'[91] This is relatively affordable, especially given all the positive outcomes for both the climate and the energy system.

Meanwhile, it will be up to various finance ministers to find creative ways of offsetting the loss of tax revenue incurred by lower fuel

---

91   Michel Derdevet, *Énergie, l'Europe en réseaux*, La Documentation française, 2015.

sales. Initially, an additional tax on cars with internal combustion engines could be envisaged, like the bonus/malus system devised by Jean-Louis Borloo, and such a measure could be expanded to penalise people still using diesel more heavily. As it happens, the worst performer when it comes to urban mobility is actually Brussels due to the idiocy of a Belgian tax system that encourages the use of company cars. This is an important aspect of the report into taxation on passenger cars that I drafted for the European Parliament in 2006:

> In some countries, company cars account for up to 50 per cent of the sales of new cars; in many cases, employees do not even have to pay for fuel. There are therefore no environmental incentives for these consumers. The proposed directive should therefore ensure that the taxation of company cars is based on CO_2 emissions.

In the longer term, once most vehicles are electric, I think that mobility taxation should no longer be tied to ownership of the vehicle or fuel (in an integrated system, it will be difficult to distinguish electricity used for lighting from that used in car batteries), but rather be based on infrastructure use – in particular, through the general application of urban tolls. Indeed, London and Stockholm already have these.

When Juncker presented his new Commission in 2014, Brussels could scarcely believe its ears: how could Angela Merkel have agreed to the representative of German industry Günther Oettinger being removed from the strategic Energy portfolio to the much less prestigious Digital? I myself was far from surprised, though; on the contrary, this decision strengthened my conviction that the German automotive industry sees success in the realms of electric mobility and digital technology as vital. Germany has realised that its leadership in carmaking could be under threat from Tesla, BYD, Google and other new players entering the market. And these new cars are now pretty much computers on wheels. There was thus method in Angela Merkel's decision to consign Commissioner Oettinger to Digital. After having spent his first mandate doing the bidding of E.ON,

EnBW and RWE, he is now responsible for protecting the interests of Mercedes, BMW, Volkswagen and the like, as they refocus on electric and digital technologies.

What about hydrogen-powered cars? Are they currently a credible alternative or desirable complement to the electrification of road transport? This technology would require a completely separate infrastructure. How much would the latter cost? And where would the hydrogen needed to supply a huge car fleet come from? Electrolysis of water is not an efficient process, and its energy performance is poor. In view of this, it is not easy to see how the numbers could add up to massive penetration of the market by hydrogen-powered cars. Not to mention the safety issues involved in transporting an unstable, highly flammable fuel on board passenger cars. Here too, however, we can expect some technological breakthroughs. The fact is that the automotive industry does not have that many options; and whether it's electrification, compressed air or hydrogen, innovation is the key for the sector.

Trucks will also have to follow suit

Freight transport, fuelled in particular by the success of online shopping and all the related logistics, is not about to stop growing. By 2030, freight transport will account for 40 per cent of surface transport emissions. Despite this, Europe has not as yet passed any legislation to reduce the CO_2 emissions by this sector.

Modal transfer, the panacea put forward during the Lamoureux years at DG Energy and Transport, in the early 2000s, is in free fall. Rail freight did win some market share in Western Europe, but this was quickly wiped out by the 'all-truck' habits of Eastern Europe. Switzerland, however, has led the way by imposing fees on heavy goods vehicle (HGV) traffic, in particular the 'RPLP tax' on services provided by HGVs, to encourage multimodal transport. One of the ways the resulting revenues are used is to improve rail infrastructures. For instance, the tax paid two thirds of the bill for the new Gotthard Base Tunnel, the world's longest at 57km, opened on 1 June 2016.

The Swiss system has proved highly effective in combating all-truck transport, by combining two elements: good rail infrastructures and taxation that encourages accompanied combined transport. The system in force in the EU, meanwhile, has been misappropriated by the haulage companies' lobby.

Indeed, the Eurovignette[92] has reinforced the dominance of HGVs, the opposite of the originally intended outcome. Tolls have been capped at ridiculously low levels which do not correspond to the actual cost of greenhouse gas emissions, air pollution or the damage caused by wear and tear on road infrastructures. The revision of the Eurovignette directive is far from certain; on the one hand, central European countries would love to do away with their interminable queues of trucks, but the outermost European countries depend on all-truck transport for just-in-time supplies. The fact that some national railway networks are verging on the obsolete does not help, either.

There is, however, one encouraging trend: national road use charging schemes for trucks, already in force in some fifteen countries, including Belgium since April 2016. It would appear that this solution discourages half-empty trucks, and encourages both shorter journeys and more especially, modal transfer to rail. The influence on vehicle performance is limited, though. Obtaining cleaner trucks would require road use charging to be distinguished from CO_2 emissions taxation. Something like this almost saw the light of day in France with the *écotaxe*, before the government backed down in the face of pressure from the road haulage lobby and broader social discontent.

It is therefore high time to pass laws on HGV emissions standards similar to those for cars and LGVs. There are applications for industry: Europe has a significant lead in the truck market. Daimler is a robust world leader, while Volkswagen and Volvo are also in the top five. In a global market which will shift towards the adoption of fuel

---

92   The Eurovignette is a usage fee charged by member states to hauliers allowing the latter to use their transport infrastructures, particularly roads. It is levied to recover the costs of construction, maintenance, repair and environmental protection. It was set up in 1999 with a view to harmonisation between countries (minimum vehicle weight covered by the tax, maximum rates etc.) and ensuring fair competition.

efficiency standards and increasingly stringent demands on engines, European manufacturers will have to adapt.

What about electric trucks? Hybrid models already exist; Siemens is working on one, using overhead power lines and induction coils. Working in partnership with Scania, the German manufacturer has built the first ever section of electric motorway in Sweden. The idea could be expanded by installing overhead power lines above the near-side lines of main motorways. Shared electric cargo bikes also exist, such as Carvelo in Switzerland, as do electric vans, such as Nissan's NV 200. These all offer alternatives to oil for freight distribution from logistics centres to outlying areas. Many cities are watching these technological developments closely.

Aviation and shipping: the climate's worst enemies

Air and sea transport pose unavoidable problems for the climate. In total, these two sectors pump out the equivalent of two industrialised nations when it comes to global emissions. According to a study by the European Parliament, they could account for 40 per cent of global emissions by 2050.[93] Aviation is both the most carbon-intensive mode of transport and the fastest-growing. The emissions of European aviation alone are equivalent to those of a country the size of the UK.

The main problem resides in the tax advantages from which aviation benefits: it is exempt from VAT on tickets and from aviation fuel taxes. This represents a huge tax gift: according to Climate Action Network, VAT on air tickets would amount to over €10 billion per year for the EU alone. Aviation must start paying for its emissions, either through taxation, or through market mechanisms. One way of doing this would be to implement a special tax on air travel to be paid by passengers, as suggested by Hervé Kempf in his book *Comment les riches détruisent la planète*[94] ('How the wealthy are destroying the planet'). Another option explored by the EU was that of including aviation within the ETS. However, Russia, the United States and China

---

93   'Emission Reduction Targets for International Aviation and Shipping', November 2015.
94   Op. cit.

opposed this head-on, and won hands down, with the EU backpedal-ling: only flights within Europe will be subject to the ETS, at least until the end of 2016. The only hope of extending the scope of application to all flights would be a multilateral agreement by the ICAO (Inter-national Civil Aviation Organization) that is more ambitious than the one achieved in Montreal in October 2016.

Aviation and shipping even managed to exempt themselves from the COP21 Agreement by invoking old, obsolete international con-ventions established by the International Maritime Organization (IMO) and the ICAO. In 2009, they were already promising to make proposals at the COP15 summit, but they turned up empty-handed. In 2015, while small islands were battling to have the 1.5°C threshold recognised as an upper limit for global warming, negotiators empha-sised the importance of air travel for tourism and refused to budge on this issue.

For shipping, as in other sectors, the challenge is to get rid of the dirtiest vessels which are little more than mobile incinerators of highly toxic materials. One solution would be to use regulations to ban the least efficient ships; this would be relatively inexpensive, and could be good for the climate, according to T&E. For instance, the IMO's Energy Efficiency Design Index for 2020 and 2030 could be made more stringent. However, there is not much hope of this actu-ally happening.

Another possible regulatory measure would be to prohibit the use of combustion engines for manoeuvres in port. Cruise vessels are now anticipating restrictions pertaining to pollution when entering harbour, and are having electric propulsion fitted for in-port manoeu-vring and power supply while they are in dock. These motors could be powered by green electricity from offshore wind farms, solar power or cogeneration within the port. Given that ten of Europe's ports ac-count for 60 per cent of its freight traffic, the potential leverage of such measures is clear.

Clean technology is available, both for shipping and for aviation. Norway recently organised a conference in Brussels on hybrid gas/

electricity propulsion for shipping. This offers a twofold advantage, cutting not only CO_2 emissions but also atmospheric and noise pollution. Research is also ongoing into whether liquid fuel can be made using electricity. Another development involves a prototype for a kite-boat, a cargo vessel pulled by a kite, developed by German firm Sky Sails, which made a successful crossing from Europe to the US in 2008. For their part, the Norwegians have Vindskip, a hybrid cargo vessel combining liquefied natural gas and sail power. Sailing vessels have also come back into fashion for coastal shipping.

In the field of aviation, Betrand Piccard's Solar Impulse is pushing back the frontiers of technology, with a successful round-the-world flight in a plane powered by solar energy – for which support came not so much from the traditional aviation industry, but rather from the manufacturers of carbon-fibre boat hulls. Newcomers, such as the Slovenian start-up Pipistrel, are also entering the market. For their part, airlines have suggested that biofuels could be a solution; however, they have resisted any binding measures along these lines. This type of kerosene could be a second or third-generation biofuel. Today, light aircraft can already be powered by electric motors. For larger planes, electricity could be used just for take-off and landing phases, as well as taxiing, with biokerosene taking over during cruise flight.

In any event, it is clear that both aviation and shipping quickly need to find a carbon-free source of energy. Electrification of port and airport infrastructures is also vital. The message for '100 per cent renewable' ports and airports is: yes, we can! To achieve such a result, though, legislation needs to gradually introduce prohibitions, at the same time as providing incentives for changing fuels. Without these, fossil-based aviation fuel and marine fuel oil are not going to disappear any time soon.

My proposals
- Setting up a European alliance of green cities that promote alternative mobility.
- Adopting new EU regulations that gradually prohibit the marketing

of diesel and petrol vehicles, combined with the setting up of a European control agency.

- Requiring vehicle manufacturers to ensure that the electricity powering electric vehicles on the road is 100 per cent renewable in origin or failing this, assigning vehicles the average emissions level of the European energy mix.

- Changing the way road haulage is taxed in order to encourage modal transfer to rail and innovation in the field of electrification.

- Putting an end to tax dumping on the part of aviation by introducing high taxation on aviation fuel and plane tickets; developing aircraft electrification for taxiing, take-off and landing, as well as airports powered by 100 per cent renewable energy; including aviation in international negotiations carried out under the auspices of the UNFCCC.

- Developing the electrification of shipping for in-port manoeuvres and dockside power supply, with ports powered by 100 per cent renewable energy, combined with the use of liquefied natural gas when at sea.

CHAPTER 15

HEATING AND COOLING: TOWARDS ZERO-CARBON BUILDING STOCK BY 2050

The amount of heat and cooling consumed in the residential and service sectors amounts to 40 per cent of Europe's energy consumption, ahead of transport and electricity production. Heating and air conditioning are used in all buildings, be they private houses or apartments or retail premises, and irrespective of whether they are occupied by owners or tenants. At present, average consumption for the sector is high at some 280kWh/m²/year in Europe.[95] What is more, 80 per cent of the buildings that will be in use in 2050 are already in existence today. However, achieving zero-carbon real estate by 2050 is a vital necessity if we are to honour our climate commitments. How can this be done? Counting on new builds will not be enough; above all, we need to develop a strategy to renovate existing buildings.

Construction: an innovation-averse sector

'In Europe, there is high-tech, low-tech, and … the construction industry.' This soundbite from Claus Bugge Garn, former vice president of insulation materials manufacturer Rockwool – and a connoisseur when it comes to the construction industry – speaks

---

thought-provoking volumes about the reluctance of this sector to modernise. Construction accounts for 9 per cent of Europe's GDP, not to mention 18 million jobs, many of them badly paid, poorly qualified and itinerant. It is, however, highly dispersed with 92 per cent of firms working in the industry employing fewer than ten people. No single company accounts for more than 1 per cent of the sector's total revenues. This means that it is not simply a question of mobilising multinationals such as Vinci, Bouygues, ACS, Eiffage, Strabag and Skanska to move things forward; the myriad of small and medium-sized contractors need to get on board, too.

The demand for optimised, high-value products such as windows and boilers is relatively low, as is demand for facade renovation works. This is due largely to the fact that occupiers are unfamiliar with the energy use of the place where they spend most of their time: their house or flat. In view of this, how can the market alone be expected to draw people towards innovative products? The only way forward is by means of political intervention: even if there is risk of the political class being seen as mounting an over-intrusive invasion of the homes of EU citizens, clear and demanding regulations could be a positive game-changer.

Near-zero-energy buildings

The first passive houses, or at least homes with near-zero consumption, were built in the 1970s. Building houses facing the sun, with thick insulation and high-performance windows, is enough to make a huge difference in energy consumption. However, despite the efforts of certain governments, particularly in Scandinavia, and of inventors such as Wolfgang Feist and his Passivhaus Institut, this kind of construction did not spread widely throughout Europe. The big change only came later, when EU lawmakers stepped in. In recent years, the EU has introduced a number of political measures that, although as yet insufficient, are well worthwhile.

The 2010 Energy Performance of Buildings Directive promotes 'deep' building renovation. It includes a long-term roadmap, to provide details of the types of building stock in each member state, including construction dates and the measures applicable to each category. This makes detailed analysis of how real estate is structured in each country possible. The biggest advance, though, has been that of near-zero-energy buildings ('nZEBs'): the directive requires all new buildings erected in Europe from 1 January 2021 onwards to have virtually zero energy consumption. This provision is already being implemented by pioneering countries, including Luxembourg, which is anticipating the existing directive's requirements by four years (the nZEB rule will be effective there as of 2017). Inevitably, nZEBs are more expensive to build. However, the resulting property is worth more, since it offers a lifetime safeguard against spiralling energy prices.

That being said, 'near-zero' consumption must be defined in practical terms. So far, there is no common definition that applies to the whole of the European Union. Some governments, such as that of Poland, are attempting to wriggle out of their obligations by accepting net energy use of 50–$70 kWh/m^2/year$: low, to be sure, but quite a lot more than 'near-zero'. In Denmark, the nZEB definition is 20–$25 kWh/m^2/year$ – an application of the very same directive, but three times more stringent. The European Commission has just addressed this loophole by publishing a recommendation on 29 July 2016. This specifies the upper and lower bounds for the definition, depending on the context, including climate considerations: after all, energy use cannot be expected to be the same in Lapland as it is in Sicily.

The current review of the 2010 Directive should also plug another gap in existing legislation: so far, nobody is really checking how much energy new buildings are using, and whether they actually comply with the relevant standards. Proper monitoring is required to measure a building's energy use in real conditions, as opposed to the figures stated on the plans, in much the same way as vehicle emissions need to be measured in real-life conditions, and not in the lab. This could be done by means of random inspections coupled with fines for contractors found to be in breach of the standards.

Faster and deeper: a twofold challenge for Europe

At the time when the Energy Performance of Buildings Directive was being drafted, very little renovation was being done. For instance, a report by DIW Berlin found that only 0.8 per cent of building stock was being renovated every year in Germany. This figure has risen slightly since, and currently stands at 1.2–1.4 per cent on average across Europe. However, it needs to increase still further, to annual real estate renovation levels of 2.5 or even 3 per cent. This is a vital prerequisite for making Europe's building stock carbon-neutral by 2050. There needs to be more renovation; it also needs to be better and more uniform. How can homeowners be encouraged to invest more in domestic energy renovation?

If a homeowner decides to renovate their house's roof, facade or windows, they need a performance analysis covering each product and technique; and if the building's energy performance is to be profitably improved, an overall analysis, rather than a piecemeal approach, is required. To achieve this, the homeowner in question needs to have intelligible and above all bespoke information at their disposal. Deep renovation also requires the existence of trained labour: artisans, installers, heating engineers and all the various other trades in the construction industry. This in turn calls for a qualification process. Not only would this help achieve European climate and energy targets, it would also help improve both social dialogue and workers' employability.[96]

However, against a backdrop of low oil, gas and electricity prices, possibly for some time, the fossil fuel price signal offers little encouragement to carry out thermal renovation that is extensive enough to achieve zero-carbon building stock by 2050. In view of this, some are recommending shock measures. One would be to determine performance levels below which the sale or rental of buildings would be prohibited. So, for instance, on a scale of A to G, a minimum rating of D would be required initially, and gradually raised subsequently. Such

---

96   See Chapter 24, p. 320.

a scheme would certainly bring down the huge levels of energy waste for which our buildings are responsible.

However, the thirteenth floor of the Berlaymont building, where the president of the European Commission's office is located, is terrified of populists of all stripes. Memories of the all-out attacks by UK and German tabloids against regulations dealing with light bulbs and vacuum cleaners are still painfully fresh. It is all too easy to imagine an alliance between landlords and populist parties taking a stand against Brussels' latest dictates. In these circumstances, most governments of member states are unwilling to accept any review of the directive drastic enough to involve anything along the lines of a binding roadmap to renovate all real estate. Instead, the EU will probably confine itself to less ambitious measures, such as improving certification procedures, the renovation of public buildings, innovation, training, and the roll out of financial instruments to speed up the renovation of the worst-offending buildings, particularly in social housing.

A European thermal renovation fund

Nevertheless, thermal renovation of buildings offers a powerful source of leverage, firstly for job creation and secondly for demonstrating that the EU actually does some good for its inhabitants. In 2015, with this in mind, and drawing on successful national models, I floated the idea of a dedicated investment fund totalling €50 billion over a three-year period. In Germany, for instance, a renovation programme funded by the state-owned bank KfW offers a combination of low-interest loans (around 1 per cent) and subsidies, and has helped raise additional private equity, thanks to a leverage factor of 20. This mechanism benefits public finance, delivering significant financial returns based on an increase in economic activity: for each euro invested, the state gets €4–€5 in return, in the form of VAT levied on renovation products and works. In Lithuania, the JESSICA Fund, together with the EIB, has made it possible to combine loans and subsidies to fund the thermal renovation of a great many buildings.

The European Energy Efficiency Fund represents a first attempt at the EU level. However, it is available only for public-sector authorities, not private buildings, and it amounts to no more than €125 million. I believe that the Juncker Plan, launched by the new president of the Commission on his arrival in Brussels to counterbalance the harmful effects of austerity policies, would be a good vehicle for a large-scale initiative. The concept of the plan would be to offer a European public-sector guarantee to prime the pump and leverage significant amounts of private-sector investment. At the same time, member states could also commit more resources, via European Structural Funds (as was the case with the Lithuanian programme). That is why, as soon as the Juncker Plan was unveiled, I leapt at the opportunity, arguing for at least €50 billion of the €315 billion planned for by the Commission in its proposal to be earmarked for energy efficiency, accompanied by the requisite Technical Assistance.

Shortly after that, four MEPs from four different political groups tabled an amendment suggesting the setting up of such designated funding: the Danish Social Democrat Jeppe Kofod, the Danish liberal Morten Helveg Petersen, the Irish conservative Seán Kelly and, on behalf of the Greens, myself. This amendment quickly gained the approval of the rapporteur, Belgian socialist Kathleen Van Brempt. However, not everyone in Brussels was of the same mind. For various reasons, despite garnering quite a degree of consensus, the idea was bothersome for many others – not least ultra-liberals of all stripes, who took the view that the almighty market, rather than politicians, should determine the Juncker Plan's priorities. It also upset all those who, not being properly informed, thought that energy efficiency was the least of European citizens' worries. Besides, the EIB – a major winner under the Juncker Plan – did not shrink from meddling in the MEPs' vote, publishing a press release in which it restated its preference for funds not to be earmarked for any particular sector: when elected representatives are being issued orders by bankers, there is something very wrong.

And so it was that despite an initial victory in the ITRE Committee, the amendment was defeated on 20 April by dint of a block vote

on the part of a 'grand coalition' between socialists and conservatives in the Economic and Budget Committees. In this instance, the
Schulz/Juncker system managed to get the better of the European
Parliament.[97] After the failure of Barroso's stimulus plan, the EFSI
programme was another missed opportunity, even if the final text
does mention energy efficiency as a priority on a number of occasions.

**Technical Assistance, accounting rules, and standardisation: the
devil is in the detail**
One of the problems to be solved in this area is that of Technical
Assistance: invaluable expertise that allows small projects to be incor-
porated within larger investment portfolios, and helps member states
and local authorities to adjust financial instruments to local needs.
For instance, the EU's ELENA programme has directed €72 million to
Technical Assistance since 2009, and the results speak for themselves.
Over €3 billion worth of private equity has been leveraged, with ambitious projects completed in many European cities. Unfortunately,
Technical Assistance is one of the Juncker Plan's weak spots. Instead
of the €400 million or so promised by the Commission, it has only
granted €20 million more per year for the EU as a whole, with the rest
remaining in the hands of capital cities via the Technical Assistance
provided for structural funds. This is nothing less than a swindle.
Roughly speaking, this tiny amount corresponds to three positions
at the EIB devoted to energy efficiency; hardly enough to achieve any
real change.

One year on from its implementation, the Juncker Plan is a long
way from keeping its promises as regards energy efficiency. Out of
the €22 billion assigned by the EIB to this infrastructure investment
programme, the sector has received only €1 billion – a mere 4.5 per
cent of the funds engaged. This can fairly be described as a failure.
Nevertheless, thanks to ongoing dialogue with the Commission's vice
president Jyrki Katainen and Wilhelm Molterer, managing director

---

97   'Voici comment socialistes et conservateurs ont torpillé le plan européen d'économies d'éner-
     gie', *Reporterre*, 29 April 2015.

of the EFSI, the proposed continuation of the Juncker Plan for three additional years is to be combined with at least 40 per cent being earmarked to combat climate change – which includes energy efficiency.

Centres of excellence devoted to energy efficiency need to be set up. Technical Assistance units should go together with financial instruments within national administrations, where national experts, part funded by structural funds, could set up project development centres. To plug this gap in the Juncker Plan, I suggested this approach to the EU-28's energy ministers on 23 September 2015 in the Luxembourg Declaration. It was validated by research on the part of leading financial institutions working together within the EEFIG, which made it one of its recommendations: 'Support the extension of Project Development Assistance facilities … which will build capacity among SMEs, and the developer and certified energy auditor networks serving SMEs, to develop and launch investment-ready energy efficiency projects [in the real estate sector].'[98]

This need applies to the EU as a whole, but is particularly acute in south-east Europe. Indeed, real estate in this region has some distinctive characteristics: large, low-performance buildings from the communist era; the fragmentation of property bequeathed by the breakup of the communist bloc; and widespread energy poverty, making it very difficult for owners to contribute to the renovation effort. Why not pool Technical Assistance in this region in order to find joint responses to the challenges, as I proposed in the Luxembourg Declaration? More specifically, this could involve using some of the structural funds allocated to these member states and, for countries that are not yet part of the EU, pre-accession funds, as well as those allocated by the European Bank for Reconstruction and Development. Several governments in the region, fully aware of the gains that such an initiative could result in, have followed Slovenia's lead and approached the European Commission in order to suggest practical ways it could be implemented. These were discussed on the

---

98   'Energy Efficiency: The First Fuel for the EU Economy', EEFIG, February 2015, ec.europa.eu.

fringes of an informal meeting of the Council of Energy Ministers under the Slovakian presidency on 12 July 2016.

One of the bottlenecks in the renovation of public buildings revolves around the issue of public debt: under the terms of the European Stability Pact, the state and local authorities are prohibited from building up too much of it – and Energy Performance Contracts are booked as a liability on the balance sheets of public authorities. This is the result of an orthodox interpretation of international accounting standards by Eurostat, the body in charge of statistical analysis of the European economy. However, it is also contrary to common sense. In actual fact, the related costs are mostly operational expenditure (OPEX), which are not public debt; rather, they are embedded in a service agreement under the terms of which the private-sector provider bears most of the liability.

On 7 August 2015 Eurostat hence erected yet another barrier. Published in the relative secrecy of midsummer, the revised guidelines were unambiguous: for agreements with energy providers, such as Esco, 'funding of such expenditure must be included in the public debt'. Did the Commission have nothing better to do than place further obstacles in the path of local authorities and cities? This interpretation represents a major hurdle for cities seeking to use Energy Performance Contracts to bring down energy use in public buildings. As things stand, they are penalised for trying to bring down their energy bills. Networks bringing together cities have raised this issue with the European Commission on a great many occasions. At the time of writing, the ball is firmly in the court of vice president Jyrki Katainen and DG Ecfin (the Directorate-General for Economic and Financial Affairs).

Stimulating innovation in a dispersed sector
Funding is not the whole answer, however. For building renovation to become more widespread, the sector needs to innovate. Whether the issue is 3D design, industrial solutions, prefabrication or something else, the main obstacle to renovation, over and above costs, is very often

its duration. Indeed, it is not easy to ask residents to move out of their homes for the long periods required for works to be carried out. Therein lies the potential for innovation. In the Netherlands, Energiesprong offers an example of the use of latest-generation tools to cut the times during which housing must be vacated. To achieve this, the firm offers predesign and preconstruction of standardised elements, which are then delivered to the worksite. As a result, a full renovation can be completed in less than ten days. The EU has a role to play in disseminating this good practice. With the help of the surplus from the Intelligent Energy Europe programme, it could fund networks of architects to examine new ways of renovating more cheaply, tailored to different climates, regulations and types of housing, in order to achieve a critical mass of stakeholders. Innovation also involves better coordination between all the stakeholders throughout the value chain, right from the design of a renovation project through to its execution and evaluation, together with the sharing of best practice and in-field experience.

The next stage involves addressing the unwanted effects of certain unsustainable techniques currently in use: existing buildings being clad in Styropoor or other types of polystyrene sounds like a good thing – but what will happen thirty or forty years down the road? Will these materials stand the test of time? Even if their energy balance is good, what is their long-term ecological impact? In the future, materials and installation techniques must be both sustainable and recyclable, with no recourse to harmful adhesives or solvents. The answer to all these questions is to be found in the principles of the circular economy: the buildings being constructed today, and those being renovated, must be designed to be deconstructed at the end of their lives, rather than simply being destroyed. This is not just a question of semantics. More efforts need to be made concerning materials, so as to ensure that they do not become non-recoverable waste and to hasten transition from demolition to deconstruction. Here too, innovation is called for.

Over and above the issue of buildings themselves, the challenge can also be addressed holistically, on the scale of an entire neighbourhood.

In Denmark, the same approach is taken to thermal renovation of homes as to collective infrastructures such as heating networks and solar thermal power. By coming at the issue from this perspective, the Danes have brought together electricity, heating and cooling, and transportation: they are all integrated, and all contribute to the system as a whole. For instance, surplus wind power can be used to supply electricity for heating networks. At the EU level, each municipality needs to be encouraged to draw up a plan for urban heating infrastructures. Local, case-by-case analysis would make it possible to decide which options to adopt, and how best to combine them. There is no one-size-fits-all solution: decisions need to be taken on the basis of local realities.

Advice for the residential sector

The first Energy Performance of Buildings Directive (EPBD) in 2002 introduced the principle of building certification with the aim of raising awareness. This was a good start, but the quality of the certificate in question has not been tightly controlled enough. The authorities should therefore carry out random checks to ensure that the diagnostic reports drawn up by experts are worth the paper they are printed on. Some member states, such as Belgium, are already doing so. Far too many certificates are drawn up at a distance by providers who do not even bother with site visits. One key feature of the review of the Energy Performance of Buildings Directive proposed by the Commission should be the obligation to automate control, monitoring and measurement mechanisms for all buildings with energy consumption in excess of 250MWh/year. This threshold is still too high, but it represents a step in the right direction. Nevertheless, these provisions disappeared in the final version of the text proposed by the Commission.

However, even when properly performed, certification may not be detailed enough to offer much help to private individuals. I believe that the way forward is to separate certification from advice. Investors and occupiers need to have the benefit of personalised advice, with a level of precision and responsibility over and above what can be provided by a generic certificate. This could take place using a network of independent, expert advisers, capable of providing individuals with appropriate recommendations. They could be grouped together into local structures such as local climate and energy agencies: in France, such Agences locales de l'énergie et du climat ('ALEC') have now been officially recognised in the country's Energy Transition and Green Growth Act.

Green offices, supermarkets and stores

Transitioning towards zero-carbon real estate by 2050 is a huge undertaking. There are many obstacles along the way, particularly for private homes. However, progress could be much faster for non-residential buildings, such as office blocks and service sector premises. In fact, these could become catalysts to usher in the new world of energy.

For a start, measures to improve energy use in these buildings have a much shorter time-to-ROI (return on investment) of between three and five years. What is more, thermal renovation work on such buildings can go hand in hand with improvements to space management, the use of resources, and computer networks, by using so-called smart solutions such as Schneider Electric's SmartStruxure. Renovation can also include putting in renewable energy installations such as photovoltaic power, solar thermal power and heat pumps, along with storage equipment (batteries), grid services (such as load management during demand spikes) and electric mobility facilities (electric vehicle charging stations, for instance). This specific positioning of non-residential buildings makes them an ideal platform for innovation – one that is much less problematic when it comes to privacy issues: data gathered in the workplace is less sensitive and intrusive than data concerning individuals in their own homes. Lastly, such buildings are far more standardised, thereby allowing replicable solutions to be tested, and opening up export markets for European providers.

To exploit the full potential of this type of building, there should be a European initiative directed at 'green buildings': this could create a virtuous circle, launch the market and increase the rate at which renovations take place. There is a market to be had, provided that at least four stakeholders can be mobilised: technology providers such as ABB, Schneider Electric, Siemens, Honeywell and Johnson Controls; property management firms, under the aegis of EuroFM, the European Facility Management Network; energy and environmental ratings standards such as Breeam, LEED, BBC (Low-Energy Buildings), HQE (High Environmental Quality), and of course investment funds: in France, for example, these account for 88 per cent of all property investments. This type of 'green buildings' initiative could be modelled on the Green Light Programme launched in 2000 by the European Commission. It could be combined with an initiative in favour of building-integrated photovoltaics, a segment in which Europeans excel and in which Chinese competition has not yet emerged.

This integrated vision of energy, digital technology and transport, already embodied in demonstrator sites such as those of Passivhaus in Germany and Bepos in France, would align with the vision of Jeremy Rifkin: 'The new buildings coming up are positive power: they actually suck up so much sun and wind that they can power their entire complex and send surplus electricity to the grid.' That is where we should be heading – without delay.

My proposals
- Acknowledging the importance of energy efficiency as the EU's 'First Fuel', and treating investments in the thermal renovation of buildings as fully fledged infrastructure projects.
- Applying legislation in force properly and anticipating the roll out of the concept of 'near-zero-energy' buildings and neighbourhoods by funding full-scale demonstrator projects as of now, before transitioning towards models for positive-energy buildings and districts, such as the Passivhaus and Bepos initiatives.
- As provided for in the Energy Efficiency Directive, drafting long-term roadmaps for each member state for the renovation of its building stock, identifying building types and the most appropriate

mechanisms for carrying out works (loans, tax incentives and grants); hastening their implementation through enhanced Technical Assistance and reviewing these roadmaps at regular intervals.

- Prolonging and extending the Juncker Plan, with the setting up of a fund dedicated to the thermal renovation of buildings worth at least €50 billion over three years.
- Reforming the Eurostat interpretation of international accounting rules in order to allow cities and local authorities to use Energy Performance Contracts without being subject to public-sector debt control constraints.
- Using structural funds to set up local energy agencies that can deliver precise, personalised and independent advice to residents, SMEs and municipalities seeking to carry out thermal renovation works on their buildings.
- Launching a wide-ranging EU programme to bring together residential property players and create forums for the discussion of deep renovation by the various stakeholders.
- Launching a large-scale EU initiative for innovation in retail and office premises, in partnership with building energy performance certification agencies, facilities management firms, property investors and technology providers. This could make the EU the world leader in green buildings and building-integrated photovoltaics.

CHAPTER 16

GREEN TECHNOLOGIES: A REAL ASSET FOR INDUSTRY

Europe's manufacturing industry has everything to gain from energy transition. All the more so since, following the COP21 Agreement, the national climate plans (NDCs) of the signatories to the Paris Agreement essentially transpose the transition that Europe has been implementing since 2005 to a global level. The commitments, which cover transportation, buildings and energy systems, open up as many new markets for European industry, which has been a pioneer in these fields.

Proof that European leadership exists

Europeans have been forerunners in a number of technologies: photovoltaics, wind power, electrical cables for high-voltage power lines, heat pumps, green mobility in cities, trams, positive-energy homes, thermal renovation and the related innovative materials and more. There is no denying that Europe has gone through dark times when it comes to heavy industry, particularly the traditional automotive industry, steelmaking and metalworking, due to the austerity policies put in place in the wake of the 2008 crisis. These have dragged down domestic demand for steel, concrete, glass and chemicals. Nevertheless, it is still home to the brightest and best when it comes to energy transition.

To cite just some examples, ABB is working on electric propulsion

motors for ships in anticipation of hybrid gas/electricity motors gradually becoming the norm, firstly on cruise vessels and later on container
ships. Siemens has extended its wind power business, buying out
Danish turbine manufacturer Bonus in 2005 and successfully pulling
out of nuclear power by selling off Framatome in 2009. Enercon is
another success story: Aloys Wobben, a German anti-nuclear activist
from Lower Saxony, set up a small business in 1984, manufacturing
one of the world's first-ever wind turbines, producing 55kW. Thirty
years later, Enercon's most recent turbine can deliver an output of
4MW – seventy-two times more. Schneider Electric, a leader in the
field of smart management of energy systems, has further strengthened its position by acquiring two industrial software start-ups:
Invensys in 2015 and Aveva in 2016. Denmark was the first country
to get out of nuclear power and start taking renewables and energy
efficiency seriously, and in doing so has achieved the creation of four
world-class industrial firms: Vestas, now a giant in wind power, Dan-
foss, Grundfos and Velux. In addition to these larger players, there are
now a whole host of energy consultancy firms – a niche that is continuing to grow. With the benefit of its visionary policy, little Denmark
has today become the number one supplier of green technology to the
world's largest market: China.

The ups and downs of photovoltaics

Of course, these industrial endeavours have not been without their
difficulties. Solar power is a case in point. Initially, the technology was
developed in European laboratories, particularly in Germany. The
solar panels for the US Apollo space programme were, in part, designed in Hanau, near Frankfurt. It was also Germany that launched
large-scale deployment of solar panels in the 1990s with its '100,000
roofs' programme, and later its Guaranteed Tariffs Act in 2001 (known
as the EEG act), after which the rest of the EU also followed suit in
the form of the 2008 Renewable Energy Directive. Chinese leaders
monitored these trends closely, and invested in the sector from their
Eleventh Five Year Plan onwards (2006–2010). In their Twelfth Plan

(2011–2015), they announced their aim of becoming the world's number one in solar energy. They have brought plenty of resources to bear, injecting public funds on a massive scale and launching a frenetic race between Chinese provinces.

Today, the Germans' enthusiasm to install as many solar panels as possible, German and Swiss technology and expertise in machine tools, and the Chinese policy of doing everything it takes to become world leader have together led to the following state of affairs: German and Swiss machines have been installed in Chinese factories manufacturing solar panels for export – to Germany. This aggressive trade policy on the part of China has resulted in a disaster in industrial and employment terms for photovoltaic module and cell production in Europe, particularly in eastern Germany, where many manufacturers had set up. At the same time, however, it has also opened up markets for European equipment manufacturers, in the fields of machine tools (such as Meyer Burger), electronic components (Manz), inverters (including SMA, the world's number one), and even high-quality silicone (Wacker Neuson). It has also enabled spectacular cost reductions to be achieved – so spectacular that they defied all expectations, leading to temporary overheating on some markets.

But just as the dotcom bubble did not mark the end of the Internet, the photovoltaic bubble does not mean solar power is about to disappear. At the very least, this speculation has made state-of-the-art technology affordable for people the world over. At current prices, there is no excuse for not hastening the deployment of solar power in Europe and committing to mass electrification of rural areas, in particular in Africa.

Staying ahead of the game

If China has indeed won the battle when it comes to existing photovoltaic modules and cells, that is all the more reason to get working on the next generation. The xGWp project being developed by a European consortium is based on heterojunction, a hybrid technology to be used at the interface between thin film and polycrystalline silicon wafers. Proof of concept has already been established, so the next step will be to find funding to set up pilot production lines. Bringing this project to life calls for investment of €50 million for an initial 90MW phase, then a further €500 million for the second phase: a full-scale 1GW production line. One upshot of this would be the creation of at least one thousand jobs – provided of course that investors can be found. Unfortunately, in France, Hollande's government preferred to save Areva – at a cost of some €10 billion – and yet could not come up with even one tenth of that amount for solar power, despite the fact that France is home to the INES[99] laboratory in Chambéry, one of the best in Europe in the field of solar energy.

In the future, a scenario in which the wind power market suffers the same fate as solar power cannot be ruled out. Not only is China the world's leading installer of wind turbines, but Chinese project developers are insisting that they should benefit from systematic technology transfer. Thousands of jobs could disappear across Europe if the EU were to drop its guard. This is why we need to implement far-reaching EU legislation, combined with industrial policy and instruments to defend our commercial interests.

Industrial leadership requires the creation of a domestic market
The Magritte Group's lobbying has already had a considerable negative impact on the European solar power market: Spain and Italy are stagnating; France is lagging behind; in the UK, solar power has been stripped down to the bare minimum by the Tories; and in Germany, the CDU has ended up capping its expansion. In order to maintain our industrial lead, there is also a need to maintain fully fledged domestic markets for green technology. An appropriate legal and regulatory framework must be put in place, in order to provide investors with stability. Green procurements for the public sector are also a way of encouraging cities and local authorities to transition faster by going further in terms of energy efficiency, buildings, clean public

---

99   Institut national de l'énergie solaire (France's National Solar Energy Institute).

transport, renewables and the digitalisation of networks. Simply put, the EU must send the following message to technology suppliers: 'Stay in Europe: there is a huge local market for you here.'

In addition, I believe that the captains of heavy industry should also be made aware that energy transition offers them major opportunities: lower energy costs, high-quality energy services, economies of scale thanks to digital technology, optimised processes, financial compensation in the event of temporary load management restrictions and so on. Indeed, these are the conclusions of the 'Industrial Innovation for Competitiveness' (i24C) initiative in its May 2016 report.[100] A number of recent studies have sung the praises of energy audits in industry. Chambers of Commerce and Industry have also acknowledged this: 'Gaining a picture of a business' energy consumption, its processes, infrastructure and transport is an important first step to control and consequently cut production costs.'[101] Another report from February 2016 makes the same point: 'The positive effects of energy efficiency go far beyond energy savings. Increased productivity is the most prominent among them for industry. Complementary effects include reduced maintenance and operational costs, improved product quality, less resource consumption, etc.'[102]

In other words, even the likes of Bayer, BASF and Mittal have everything to gain from energy transition: chemicals companies can bring down their production costs; steelmakers will find new markets for high-value products such as wind turbine masts and nacelles. Meanwhile, optimising industrial processes is now easier than ever before, thanks to Big Data. And the constantly decreasing cost of renewables means that European industry can enjoy the benefit of accurate forecasts of tomorrow's energy costs and prices. Indeed, some quarters of the chemicals industry have already understood that it is in their interest to hasten the trend. Formerly historic opponents of energy efficiency,

---

100 'Scaling Up Innovation in the Energy Union to Meet New Climate, Competitiveness and Societal Goals', i24c, July 2016, i2-4c.eu.
101 'Energy Audits for Europe', Eurochambres, September 2015, www.eurochambres.eu.
102 'Enhancing the impact of energy audits and energy management in the EU', ECEEE, February 2016, www.eceee.org.

these players are starting to change their tune: in September 2016, forty of Europe's CEOs – BASF's among them – appealed to President Juncker to press forward in the field of green technologies.

Notwithstanding this entreaty, the European bosses' federation BusinessEurope unfortunately continues to view energy transition as a scourge that is killing off industry in Europe. European bosses have not hesitated to exploit the economic crisis to create political pressure and secure senseless exemptions from legislation covering competition, energy and the environment. They accuse energy transition of being the largest problem facing European industry in order to conceal other, much more significant difficulties to which they are incapable of providing any solution. Indeed, it is the decline in demand for consumer goods and equipment triggered by the austerity policies of the 'Merkozy' era, coupled with the unfair commercial practices in which certain Chinese competitors engage, that lie behind the desperate lack of investment to modernise Europe's production resources.

Outlets for European industry: developing our export strategy
Preserving a domestic market for European industry is definitely one vital component, but this also needs to be accompanied by the implementation of an export strategy. Some countries are encouraging their SMEs to export, since energy transition creates industrial opportunities internationally, but there have been no concerted attempts in this direction. If the EU were to set up a coherent instrument to promote European know-how, it could be on a par with the USA, Canada and Brazil, which all have well-defined, effective strategies in this respect. As things stand, Europe does not do enough to promote its leadership in green technologies. There is nothing in the Commission's proposals about promoting them in the islands of the Pacific, the Caribbean, Africa or Latin America. To take just one example, trams are undergoing an unprecedented resurgence worldwide. In Europe, we are lucky enough to have Alstom, one of the world leaders in this sector. What is the EU doing to help Alstom win the contracts for the tramway systems of Rio, Cape Town or Shanghai?

There are two instruments available to us to develop an appropriate export strategy, particularly for Africa. Since 2015, I have been striving to see an Energy Plan for Africa set up, alongside Jean-Louis Borloo, who managed to engage the interest of African heads of state and the leaders of the Pan African Parliament. After much to-ing and fro-ing, in September 2016 the Commission finally came up with a European external investment plan. It is up to the EU to grasp this opportunity and promote the new approach. The fund would be used mainly to bring down the capital costs involved in the deployment of renewable energy. Africa has no shortage of sunshine, but does suffer from a lack of confidence on the part of financial markets; the latter penalises country risk, in the form of prohibitive interest rates. One vital ingredient is for national budgets, national promotional banks such as Caisse des Dépôts in France, KfW in Germany and Cassa di depositi e prestiti in Italy, together with national development agencies such as AFD in France and GIZ in Germany, to be closely associated with the implementation of this plan. Europe also needs to become better at communicating what it is doing to benefit Africa: sadly, the Commission had very little to say about all this at the COP22 summit in Marrakesh in November 2016.

In addition, replicating the Covenant of Mayors, which has been an enormous success in Europe, on a worldwide scale would be an excellent idea. The Covenant of Mayors brings together over 6,000 European cities that have committed to energy transition, with carbon reduction targets over and above those of states. The same principle could help the cities in Africa and Latin America to develop robust climate strategies, and thereby create a market for green European technologies. In July 2016, the Commission's vice president Maroš Šefčovič took steps in this direction, launching the 'Global Covenant of Mayors', the worldwide equivalent of its European forebear, in partnership with Michael Bloomberg and Anne Hidalgo, amid great ceremony.[103] This initiative is encouraging, provided that smaller

---

103   See Chapter 23, p. 309.

towns and cities are not left behind, with the megacities becoming the sole beneficiaries.

All this should be providing food for thought for the Commission prior to its formulation of EURICS (the Energy Union Research, Innovation and Competitiveness Strategy). On 26 September 2016, Innovation Commissioner Carlos Moedas convened a brainstorming session to discuss the strategy. A former water treatment engineer, Moedas is one of the rare commissioners to have a global, systemic view of things. He is also the only one to have understood that the combination of digitalisation and renewable energy will result in radical change, for which European industry needs to be prepared. He lost no time in making his position clear: 'our challenge is to achieve zero carbon by 2050, in buildings, transportation and industry'. The next speaker to take the podium was Mariana Mazzucato, a rising star among innovation economists[104] and the economic adviser to 'red' leader Jeremy Corbyn. Rest assured, there is no contradiction here. Indeed, it is from such iterative discussions between visionaries from right across the political spectrum that a genuine innovation policy for Europe can emerge. Dialogue between politicians, industrialists and academics is crucial.

I am very much a believer in cross-pollination of this type. The EU should set up think-tanks that include grassroots players as well as politicians, academics and captains of industry. I am more convinced by the momentum generated by Bertrand Piccard,[105] just back from his round-the-world trip in a solar-powered aircraft, than by Airbus Industry, Air France-KLM or Lufthansa when it comes to advancing the cause of aviation electrification. Why not also invite veteran yachtswoman Ellen MacArthur[106] to encourage Europe's ports and ships to invest in wind turbines to power vessels' hybrid

---

104   Among other things, she was the joint editor of *Rethinking Capitalism: Economics and Policy for Sustainable and Equitable Growth*, Wiley-Blackwell, 2015.

105   Bertrand Piccard is a Swiss entrepreneur and inventor. In particular, he was responsible for the Solar Impulse initiative; in 2016, this resulted in him completing a round-the-world trip in an aircraft powered by solar energy alone.

106   Ellen MacArthur is a British yachtswoman who finished in second place in the Vendée Globe round-the-world race in 2001, before going on to break the solo round-the-world sailing record in 2005.

engines? Former European commissioner Pascal Lamy, subsequently a director-general of the WTO, would probably be in a good position to dislodge Mittal, BASF, Lafarge and their ilk from their fruitless opposition to European climate and energy policy. Whether it's for sail-powered shipping, solar-powered air travel or the use of 100 per cent renewable hydrogen for fertilisers, refineries, paper and steel, the solutions already exist, and need to be brought to life by leaders in order to provoke emulation on the part of stakeholders who are historically relatively resistant to change – such as shipbuilders, airlines and heavy industry. To prime the pump, in addition to pilot projects which have already demonstrated the feasibility and profitability of such solutions, these now need to be deployed on multiple, bleeding-edge sites. These could be funded by the public sector, which has always provided impetus for innovation. Until such time as Merkel and Schäuble, the guardians of German orthodoxy, loosen their grip on the Stability Pact, new financial revenues could be generated, for instance, by the introduction of a carbon floor price, and devoted to speeding up investment of this type. In order for private banks to start getting on board, the cheaper capital from 'Draghinomics' needs to be coupled with a strong dose of eco-conditionality on the part of the European Central Bank.

Modernising industry through tax reform

It has to be said that Europe is confronted with counter-productive price signals: oil, coal, gas and electricity prices are all too low and carbon prices have collapsed. There is thus no incentive to invest in green technologies. There is a risk of wasting another decade, as we did in the 1990s, when the sudden interest on the part of the media and society in general in favour of the environment in the wake of the Rio summit collapsed like a soufflé as the oil bust hit. To prevent this, a fiscal revolution is required, putting greater tax pressure on CO_2 emissions and fossil fuels. These new revenues would allow funds to be marshalled to bring down labour costs, address the issue of energy poverty and invest in energy transition by means of tax incentives for the purchase of green technologies, building renovation and green mobility. In Europe as elsewhere, the fact is that labour is too expensive and pollution is too cheap.

The European Commission has constantly encouraged adjustments to taxation along these lines, taking its cue from Jeremy Rifkin's book, *Third Industrial Revolution*. Each of the Commission's annual reports on taxation published in recent years is unequivocal in this respect. The 2013 special report could not be plainer: 'Why is a tax shift advised? … Green taxes (environment and energy) are considered to be among the most growth friendly, and also support wider policy objectives related to climate change, resource efficiency and energy security.' In the same report, the Commission 'encourages member states to take further measures to improve the existing design of taxes in this area including by adjusting the structure of tax rates on fossil fuels, indexing environmental taxes, or considering the abolition of reduced VAT rates on energy'. The song remained the same in 2015: the Commission's annual report took the view that 'employment and growth can be stimulated by shifting the tax burden away from labour towards other types of taxes which are less detrimental to growth, such as recurrent property, environment and consumption taxes'. In the most recent edition to date, that of 2016, it states the following: 'It is important to ensure efficient and growth-friendly tax systems. This includes shifting taxes away from labour.' Notwithstanding all this, the Commission cannot actually do very much, because taxation is one of the issues that must be decided unanimously by the Council. The ball is now in the court of Europe's finance ministers.

My proposals:
- Restoring a domestic market for green technologies in order to maintain European leadership by means of ambitious targets for 2030: 40 per cent energy efficiency and 35 per cent renewable energy.
- Defining an export strategy to provide active support to European technology and service firms in their efforts to penetrate foreign markets, in the form of a 'de-risking' fund for green investments

in developing countries, together with internationalisation of the Covenant of Mayors.

- As part of the EU's policy on research, innovation and competitiveness, identifying the most promising technologies and developing a fully fledged European industrial policy, coupled with quantified targets and indicators. For instance, setting a target for at least 20 per cent of the domestic photovoltaic market to be supplied by cells and modules made in Europe, and bringing to bear the resources required to invest in pilot production lines for the cells and modules of the future, such as those using heterojunction.

- Using trade defence mechanisms to counter Chinese dumping; refusing to grant China WTO 'Market Economy' status.

- Encouraging SMEs to implement energy efficiency and circular economy measures (such as energy audits, tax credits, vouchers for eco-innovation in the value chain etc.) as a key avenue to improve their competitiveness.

- Establishing transparency in the actual electricity prices invoiced to European industry in order to put an end to massive exemptions without any contribution in return to investment in European production resources; shifting taxation in member states by taxing resources more and labour less; implementing a carbon floor price.

CHAPTER 17

THE DIGITAL REVOLUTION
IS WELL UNDERWAY

Digital technology is now revolutionising energy in just the same way as it has transformed other sectors. At the crossroads of the worlds of digital and energy, the 'Enernet' is changing the game entirely. In 2018, according to French think-tank Innovation industrielle pour la compétitivité ('Industrial innovation for competitiveness'), 20 per cent of energy companies' revenues will come from energy services made possible by digitalisation of the sector. According to Cisco, the digitalisation market will be worth $14.4 trillion over the next ten years. What is more, digitalisation offers the potential for another step change: the advent of the shared economy in the field of energy.

Digital technology can be used to combat climate change, as British Telecom has pointed out: the ICT (Information and Communications Technologies) sector could reduce CO_2 emissions by 1.2Gt by 2030. Already, 53 per cent of greenhouse gas emission reductions relating to ICTs are the direct result of improved energy efficiency. The sector could bring in net economic profits of €1.3 trillion by 2030: €678 billion of new revenue and cost savings of €643 billion. To ensure that emissions avoided thanks to digital technology are not offset by exponential growth in energy use on the part of servers, it is vital for data centres to be powered by '100 per cent renewable' systems.

Not only will cost savings delivered by digitalisation result in technological improvements to production facilities, such as better turbines, better solar panels and more powerful wind turbines; they will also achieve spectacular outcomes in the field of electronics, particularly as regards sensors and miniaturisation. ABB, for instance, entered the field in the early 2000s and now has microgrids that have made the emergence of virtual power plants possible. Furthermore, digitalisation allows end users to be more actively involved in the process. Instances of digital technology being used to improve energy performance are springing up all over the place. Examples in France include AVOB, Smart Impulse and Ubigreen. Other initiatives are making it easier to become a producer of solar energy, such as Solease in the Netherlands, as well as DZ-5 and Sonnen in Germany.

However, it must also be remembered that the digital revolution raises issues of its own, the foremost of which is the protection of personal data. Without careful thought about the issues of confidentiality surrounding sensitive information, these solutions will never be fully embraced by the population as a whole and there is a real danger of a severe backlash on the part of civil society.

Electricity markets in a digital age

Digital technology is the perfect companion for renewables, as well as for demand response and storage. On the one hand, increasing the integration of variable capacity in a decentralised electricity system depends on the ability to process increasing amounts of data in real time.

A highly decentralised system is intrinsically more complex but by aggregating data from all sources of production, storage solutions and points of use, digital technology delivers better forecasting for the system, and indeed a higher degree of automation. It offers better prediction of the load curve on the basis of detailed weather forecasting, combined with consumption and production data logs. Experiments currently underway in Portugal currently have a margin of error of less than 5 per cent in load curve forecasting twenty-four hours in advance. Admittedly, more decentralised variable sources involve more day-to-day intervention in terms of grid management. The experience of German companies such as the utility EWE and the TSO

50Hz show that if these interventions are managed properly, a more renewable-intensive network is more resilient, and risk periods for blackouts and voltage drops are shorter than in a system saturated by nuclear power plants and coal-fired power stations, which are much less flexible.

Digitalisation of the system also makes it easier to integrate small production facilities into sophisticated electricity markets. Aggregating production and consumption points allows 'virtual power plants' to be created; these balance each other out. Last-minute adjustment between production and demand is therefore reduced to the bare minimum, bringing down the costs of integrating a large quantity of renewable energy into the grid.

One question does remain, however: will this increasingly digitalised electricity system automatically lead to a more dynamic intra-day market? Technically, managing production changes in real time is now quite feasible. But at present, producers must submit their supply offers in one-hour slots. This period is still too long to be ideally suited to the characteristics of renewables. In future, time slots should be no longer than thirty, fifteen or even five minutes, since IT systems now make this possible. New hedging instruments are already being developed by electricity exchanges such as EPEX to ensure that market players can protect themselves against the swift changes (and high spike prices) that would result from an ultra-flexible and highly responsive intra-day market. These instruments would also compensate load management and other short-term flexibility measures. It remains to be seen how these new markets can be combined with schemes to promote the production of green electricity; things are far from satisfactory in this respect at present. Digitalisation offers the prospect of being able to trace green electricity. However, it is soon lost in the flow of electricity generated by nuclear fuel or coal, at which point it becomes 'grey' electricity, of uncertain origin.

To promote renewables, digitalisation could also see a new electricity supply market emerge, along the lines of the model currently being developed in New York, a huge virtual trading floor allowing individuals to buy and sell electricity directly to each other, without involving traditional suppliers. Could this change the state of play? While almost 90 per cent of renewable energy production is connected to the low-voltage distribution network, in the future this trend will naturally affect the future of system operators, too.

A new role for system operators

One effect of digitalisation is that system operators (both TSOs and DSOs) will become smart grid operators. In other words, they will no longer automatically opt for traditional, physical extensions of the grid in the form of new power lines, but also envisage the use of new software – a cheaper solution than digging trenches to bury copper cabling. To curtail system costs, the copper in the ground and the aluminium used overhead must be pushed to the maximum of their current capacity. ICTs will help optimise existing electricity transportation infrastructure, more especially so when it comes to distribution.

ICTs can push the envelope of the grid by optimising transmission, and all the more so by making it possible to stretch the system right to its limits, by monitoring systemic reactions in extreme situations much more closely. Sophisticated digitalisation of grid management comprising smart data monitoring, flexible local transformers, surveillance of high-risk equipment and so on could deliver significant improvements in efficiency and delay or even do away with the need to modernise existing infrastructure. For instance, greater familiarity with the details of consumption on different sites could lead to a realisation that providing more physical capacity for an existing distribution line is not actually necessary – an insight that is simply not possible when managing 'blind'.

Connected, proactive consumers

There is no doubt that ICTs will push back the frontiers of demand flexibility, not only for major electricity-intensive firms, but also for thousands of SMEs, non-residential buildings such as retail premises

and office blocks and, in the longer term, millions of individual consumers. Today, industrial companies can already defer consumption
to benefit from cheaper prices. Individual clients can also use their
smartphone and apps to manage their consumption directly, even at a
distance, by adjusting their thermostat or switching household appliances on or off. By joining all these actions together, aggregators could
produce huge amounts of cheap load management, which could then
be sold on new, flexible, responsive intra-day markets. Connected objects are now invading our day-to-day lives, homes and workplaces,[107]
and they are easy to make use of: the barriers to entry are very few.

I see relatively few privacy issues when it comes to speeding up
the deployment of smart meters to industrial and business clients.
However, it may be that a critical number of private individuals are
sensitive to such issues. A cautious, responsible approach therefore
needs to be taken with residential consumers. In addition to confidentiality, the design of the meters and the related PR both call for careful
consideration if widespread knee-jerk opposition is to be avoided. A
compromise will need to be struck between the availability of data and
its confidentiality. It should be possible for information that is strictly
necessary for network security to be transmitted automatically. For
everything else, consumers should have the right to decide which
data can be gathered and made available to a public-interest entity
such as a TSO and/or a consortium of DSOs, or other new, public or
semi-public bodies. Individuals and citizens' organisations in Europe
would doubtless prefer this solution to a model in which data was
gathered by 100 per cent private-sector companies with no checks or
balances – and an inclination to sell their access to individual data to
third parties.

The issue of the form in which this data will be made available to
market players also needs to be addressed. If DSOs were appointed to

---

107   In one illustration of this, during a Eurofores meeting in Strasbourg in April 2015, Research
Commissioner Carlos Moedas explained how he was using his mobile phone coupled with
the Nest smart thermostat app (which has since been bought out by Google) to adjust the
temperature in his flat in Brussels, ready for his return.

act as neutral facilitators, how could abuse of dominant position be prevented, given that almost 70 per cent of such operators belong to vertically integrated oligopolies such as EDF, Enel, CEZ and Iberdrola? My position is therefore that DSOs should have to choose: either they confine themselves to the role of market facilitators, or they are themselves the players; they cannot reasonably be left to act as both. As ERDF, now Enedis, imposes the rollout of the new Linky smart meter in France, access to the data must be non-discriminatory, with no special privileges for the parent company. During this crucial time when new markets are being created, any other position would result in the creation of new monopolies. A regulatory solution covering the separation of network assets is required for DSOs, in much the same way as the one that already applies to TSOs. The Commission has not had the courage to settle this issue in its latest legislative proposals. Worse still, it is seeking to institutionalise a new pan-European body which would bring together all the DSOs; a sort of official lobby of established operators, giving them a stranglehold on how distribution network rules are defined. It is to be feared that the resulting rules would not be very favourable to the emergence of new players likely to enter into competition with their parent companies.

To avoid energy data being controlled by oligopolies, inspiration could be drawn from the positive example of data exchanges in Scandinavia, where individual data is collected and made available on an open-source platform accessible to all. A proposal along these lines was also put forward by Michel Derdevet in his 2015 report on grids in Europe ('France and Germany could lead the way by setting up an energy data platform'), aimed at enhancing security, standardisation and the development of a European Big Data processing chain.

Is there any other option? At the end of the day, what right do TSOs and DSOs have to be the sole arbiters of how information technology should be used? Individual citizens, meanwhile, couldn't care less what system operators think; they are using applications developed by third party companies directly and don't ask the DSOs for permission before doing so. All consumers want is to be able to benefit from a high-quality energy service in terms of temperature and comfort, one that is easy to adjust. Price is not necessarily the only concern, as the huge success of the iPhone demonstrates. Simplicity of use is the deciding factor.

As for consumer-producers, also known as 'consumer actors' or 'prosumers' (the number of different neologisms bears witness to just how new the concept is), they are making the most of the promising learning curves delivered by solar panels, and now batteries. Of course, it is difficult to predict just how many stakeholders will be eager to achieve energy autonomy – in other words, produce their own energy and unplug from the grid. Some parties, particularly system operators and finance ministers (who will have to transition their taxation system from being based on consumption quantities to more complex systems) are fearful of such a development – and, more especially, of losing some of their revenues as a result. I believe that a compromise based on a number of key principles should be established. For one thing, any individual or company taking the initiative to use their roof to produce solar electricity is acting for the benefit of society and combating climate change; such behaviour should therefore be encouraged rather than sanctioned. It is for this reason that I am seeking to see the right to self-generation included in the EU Renewable Energy Directive. Secondly, if consumers are inflicted with too many artificial, unfair taxes, their response will be 'if that's the way things are, I'm going off the grid'. This would make matters much worse, both for society and for system operators. I am therefore keen to see some boldness expressed in regulations, with the design of a framework that provides mutual benefits for 'prosumers' and system operators alike.

Lastly, there are many issues still to be resolved when it comes to storage and demand-side response. How can these practices be encouraged in a market which is currently not conveying any price signal? Do we want short-term storage, long-term storage or even seasonal storage? Is it up to TSOs or DSOs to organise, promote, invest or operate storage and load management? New models need to be defined for all these aspects.

A new regulatory framework needs defining

The multiple fields in which ICTs are being deployed call for a new regulatory framework. For instance, digital solutions should be encouraged over and against material solutions when it comes to investments in the network. Software is just as important as copper when it comes to rolling out a smart grid, and this fact should be better taken into account by regulators.

The deployment of smart meters could also be optimised. The Commission is recommending that they should have ten or so functionalities. Their efficiency needs to be improved, by reducing how much energy they use on standby, and by creating interfaces that are easy to read and understand, for instance on smartphones. There is no point in trying to force this issue through: instead, all the necessary consultation with civil society needs to be organised well ahead of time, so as to avoid the kind of angry disputes that have been seen in France over Linky. Initially, rollout is of more benefit to consumers using in excess of 6,000kWh/year, and for households that have opted to have solar panels, batteries or an electric car. Smart meters should also be available for any individual who has deliberately chosen to use one. Wholescale rejection of the use of smart meters, however, is simply not an option. If the authorities do not intervene to provide a structured framework for their installation via system operators, GAFA (Google, Apple, Facebook and Amazon) and their ilk will lose no time in doing so themselves, thereby drawing consumers into their nets. I would prefer a less-than-perfect regulatory framework to a disorganised rollout left in the hands of digital multinationals, engaged in a no-holds-barred race to acquire personal data.

To exploit information technology to the full extent of its potential, a system in which prices are established dynamically and change in real time must be established; failing this, digitalisation will offer no benefits that can encourage people to adopt it. For instance, connected consumers could have the option of replacing a standard profile with recommended electricity use management based on flexible tariffs. This would also help decrease energy poverty, by delivering transparent, easily understood information to consumers, enabling them to decrease their consumption and thus their bills.

However, there is no room for mistakes here and it is better to move forward slowly and ensure that everybody is on board. Data protection is a key element when it comes to ensuring social acceptance. Some principles need to be established from the outset: data anonymisation; transparency as to data use; prior consent; and non-discrimination between market players for access to the data. There needs to be a distinction made between data required to manage the energy system, which by nature needs to be passed on to the system operator, and data which is relevant for market players developing commercial offers: the electricity suppliers and aggregators.

Another question is whether cyber security could hamper this change to the system. Do we need special rules for energy system ICTs or are the standard rules for the digital world enough? Clearly, energy system data needs to be extremely reliable and be covered by the highest cyber security standards, because the electricity system of the future will, increasingly, be handled by automated decision-making installations. Regulations therefore need to provide for the case of wrongful use of a smart system and offer firm guarantees to users, along the lines of the requirements imposed on the banking sector, for instance. Moreover, a decentralised system is a very good thing in terms of cyber security, since it is less vulnerable to attack.

Lastly, these changes are of course subject to the extensive penetration of broadband Internet. This has developed much more quickly in urban centres because of the density of consumers. Energy transition could also happen more quickly in rural areas, so they need broadband too. Indeed, this is a priority if we wish to avoid a digital divide in addition to the economic divide that is already visible between town and country. It is important for the funding of broadband to be one of the priorities in the extension of the Juncker Plan for investment in Europe.

That said, excessive digitalisation does have an energy cost. According to French research agency ADEME, each email sent generates

19g CO_2e. Search engine requests account for an average of 9.9kg CO_2e per year and per web user. This enormously high consumption was brought to light by Greenpeace and its Click Green awareness campaign. Moreover, Internet giants themselves have realised this could be an Achilles heel. As a result, they have joined the RE100 initiative, designed to promote the '100 per cent renewables' vision. Could the GAFA companies actually be pioneering environmentalists? Larry Page and Bill Gates and the late Steve Jobs may no doubt qualify as environmentally aware, but they have sought above all to avoid criticisms of the carbon footprint of their data centres. If they have undergone a Damascene conversion as well, so much the better; and all the more so if it makes them our allies in accelerating energy transition in Europe.

My proposals:
- Establishing appropriate regulatory frameworks to ensure the protection of individual data collected by the increasingly large numbers of connected objects.
- Creating a data platform accessible to third parties in order to allow the development of a European industry for the smart processing of energy production and consumption data from various types of consumer; encouraging the establishment of start-ups to nurture the emergence of European alternatives to the GAFA companies.
- Developing a dynamic intra-day electricity market that takes into account all the latest progress in information technology as applied to load-forecasting.
- Implementing a regulatory framework and dynamic tariffs that recognise the right to self-generation of energy and the active participation of different types of consumer, while also encouraging them to maintain their connection to the electricity collection and distribution network.
- Setting up a European framework to implement the separation of electricity production and distribution assets, in order to bring an end to abuses by vertically integrated companies and prevent

oligopolies from having a stranglehold on the rules governing network use. This would apply above a certain threshold, in order to protect local authorities, who are also distribution system operators.

- Ensuring that data storage services in Europe are powered by 100 per cent renewable electricity in order to bring down the carbon footprint of the digital sector and generate additional investments in solar and wind power.

The five sectors we have discussed all have a role to play in implementing energy transition. However, they will not head off in this direction of their own accord; achieving this necessarily involves the mobilisation of a whole host of stakeholders. These range from the least tangible – in the public sector, EU and national lawmakers and macro-regions, and from the private sector, utilities and financial markets – through to those closest to the ground, such as cities, local authorities, workers and indeed all of the 450 million citizens of the EU.

CHAPTER 18

EUROPEAN LAWMAKERS: REVIVING THE SPIRIT OF 2008

The European Union can be proud of what it has put in place since the 2000s in terms of climate and energy policy. Nowhere else in the world, with the possible exception of California, has such a strong legal arsenal to support energy transition. Pioneered by Jacques Delors, the gradual implementation of the internal market during the 1980s and 1990s – with the free movement of goods, capital, services and people – did not include the energy sector, which was deemed too sensitive to be removed from the sole control of member states. However, the environment was added to the EU policy remit in the 1992 Maastricht treaty and has been covered by the co-decision procedure ever since. It is as a result of this that it has become possible to put forward EU law pertaining to these issues.

The EU's body of law in this area is made up essentially of four pieces of legislation on energy efficiency[108] and a Renewables Directive. These five pieces of legislation are designed to create security for investors. They have proved their worth time and again since 2008, far more than the ETS, which is a market instrument. There is also a sixth piece of legislation: the regulation governing CO_2 emissions

---

108 The Directives on eco-design, energy labelling, the energy performance of buildings, and energy efficiency.

by passenger cars, which incites automotive manufacturers to bring down vehicle fuel consumption. However, the regulation in question will lack effectiveness so long as legal (or indeed illegal) workarounds exist. Dieselgate therefore offers an opportunity to redress the balance between lawmakers and the automotive industry, which is one of the most influential in Europe, if not in the world.

The EU has established minimum performance standards applicable in every sector, in all twenty-eight member states. This has borne fruit in central and Eastern Europe, where the former Soviet bloc countries have been able to start modernising their economy. These efforts must be pursued: even today, over ten years after their accession, energy intensity in these countries is between seven and eight times higher than in Germany or Denmark. For instance, in the field of eco-design, the EU has made it possible to establish a European market for energy-efficient televisions, vacuum cleaners and cars, as well as near-zero-energy buildings. Producers everywhere, not just in Europe, have had to comply with certain rules if they want to sell their products on the world's largest market. Through such legislation, Europe has helped the whole world improve: lawmakers in other countries draw inspiration from our laws, and our green technology is being exported.

Now is the time to act
The COP21 Agreement has given us a unique opportunity: the whole world has now set off down the path of energy transition. However, we must lose no time in giving ourselves the resources to become the world number one in renewable energy by having a vivid domestic market. Failing this, we could lose our technological lead over other industrialised countries and countries such as China, which are well placed to catch up both economically and industrially. There is absolutely no benefit in waiting until the last minute to take action in the face of urgent climate issues, as we did in the face of the financial crisis and the migrant crisis. All twenty-eight nations face the same crises, but all too often we find ourselves ill prepared to respond.

The European carbon market is dead on its feet, and doing nothing to generate green investment. For this system to work regularly and predictably, a much more ambitious greenhouse gas reduction target needs to be set well above the 40 per cent planned for 2030, together with higher carbon prices. The latter are currently ridiculously low, at around five euros per tonne; this is preventing any far-reaching change in our production and consumption habits. Given all this, we need to draw lessons from the successful aspects of the 2008 Climate and Energy Package to prepare the future, by means of robust legislation and active innovation policies, rather than twiddling our thumbs while we engage in the fantasy that the carbon market's invisible hand will do the job for us.

In the wake of the COP21 Agreement, the EU must decide what it will do between 2020 and 2030 to stimulate the necessary investments in renewables and energy efficiency. What laws should it adopt to this end? The electricity system is currently very inflexible since it is based mostly on coal and nuclear power. It too will have to change to incorporate more and more photovoltaic and wind power production facilities, which by nature are flexible and decentralised, and ensure overall security. These are the challenges we face in the coming years, the idea being to achieve a far-reaching framework by the end of MEPs' current mandate in 2019.

Energy efficiency: the need for a revised directive as industry transitions

According to the IEA, in a world in which the temperature is set to rise by 2°C, 40 per cent of emissions reductions can come from energy savings.[109] Wasting less is therefore the top priority; it is much more beneficial than starting up fresh production capacity. While there is something of a 'rebound effect', technological progress in this field is such that the net gains are significant.

Policy promoting energy efficiency is based on cutting energy wastage in industry, construction, household appliances and mobility.

---

109   'Energy Efficiency Market Report 2015', International Energy Agency, www.iea.org.

A newly revised directive on this issue is to be adopted within the next few years, on the basis of the Commission's proposal published in November 2016; what will end up being in it? In Brussels, the battle will be that of setting a binding target of 40 per cent for energy efficiency by 2030; this corresponds to a reduction in consumption of 2 per cent per year, coupled with a whole array of instruments. Since the European elections in 2014, this 40 per cent target has been requested four times by the European Parliament. The figure has not been plucked out of the air: it represents the optimum amount for Europe. However, the modelling used by the Commission has not taken into account all the positive outcomes of energy efficiency, including bringing down energy bills, decreasing our geopolitical exposure to Russia and oil sheikdoms, job creation and increased competitiveness. Research[110] published in summer 2016 by the Joint Research Centre lends support to the Parliament's approach: by 2015, European energy demand was much lower than the levels taken into account by the Commission in the impact assessment study on which the legislative proposals of 30 November 2016 were based.

This is a far cry from the paltry 27 per cent proposed by Barroso in January 2014 and imposed by Cameron on European leaders ten months later at the European Council meeting of October 2014.[111] Indeed, a 27 per cent target would actually entail making less effort between 2020 and 2030 than between 2010 and 2020. How would co-legislators be able to bridge such a huge gap and achieve a position consistent with the Paris Agreement of December 2015?

Many stakeholders also agree that it is in the EU's geopolitical interest to aim for 40 per cent. Commissioner Arias Cañete is fond of repeating that 'for every 1 per cent of improvement in our energy efficiency, gas imports come down by 2.6 per cent'. Eastern European countries have grasped the fact that energy efficiency is the best way of ensuring security of supply and reducing their dependence on Russia in this respect.

---

110   'Energy Consumption and Energy Efficiency Trends in the EU-28 2000–2014', Joint Research Centre, June 2016, iet.jrc.ec.europa.eu.
111   See Chapter 11, p. 145.

This is clearly the EU's best possible response to the energy blackmail in which Vladimir Putin and the OPEC cartel love to engage.

What is more, energy efficiency policies are also strengthening convergence between the countries of eastern and western Europe. Historically, Eastern European countries are at a competitive disadvantage compared to western European countries, due to the energy intensity they have inherited from the former Soviet bloc's culture of energy wastage. Incentives are therefore required to close the gap between the least efficient and the most efficient, by tying energy efficiency to discussions on burden-sharing pertaining to greenhouse gas emissions reductions. If Eastern European countries' energy efficiency is improved, it will be easier for them to surpass their greenhouse gas emissions reduction targets, which are broadly determined on the basis of GDP. Given a suitable flexibility mechanism, they could resell their surplus to western European countries. This is a win-win situation, thanks to which Europe could also modernise its economy. A west-east transfer in the form of payments would also shrink the energy performance gap.

Not only do ambitious goals need to be set but the means of achieving them must also be devised. Today, energy firms' business model is focused on the production and sale of energy. Since Europe has already adopted a target of 20 per cent energy efficiency, demand is decreasing, reducing the size of the pie shared out between energy producers such as EDF, Engie, E.ON, RWE and their kin. In addition to sectoral regulations covering topics such as eco-design, more energy-efficient cars and passive buildings, the EU therefore has every interest in developing a market to remunerate not only the provision of energy itself, but also the provision of advice on how to use it. This is at the heart of the battle over Article 7 of the Energy Efficiency Directive, which establishes an obligation to control consumption. Indeed, in Denmark, electricity resellers have already transformed the energy savings obligation, in force there since the 2000s, into an opportunity: they generate significant revenues from departments working in services, consultancy and investment in energy efficiency.

How could Article 7 of the Directive be strengthened? Today, each energy supplier must achieve 1.25 per cent annual energy savings, either by investing in their own company or externally, to the benefit of private individuals or other companies. Article 7 specifies that if this quota is not met, the party in question is liable for penalties. In France, on the basis of the first Directive, 'white certificates' have been created and the amount of savings to be achieved has been multiplied six fold for the third period (2015–2017). Establishing such a market encourages both energy firms and new players to support energy efficiency and virtuous behaviour. For instance, in France, mass retailers sell petrol in superstore car parks, and thus find themselves subject to energy savings obligations. To meet the related targets, stores such as Carrefour and Mr Bricolage run campaigns, hand out vouchers to buy back energy savings certificates and compensate clients who commit to energy efficiency in the form of an 'eco-works bonus'. A market is therefore emerging, together with economic stakeholders with an interest in eliminating energy waste.

Looking more closely at the Danish example, it becomes apparent that most of the energy efficiency efforts benefit SMEs and major industrial firms. Indeed, the obligation to control consumption that forms part of the Directive is also an instrument designed to help industrial firms invest. Generally speaking, industry looks for very short time-to-ROI and this approach makes them reluctant to commit to spending on energy management. To address this, the law allows for a partnership with a third party such as an energy services company or an energy provider to carry out an audit, launch investment in new equipment or processes and, ultimately, save energy. In this way, industrial firms benefit from improved energy productivity thanks to investment shouldered by the third-party investor, who receives compensation based on the savings achieved. This is a win-win model.

It could become a success factor for European industry, becoming more competitive globally. Even if the unit cost of energy in Europe is higher, its absolute energy costs are lower. Research funded by Philips recently shed light on this concept of energy productivity.[112] This represents a major step forward in how energy efficiency is perceived by industry: that it can nurture competitiveness. To make it easier for SMEs to identify their consumption savings potential, the scope of the energy audits provided for in Article 8 of the Directive should now be broadened. The flaws in how these reductions are measured need to be ironed out, and greater security needs to be provided for investors by extending the Directive to 2050.

Eco-design and energy labelling: vital in Europe and beyond

Europe's policy of promoting energy efficiency is also apparent in the standards for energy-using devices and consumer information. It has resulted in less waste by encouraging progress in the entry-level market for electronic and household appliances. A new fridge sold in Europe today uses far less electricity than the equivalent product did ten years ago. LEDs use between ten and sixteen times less electricity than incandescent lightbulbs, which generate more heat than light – literally.

The bogeyman of bureaucracy

Despite this, the scheme was attacked at the highest level by the president and first vice president currently in charge of the European Commission. During the last European election campaign in 2014, Jean-Claude Juncker and Frans Timmermans both raised the issue of EU legislation extending 'even' to vacuum cleaners as an illustration of overregulation in the EU. According to them, EU citizens are opposed to regulations governing the energy performance of vacuum cleaners. This is misinformed. After the elections, I challenged Frans Timmermans about whether Europeans are really fed up with the EU institutions because they are encouraging more efficient, quieter and more comfortable products? Faced with the Green group, he finally conceded (just about) that he could perhaps have chosen a better example.

---

112 Kornelis Blok, Paul Hofheinz and John Kerkhoven, 'The 2015 Energy Productivity and Economic Prosperity Index', 2015, www.ecofys.com.

Why did Juncker and Timmermans take a public stand against legislation on vacuum cleaners? Since its defeat in 2006 on the "REACH" legislation, a landmark initiative that regulates chemicals within the EU, the industrial lobby led by BusinessEurope has orchestrated a campaign against European legislation. Their mantra is 'better regulation' which, in effect, comes down to 'no regulation'. In this narrative, the EU is described as a bureaucratic monster determined to spew out regulations with the ultimate goal of attacking industry, decreasing its competitiveness and thus destroying jobs. For my part, I believe that REACH represents tremendous progress. This EU regulation protects the health of Europe's citizens against the chemical industry's desire to make money at all costs. Legislation also stimulates innovation, which in turn is good for industry. Not only that, but where Europe leads the rest of the world follows; even China has ended up adopting similar measures to REACH in order not to disqualify itself from the EU market.

The second reason why Juncker and Timmermans attacked the energy performance of appliances is the poor communication at the time when incandescent lightbulbs were being phased out, which created a bad image of the relevant regulation. The decision itself was a courageous one and led to an explosion in the market for LEDs. But when the measure took on visible form on supermarket shelves, the general public simply noted a sudden increase in the price of lightbulbs, without any explanations as to the improved performance justifying these increases. Member states' policymakers suddenly found reasons to be elsewhere, and criticised 'a measure imposed by Brussels'. All of this criticism was directed at the Commission, which suffered a hail of insults for several months. This was extremely hypocritical on the part of national governments. As co-decision-makers, they also have their share of responsibility when it comes to explaining the decisions of European democracy to their respective electorates. If they do not, the inevitable result is that the less understood the EU is, the more unpopular it becomes, as demonstrated by the reprehensible – and successful – campaign conducted by the Brexiteers in the first half of 2016.

Steps in the right direction

Once Juncker and Timmermans were at the top of the Commission, however, they shifted towards more reasonable stances than could have been expected from their off-the-cuff remarks during the electoral campaign. If, as they assert, the EU should be 'big on big things and small and modest on smaller things', then these framework laws on eco-design and energy labelling should continue; indeed, these measures have been an unmitigated success. Moreover, one of the first legislative proposals of the new Commission in the field of energy was a revision of the existing Energy Labelling Directive, designed to make the consumption categories more easily understandable for purchasers.

An attempt to make the system more dynamic in 2008–2009 failed, with the industry rejecting the automatic recalibration of labelling as the market progressed. The A+, A++ and A+++ classes, indecipherable for consumers, had been added to the A-B-C-D-E-F-G classes. Industrial players thereby sought to weaken the effect of the legal instrument in order to be able to play on the positive psychological effects of the A category, whereas an A+ device in fact belongs more rightfully in category C. In the new proposal, the Commission and many governments have acknowledged the problems caused by the system, which henceforth will be much easier to understand thanks to a return to a scale running from A to G. Unfortunately, industry has not given up and its frenetic lobbying of the Parliament and the Council throughout 2016 was designed to delay this automatic recalibration for as long as possible. Recalibration would happen once between 10 per cent and 15 per cent of all products have reached the level of class A in a given sector. This obstructionism was undoubtedly successful: the inter-institutional deal reached in March 2017 foresees that recalibration would happen no earlier than 2023 for most appliances (e.g. vacuum cleaners, tumble driers) or even 2026 and 2030 for boilers and heaters respectively.

Another battle relates to market supervision. At the national level, some governments do not want the EU to be in charge of monitoring product conformity. However, it is precisely because of this lack of control that organised cheating has appeared, such as in Dieselgate. In a single market, EU-wide policing is required since many electronic products are not made in the EU and so are imported. I believe that all producers should supply information about their products to be recorded in a European register, as this should make it easier to detect fraud. A 'Fridgegate' is all it would take to undermine consumer confidence in European labels.

Another step forward would be to link energy performance and eco-design to the principles of the circular economy, starting with a priority list of between fifteen and twenty products for which, in addition to cutting energy consumption, water consumption and programmed obsolescence could be reduced, while also improving recycling. A test phase involving a selection of products could introduce the criteria of the circular economy and the efficient use of resources, including aspects such as water consumption by dishwashers and washing machines, the use of reduced quantities of metals and their replacement by other materials. The good news is that all this is already possible under existing legislation. All that is lacking is the political courage to act.

Promoting labelling and eco-design through European soft power
Lastly, in the wake of the ratification of the Paris Climate Agreement, one of my hopes is that international cooperation on energy labelling and eco-design may be established. Indeed, the standards that apply to our European market and its 450 million consumers could inspire the rest of the world still further. Europe must stay at the cutting edge of such practices, but it should also encourage the creation of a global network of regulators to promote ambitious standards for mass consumer products. A talking shop bringing together regulators from the leading industrialised nations would be relatively cheap to implement and would help redress the balance of power between regulators and industry lobbyists. The fact is that lobbyists working for multinationals take part in standards consultations for Europe, the US, Korea and

Japan, attempting to drag them down in order to minimise the environmental constraints involved. Regulatory authorities do not have enough resources to join forces and counter such attempts.

In countries bordering Europe, particularly Egypt and others in north Africa, the demand for electricity is exploding, running parallel to huge demographic growth and much-needed economic growth. The swift adoption of energy efficiency standards would be a powerful source of leverage to control this increase. Failing this, it will be impossible for local renewable production to be enough to cater for demand, and coal will once again come out on top. Europe should therefore be helping these countries to expand their institutional capabilities, enabling them to implement appropriate policies on energy labelling and eco-design for their markets. This is known as soft power. Just as the USA has exported its lifestyle worldwide through Hollywood films and fast food, Europe can export its environmental standards! Developing countries certainly have everything to gain from imitating our legislation on energy labelling and eco-design. This would also have the advantage of avoiding a top-of-the-range market with high-quality products in Europe existing cheek by jowl with a 'junk' market for harmful products wasting too much energy and water.

Renewables at the centre of a restructured electricity market

The EU is heading towards 100 per cent renewable energy, especially as regards electricity, for which renewables are the best solution to provide a wholly carbon-free electricity system. In the longer term, the same will also be true for transport and heating. This is fully in line with the Treaty; Article 194.2 allows each member state to choose its mix of renewables and promote both diversity and complementarity.

In the space of ten years, the Renewables Directive has triggered an investment boom that has borne fruit all over the EU. Many governments have invested in the sector, particularly those of Germany, Portugal, Denmark and Sweden, as well as their counterparts in Lithuania, Italy, Bulgaria and Romania. Some member states are lagging behind with respect to their 2020 targets, though, as the Commission pointed out in its 2015 progress report:

> France and the Netherlands failed to meet their 2011/2012 interim target … some member states, including France, Luxembourg, Malta, the Netherlands and the United Kingdom, and to a lesser extent Belgium and Spain need to assess whether their policies and tools are sufficient and effective in meeting their renewable energy objectives.

Luxembourg and Malta are small countries that will need to resort to statistical transfers to meet their obligations. Neither the Netherlands nor the UK have any such excuse, though; the fact is that successive governments in London and The Hague over the past ten years have not always sought to promote renewables. Spain has fallen behind due to manoeuvring on the part of the oligopolies, designed to preserve their economic rent derived from fossil fuels and nuclear power. The same is true in France, where EDF and Engie have forced the government to join the race for renewable energy – with the handbrake on. Prior to the 2017 French election result, there were fears that a right-wing government would doubtless be delighted to renege on the Energy Transition Act and slow down the deployment of renewables, despite the French territory having geographical and meteorological potential that is unparalleled anywhere else in Europe.

There is no denying that the Renewables Directive has changed the electricity market's business model. A major part of the economy, formerly to be found in many instances to be in the grips of a single operator or an oligopoly, has inevitably become more democratised. How can this trend be extended? Will the forthcoming directive promote a democratic model for renewables, or will it mark a return to an oligopolistic market structure? We have seen how the European Council carried out something akin to an institutional coup d'état when it came to the future 2030 Climate and Energy Package.[113] Under

---

113   See Chapter 11, p. 142.

the threat of a veto by David Cameron against a backdrop of Brexit blackmail, the heads of state and government decided to scale back the progression of renewable energy between 2020 and 2030, and to hack away at existing governance. The European Parliament and the Commission must not cave in to this brute-force attack; instead, they should make the most of Brexit to return to a more ambitious policy, with binding targets.

The European target for renewables in 2030 should, at the very least, reflect the 'cruising speed' achieved over the past ten years as, failing this, the development of renewables will slow down. Today, the cost of renewables, particularly for solar and offshore wind power, has decreased enormously. Current investments cost no more (and in some cases even less) than traditional energy, with no indirect costs for society in the form of climate change, pollution or radiation. Europe cannot allow itself to keep on investing less than China and the US as it did in 2015. In that annus horribilis, European investment fell by 18 per cent to 2006 levels – equivalent to scarcely more than half of Chinese investments that same year.[114]

Despite all this, the target advanced by the Commission in its November 2016 proposal is pathetic: just 27 per cent. In absolute terms, when energy use reduction achieved through ambitious policy in the field is taken into account, this target is equivalent to a threefold decrease in total investment in renewables across the EU. How can Jean-Claude Juncker possibly hope to honour his commitment to make Europe the 'world number one' in this respect with a shrinking domestic market?

The argument for robust governance
The EU must preserve the aspects that make the current directive a success: robust governance with binding national targets. If the directive does not assign national responsibilities, it is pointless. This

---

114   'Clean energy investment', Bloomberg New Energy Finance, www.about.bnef.com/blog/clean-energy-defies-fossil-fuel-price-crash-to-attract-record-329bn-global-investment-in-2015/

means that national targets and national support schemes should not be done away with. Moreover, the legality of national schemes was upheld by the European Court of Justice in 2014 (the Ålands Ruling):[115] a member state has the right to restrict the scope of its support schemes to installations located within its national territory.

It is worth explaining why, despite being a committed federalist and Europhile, I am so strongly in favour of national support schemes and not in favour of creating an integrated European renewables market. There are two fundamental reasons for my position. Firstly, it is impossible to transport and store electricity on a massive scale in the same way as other goods. It is ridiculous to promote the idea of simply having wind power in Scotland and solar power in Greece, since the reality is that energy is lost in the form of heat when transporting electricity over great distances. In addition, there is the issue of the inevitable backlash against the prospect of building the thousands of kilometres of power lines that would be needed to make such a scenario a reality. Secondly, there is always a local dimension to renewables as neither wind nor solar power can be delocalised, so the production site is key. In addition, research and development means that wind turbines can be adapted, both to areas with little wind and to areas with extreme climate conditions. A similar logic applies to solar power; innovation has led solar power to make a breakthrough in northern Europe, despite the fact that these latitudes benefit from less sunshine. This runs counter to the overblown theory of hotspots, according to which solar power belongs in countries where the sun shines and wind power in countries where the wind blows – an idea dear to German energy firms and Commissioner Oettinger, along similar lines to the Desertec project,[116] which was swiftly abandoned.

The future is nevertheless one in which there must be strong, highly

---

115   Court of Justice of the European Union, ruling dated 1 July 2014, C 573/12, Ålands Vindkraft AB vs. Energimyndigheten.

116   Desertec was an enormous project briefly supported by German industry which envisaged covering the Sahara with solar panels and importing the electricity they produced to Europe. Over and above issues of technical and economic feasibility, the project also revived the spectre of neo-colonialism, since it involved the exploitation of domestic African resources by and for Europeans.

structured regional cooperation in the fields of network-planning and the optimised deployment of renewable energy production capacity. For instance, if all the countries with a North Sea seaboard could agree on an ambitious, coordinated plan to develop offshore wind power, the costs would decrease far more quickly than if each of them worked to pursue such a project separately. Regional cooperation is a catalyst that would favour the completion of a 100 per cent renewable energy system. Consequently, the cooperation schemes provided for in the existing directive should be allowed to continue.

Today, the question is one of ensuring payment by off-target countries, i.e. those who do not comply with EU legislation. In this respect, I invite the Commission to commence infringement proceedings against those member states that are lagging behind and making no effort to achieve their 2020 targets.

Encouraging democratisation

By pushing the Commission to impose an auction system rather than guaranteed tariffs, traditional producers sought to ensure that support schemes would favour major investors and deter small investors. However, thanks to the de minimis rules, member states can continue to apply guaranteed tariffs, provided that the projects are beneath certain thresholds. It is imperative that the new directive gives these exemptions for small installations with a firm basis in legislation. Similarly, the upcoming 2020–2025 guidelines on state aid for environmental protection and energy should duly note the decision by the European Parliament and the twenty-eight member states of the Council in favour of common principles for national support schemes.

There is another vital component for democratisation of the energy system to be achieved. Some 70–80 per cent of European distribution systems are in the hands of ten or so oligopolies. It is therefore hardly surprising that the latter are increasingly using these systems as a weapon to restrict the penetration of renewables. For instance, DSOs are starting to complain that an excess of renewable energy from self-generation is creating solidarity problems when it comes to paying for grid costs. They are arguing that everybody connected to the system should pay a fixed subscription charge, regardless of whether they use the grid permanently or only for a few hours a year. DSOs want to drastically increase the fixed component in their tariff system, while some member states such as Spain have even implemented a special tax on self-generation in order to protect conventional operators.

This is a full-scale attack on the business model for renewables. The new directive should prevent this form of indirect penalisation of self-producers by means of abusive tariffs.

The right to produce and resell electricity should be properly established. Individuals producing electricity on their roofs should not be sanctioned by society; they should be rewarded. This should be done by defining a new legal framework in which the neutrality of DSOs is guaranteed and, more especially, their independence from the oligopolies is assured. A first symbolic step in this direction in France was the separation of EDF as a producer from ERDF, when the latter became Enedis after the regulatory authority ruled that the EDF and ERDF acronyms were too similar and liable to create confusion between the two enterprises in the minds of consumers. However, much more than a change of name is needed. The main thing is to continue to grant priority to renewables in requests for access to the grid.

Grid access and priority dispatch

Thanks to priority grid access and priority dispatch, the existing directive has forced TSOs and DSOs to innovate. As a result, operators have used all the technical resources at their disposal to integrate renewables. However, electricity firms are now invoking the argument of network limitations to slow down the growth of renewables. The fact is, however, that the problem is not one of too much renewable energy in the system, but rather the surplus of inflexible, conventional capacity. Access and priority dispatch must be maintained until this issue of overcapacity has been resolved.

In the event of production far exceeding electricity demand – a state of affairs that is likely to occur with increasing frequency, since the oldest power stations are not always shut down – TSOs and DSOs have to take certain installations offline in order to balance the network. In the absence of any priority access and dispatch for renewables, they would naturally be inclined to start by unplugging those power stations with the lower marginal costs of production, since it would be the least expensive option. This is an upside-down 'merit order' which would benefit nuclear power and coal, the most inflexible power plants. Traditional producers are therefore hoping to establish a market model in which the system operator will be compelled to halt renewable production. The next step is obvious: the very same operators would point an accusing finger at wind turbines that are not rotating even when the wind is blowing. They would focus attention on the costs of redispatching, and if these increase, it would be an indication that the system is saturated by renewables. They would then demand that existing renewable power is shut down, followed by the development of all renewables being halted until new power lines have been built or legacy power stations have reached the end of their lives.

If renewable energy from cogeneration in the form of biomass, geothermal power and thermal solar power did not benefit from priority dispatch, it would drop down the merit order because electricity produced by cogeneration with renewables will always be slightly more expensive than the same procedure using coal or gas combustion. Without clear priority access for renewable electricity from cogeneration, some countries such as Poland are likely to continue to power their heating networks using fossil fuels.

How much biomass after 2020?

First-generation biofuels should comply with the Indirect Land Use Change (ILUC) Directive, which regulates their carbon footprint. Thanks to mobilisation on the part of the Greens and civil society, the EU has imposed a cap in this respect. In a world which will soon be home to 10 billion people, food production must be one of the top priorities, well ahead of energy crops. Today, politicians have a responsibility to encourage biofuels and biogas to progress to second- and third-generation fuels, based on organic waste and agricultural and forest residues rather than dedicated crops, and to gradually abandon first-generation biofuels.

The revised EU directive should also put forward ambitious sustainability criteria, with the imposition of environmental standards on biomass, including solid biomass for wood energy. This is also in the interest of the European forestry industry, since it would put an end to the unregulated deforestation currently taking place in some countries. Without a European standard, it is impossible to impose standards on imported timber, since the WTO requires equal treatment of both domestic and foreign producers. Sustainability criteria for renewables should therefore remain in the directive and not be the subject of separate legislation, in order to provide a comprehensive overview.

The co-firing of biomass in coal-fired power stations should be brought to an end as a top priority. The practice is environmental nonsense, in particular because of the imports of millions of tonnes of biomass from the Americas, Ukraine and Asia. It is also an economic 'con trick', since the producers win both ways: the system allows them to artificially extend the lifespan of their creaking coal-fired power stations, while also benefiting from subsidies earmarked for renewable energy. The Dutch Parliament is currently examining a solution to this problem with regard to their more recent installations: a redistribution of co-firing subsidies to operators in exchange for the early closure of their coal-fired power plants.

In addition, over and above the legitimate criticisms of biofuels and the unsustainable use of biomass, the issue of biodiversity must be considered holistically as only a small amount of arable land is currently being used for energy production. The debate on climate change must include the whole of agriculture, including livestock farming that is due to the overconsumption of meat, the carbon footprint of which is far in excess of that of bioenergy. Indeed, livestock farming is responsible for 18 per cent of greenhouse gas emissions, more than the whole of the transport sector. Most of these emissions come from feed crops, animal digestion and animal waste. Methane is a greenhouse gas that is thirty times more harmful than CO_2, making the emissions from the 3.6 billion ruminants being reared on the planet our leading source of greenhouse gas emissions. The farming lobby has succeeded in countering measures designed to bring down methane emissions in the Air Quality Directive, but the vast majority of agricultural emissions (65 per cent) relate to cattle, the energy yield of which is disastrous. Beef alone is responsible for one third of the entire sector's greenhouse gas emissions and the prospect is even worse if the huge quantities of water consumed during livestock-rearing are taken into account. Simply put, if the whole world's cattle were to constitute a single nation, it would be the third most-polluting country, surpassed only by China and the USA.

My proposals:
- Using the revision of the Energy Efficiency Directive to increase the European target for 2030 to at least 40 per cent, with binding national targets; extend the application of Article 7 by increasing energy savings obligations to 3 per cent per year, and including the transportation sector; broadening the scope of energy audits and implementing the recommendations of these audits; stimulating the Energy Performance Contract market.
- Using the revision of the Energy Labelling Regulation to abolish A+, A++ and A+++ and similar categories, and return to a scale running from A to G that includes automatic recalibration as the market progresses; create a centralised database allowing consumers to compare the energy performance of different products across the whole of the EU, and allowing the Commission to supervise the entry into the market of products manufactured outside Europe more closely.
- As part of the Ecodesign Working Plan, increasing the list of

products concerned to cover all household appliances, heating appliances, and office equipment, and extend the text in the direction of the circular economy by including other elements such as water consumption.

- Using the revision of the Renewable Energy Directive to increase the EU's 2030 target to 35 per cent, with binding national targets; maintain the principle of national technology-specific support schemes (these should be a combination of feed-in tariffs for small projects and premiums allocated via competitive auctions for large projects); encourage progressive convergence at the macro-regional level, and the implementation of cooperation mechanisms (for instance, by means of a renewable energy exchange allowing member states with a surplus to sell it to other member states with a deficit); maintain the principle of priority access to the grid and priority dispatch for renewable electricity; add a new clause devoted especially to the management and promotion of self-generation by individuals and cooperatives; extend sustainability criteria to include solid biomass.

CHAPTER 19

MACRO-REGIONS: HALFWAY BETWEEN NATIONAL SOVEREIGNTY AND COMPLETE HARMONISATION

On the one hand, national sovereignty is guaranteed by Article 194.2 of the Treaty on the Functioning of the European Union in matters pertaining to the energy mix and security of supply. On the other hand, there is complete harmonisation for all twenty-eight member states when it comes to the internal gas and electricity market. Is there no room for an intermediate position between these two extremes? Are we stuck forever with a binary system in which each member state conducts energy policy either in splendid isolation, or under the sole control of the European Commission? I am convinced that institutional cooperation bringing together several countries facing the same regional challenges would be well worth exploring as a compromise position. The creation of macro-regions, stimulating cooperation between neighbouring countries, could even be the greatest innovation of the Energy Union.

Indeed, while the governance of the Energy Union is being drawn up with national plans and pan-European targets in mind, it is also set to provide plenty of room for macro-regions as a new, established stakeholder. Legislation will thus provide an environment that facilitates working together at the regional level. The idea here is to optimise energy systems beyond borders, without necessarily aiming for complete European harmonisation, at least initially. Before achieving such a thing across Europe, the logical halfway house is that of macro-regions.

This is absolutely not about stripping national governments of their responsibilities. They are the main providers of the existing legislative framework, thanks to their sovereign powers and the degree of discretion they enjoy in the transposition of EU directives, their choice of energy mix, their external and bilateral relations and in how they guarantee security of supply. And too, it is them, and not 'Brussels', who structure their territory and grant permission for the construction of wind farms and photovoltaic power plants. Besides, a European commissioner will never have more legitimacy than a minister when it comes to defending a local infrastructure project. Rather, the idea is to provide reassurance to member states and counter the current trend in favour of the renationalisation of energy policy. It would also allow those who want to press on in a particular area to do so with others, without falling victim to obstruction on the part of other member states. Clearly, it is easier to reach an understanding between four or five ministers or heads of department in neighbouring countries than for twenty-eight partners to do so.

Flexibly defined geographical regions

The main barrier to regional cooperation is the geographical definition of the regions themselves. Which countries should be brought together, and on what basis? I believe that this difficulty could be overcome by making the scope of regional cooperation dependent on the particular fields in question. A region might consist of different countries depending on whether electricity or gas is being considered. Of course, there are some regions that are 'naturally' quite stable, such as the three Baltic states, Scandinavia or the Iberian Peninsula. In other cases, however, the definition of regions needs to be based on specific criteria: physical grid interconnections, market coupling, the amount of trade or the complementary nature of their respective energy mixes.

Regional cooperation is not a new idea. For several years now, certain member states have been engaged in it – sometimes in a rather haphazard fashion, but always proactively. Existing cooperation pertains mostly to the field of electricity. For instance, there is the Pentalateral Energy Forum (now known as the 'Central West Electricity Regional Energy Market') set up in 2005 between France, Germany and the Benelux countries in order to coordinate and then couple their electricity markets. This initiative has proved highly successful, with Austria and Switzerland joining later. In this instance, the scope of application has been deliberately circumscribed: coupling the electricity market and increasing cross-border trading. The Scandinavian countries offer another example; they are grouped together in Nord Pool, a single electricity market, later joined by the Baltic countries. Here again, the scope of cooperation is very narrowly defined as establishing a common electricity exchange for these countries – the oldest one of its kind in the world.

This begs the question of why these initiatives cannot simply be left to emerge and thrive on their own. The reason is that regional cooperation without European oversight carries with it a significant risk: that of each region developing its own markets, mechanisms, standards and procedures, each thereby drifting apart from the others and putting a strain on the Single Market. That is why I am in favour of structured regional cooperation being established, with a role for the Commission and other pan-European bodies, such as the Agency for the Cooperation of Energy Regulators (ACER) and the involvement of other stakeholders including national MPs, cities, civil society and industry. This would provide genuine coherence between regions that are supposed to be converging, rather than drawing apart.

Models worth looking into
BEMIP

The MoU for BEMIP (the Baltic Energy Market Interconnection Plan) signed in June 2015 is without doubt a good template for others to follow. It includes a top-level group that meets once a year, chaired by a European commissioner. This offers a good guarantee of overall coherence, along with other, more technical working groups. More importantly, while it does focus on network interconnections, it also deals with a whole host of connected issues by allowing for exchange of information about renewable energy, energy efficiency, gas and even nuclear safety. The big job currently being dealt with by BEMIP is the de-synchronisation of the Baltic states from the Russian electricity system. This political priority for the Baltic countries has the potential to become a flagship project for Europe as a whole if it can be tied into a broader discussion about improving the integration of Estonia, Latvia and Lithuania into the Scandinavian market. The new cables required for synchronisation between the Baltic states and the rest of Europe's electricity grid could, for instance, be used to help develop offshore wind power in the Baltic.

EU participation in laying a cable between Poland and Lithuania via offshore wind farms would also be the best way of convincing the Polish authorities that alternatives to coal exist. Furthermore, this would offer future prospects to factories in Gdańsk, Gdynia and Szczecin, which have successfully retooled in order to enter the market for underwater steel structures to anchor wind turbines. Another potential item for BEMIP's agenda would be the conversion of district heating networks in the Baltic countries and Poland, many of which are still being powered by fossil fuels, to renewable energy from biomass, geothermal power and thermal solar power. Such a cooperative project would make BEMIP a powerhouse for energy transition across the entire region.

An action plan for the North Sea
One year after BEMIP, in June 2016, countries bordering the North Sea finalised a policy declaration, along with an action plan and a specific governance structure. Here again, the Commission is included as co-president of the high-level group, in order to prevent the emergence of loose cannons. The declaration concerns a specific objective: the development of an interconnected electricity grid in the North

Sea with a view to rolling out significant wind turbine capacity. The prospect of 100GW of wind power in the North Sea by 2030 is by no means unrealistic. In the first half of 2015, the Dutch presidency of the Council made this issue one of its priorities, with the encouragement of a score or so of MEPs convinced of the need to make the North Sea, with its huge wind power potential, north-west Europe's 'power house'.[117]

Eight EU member states, the Commission and one third country, Norway, formally acknowledged that regional cooperation in this field could result in huge cost reductions for a technology which is as yet relatively expensive. This decision made sense: these cost reductions will occur once European industry feels confident enough about the development prospects for the market to commit significant investments to devising new materials, new production processes and new installation techniques. Harmonising safety regulations is another avenue to be looked into in this respect. And in a post-Brexit world, electricity cables might be a good way of maintaining ties between the UK and the EU, ensuring that it does not gradually drift further westwards across the Atlantic!

CESEC

One final example of particularly noteworthy cooperation is CESEC, a high-level group dealing with gas connectivity in central and south-eastern Europe. Here too, the terms of reference provide for leadership by the European Commission and third countries adjacent to member states are also invited to participate (in this case, the western Balkan states). Set up in the wake of the political turmoil following the abandonment of the South Stream gas pipeline, this group is seeking to find solutions to an extremely pressing problem for the countries in the region: the risks pertaining to their security of gas supply. This difficult state of affairs, in which these countries are overexposed to a single country of supply, Russia, with supply passing

---

117   'Northern Seas as the power house of North-Western Europe', January 2016, bit.ly/NorthernSeas.

through a fragile transit country, Ukraine, has strengthened the legitimate need for greater liquidity of the gas market in the region, achieved through the construction of some priority infrastructures, such as bidirectional gas pipelines and storage sites.

That said, it is disappointing to note that this is the only response being envisaged by the region's policymakers, even though other solutions, such as energy efficiency, would be more long-lasting when it comes to reducing dependence on Russian gas and stimulating the local economy over the long term. There is also the issue of the western Balkans escaping the tyranny of coal. In view of this, in June 2016 some fifteen MEPs published a manifesto[118] arguing for regional cooperation in south-east Europe to be broadened to other key areas, including the electricity market, renewables and energy efficiency. Their efforts finally paid off, as shown by the decision on 9 September 2016 to extend CESEC's scope of cooperation beyond gas.

This is very much in line with the Commission's Energy Union strategy:

Given its particular vulnerability, there is a need to improve cooperation, solidarity and trust in the central and south-eastern part of Europe. Dedicated cooperation arrangements would help to accelerate the better integration of these markets into the wider European energy market which would improve the liquidity and resilience of the energy system and would allow full use of the region's energy efficiency and renewable energy potential.

Moreover, there is a huge potential for energy efficiency both in buildings and in industry for the countries in the region, which have fallen far behind in terms of the energy intensity of their economies, partly inherited from a communist system that paid little heed to energy wastage. Regional leaders, including those from countries that are not yet members of the EU, have become aware of this, as illustrated by

---

118   'South-eastern Europe: more than just a gas corridor, a lighthouse for Europe', June 2016, bit. ly/SouthEastEurope.

the Tirana declaration on energy efficiency in the Balkans, adopted on 15 September 2014.

To move things in the right direction, there should also be more Technical Assistance offered to national administrations and project developers in the region. This could be achieved via a cluster of excellence, partly funded by the EIB and partly by structural funds, as I suggested in the Luxembourg Declaration.[119] There is also every reason to couple the electricity market across the region as a whole. In initial stages, in February 2016 a trading platform was set up in Belgrade by EPEX, the European Electricity Exchange; in 2017, the Serbian 'day-ahead' market is due to be coupled with that of its neighbours (Hungary, the Czech Republic, Slovakia and Romania), to be known as 4MMC.

However, what is the point of coupling the south-east European markets if the electricity in question is generated using coal and lignite, as is widely the case today? Some governments are even keen to see this state of affairs carry on, with no fewer than 6GW[120] of new coal-fired power stations planned for in the Balkans, whereas the aim should rather be to develop the region's huge potential in renewables. There is plenty of sunshine; some regions are very windy, particularly the Danube Delta, home to the largest onshore wind farm in Europe; biomass is abundant and the region's hydroelectric potential has scarcely been tapped at all. Envisaging a future well on the way to 100 per cent renewables is therefore not a pipe dream, as shown by scenarios drawn up under the aegis of the International Renewable Energy Agency (IRENA) and the 'SEE 2050' model.

The Pentalateral Energy Forum

France, Germany, and the Benelux countries were among the forerunners of regional cooperation, launching the Pentalateral Energy Forum in 2005. Cooperation between the most ardent fans of nuclear

---

119   Claude Turmes, 'Luxembourg Declaration', 23 September 2015, http://bit.ly/LuxDeclaration.
120   'Beyond Borders: How Energy Union Can Turn the Tide against Coal in the Western Balkans', CAN-Europe, August 2015, www.caneurope.org.

power and those leading the charge to abandon nuclear power was not self-evident. In actual fact, it was the three small Benelux countries – quite possibly tired of having to put up with choices made by their two larger neighbours – who created the impetus for this forum to be set up. The Netherlands, for instance, have had to shut down a great many coal-fired power stations to cope with huge influxes of German electricity. This is due to the fact that Germany has fallen behind in the construction of high-voltage lines to transport surplus electricity from its wind farms in the north of the country southwards, and is continuing to protect its own coal-fired power stations, invoking the 'must run' principle. Belgium does little better with its much larger neighbour, France, which has to import huge amounts of electricity in winter, having encouraged electrical heating as a means of absorbing its nuclear electricity: for every 1°C drop in temperature, 2,400MW of additional production is required.[121] As a result, France sucks up its neighbours' electricity during winter spikes, despite its over large nuclear fleet, while remaining, on average per year, a net exporter. Meanwhile, Luxembourg has been living with the spectre of blackouts since September 2004, when a failure in the connection with Germany crashed the Grand Duchy's grid.

To avoid being at the mercy of the slightest problem with their two larger neighbours, the three smallest countries therefore formed the coalition and suggested working together at the regional level. This began by coupling the markets, followed by the calculation of generation adequacy. Market coupling was an unqualified success, and helped to bring wholesale electricity prices down. Unfortunately, however, the joint work on security of supply was not completed. On the eve of this work being finalised, France unilaterally decided to launch its own capacity market to subsidise its power stations. Keeping national egos in check can sometimes be difficult. In Belgium, Electrabel, a subsidiary of the French firm Engie, formerly GDF Suez, behaved just as badly. Instead of entering into a partnership with its

---

121   'Bilan électrique 2014', RTE, 29 January 2015, www.rte-france.com.

neighbours in the Netherlands and Luxembourg to ensure security of supply by means of gas-fired power stations just over the border, the group headed up by Gérard Mestrallet devised a blackmail scheme leveraging security of supply to wrest an agreement extending the life of its nuclear power plants. It achieved this end with the help of the kingdom's liberal government. Another factor dampening the spirits of the Pentalateral Energy Forum is the presence of three dangerous nuclear power stations in border regions that are cause for concern on the part of their neighbours: Fessenheim on the border between France and Germany, Cattenom on the border between France and Luxembourg and Tihange, the Belgian power station located close to both the Dutch and German borders.

Today, I think there are two flagship projects that could give cooperation in the Pentalateral Energy Forum a new lease of life. Firstly, an agreement to decrease overcapacity, which would allow the electricity market and the carbon price to be adjusted across the area as a whole. Overproduction in Europe, and the resulting low wholesale prices, are direct consequences of the continuing use of coal in Germany and the Netherlands and of the continuing use of nuclear power in France and Belgium. I therefore propose closer cooperation for the development of renewables by optimising the extended area covered by the Pentalateral Energy Forum. It could be done through the use of common cross-border calls for tender: Germany and Denmark already launched one; others, such as Germany with France, and Belgium with Luxembourg, may soon follow. Meanwhile, gradual, negotiated abandonment of coal and nuclear power by 2025–2030 accompanied by a regional carbon floor price, is the only way to breathe new life into the moribund carbon market. It is worth pointing out that EDF would not be opposed to such a measure.

Secondly, I propose that a major cross-border electric mobility project should be launched. The automotive industry is situated right at the heart of the Pentalateral Energy Forum's area: Baden-Württemberg, Alsace-Lorraine, Luxembourg, Belgium and even the Netherlands (for trucks). The region could put forward a joint car-sharing offering and 100 per cent renewable electric mobility, together with unified charging and payment systems. This electric mobility corridor would be accompanied by a network of fast charging stations along the region's motorways.

Other projects for the future

What about southern Europe? The Iberian Peninsula is a de facto integrated market, with aspirations for interconnection with north Africa and France. While Spanish motivations are largely praiseworthy – resolving the problem of the bottleneck at its border with France – the Italians' long-standing dreams of much better interconnection with the Balkan countries conceal less honourable intentions. The Italians hope to delocalise coal-fired electricity production to third countries and then import electricity back to Italy, thus evading European carbon market strictures. These notorious 'cables for carbon' are a dangerous project.[122]

Countries bordering the Mediterranean, meanwhile, on both its northern and southern shores, have everything to gain from cooperation that respects regional particularities and nurtures renewables, for which the region is undeniably suited. Why not encourage the emerging democracy in Tunisia to develop renewables, along with export potential to Italy in the long term? The same principle could apply between Morocco and Portugal. What is more, the Mediterranean basin is not just good for solar power: technological advances in the field of floating wind power mean that the Mediterranean itself offers huge potential. A marine link between Catalonia and Occitania would not only preserve the landscape of the Pyrenees, it could collect electricity produced at sea thanks to the Tramontane wind. Malta's presidency in the first half of 2017 offered a good opportunity to move forward on this issue.

As a convinced Europhile, I am delighted to see these strategic initiatives involving structured, coherent micro-regions. However,

---

122   Claude Turmes, 'Cables for carbon?', March 2010, stopclimatechange.net.

I regret the fact that they are incomplete, since they are not legally binding and are based on structures that are wholly ephemeral due to their being dependent on the goodwill of policymakers who can come and go at any time. There is only one way to ensure their long-term future, and that is to enshrine them in legislation. Indeed, this is what the Commission attempted to do when reviewing the regulation on gas security of supply.

Towards institutionalised cooperation, with gas as a precedent

February 2016 was a watershed in the history of regional cooperation on energy in Europe. For the first time ever, the European Commission looked at making cooperation between neighbouring countries mandatory. It chose a promising topic – the security of gas supply – and an audacious approach: the ex-ante definition of regions (listed in the annex to the proposed regulation). The proposal was based on the principle that 'stronger regional cooperation, with certain standards being set at EU level, is necessary to sufficiently address the deficiencies of the current system (national risk assessment and national plans) and enables problems to be solved at regional level, without being unnecessarily prescriptive'. Under the terms of the regulation, each of these regions would have to design a common risk assessment plan, a risk management plan and an emergency plan (in the event of disruption of supply), approved by all of the member states making up the region. Vice president Šefčovič and Commissioner Arias Cañete did not shrink from putting forward this courageous proposal, despite it going against the desire of certain member states to keep regional cooperation beyond the reach of Brussels.

Reactions were not long in coming, first and foremost from Berlin and Vienna, supported by Paris, Rome and Brussels (Belgium, not the Commission). These governments lost no time in publishing an incendiary statement criticising a rigid, artificial division by the Commission. Austria was furious to find itself lumped in with Hungary and not with Germany or Slovakia; for its part, Germany saw its inclusion in a region including Poland as an insult. Admittedly, definition on the basis of geography is a perilous exercise, but I am of the opinion that these attacks by Germany and Austria conceal a rather nationalistic tendency to want to hold onto their gas policies as their prized possessions. This is a 'rich people's problem' for Germany, keen to exploit its privileged bilateral relationship with Russia and continue with its project to build the controversial Nord Stream 2 gas pipeline, which links Russia directly to north Germany, passing beneath the Baltic Sea.

On the other side, those threatened by possible gas shortages, the Visegrád countries and the Baltic states, were delighted by the Commission's proposal and took the view that regional cooperation would be a powerful source of leverage to reduce their dependence on Russian gas. While the European Parliament is tending to favour the latter, the matter was still in the balance at the time of writing. Either way, this will set an important precedent when it comes to the establishment of macro-regions for energy in Europe. Undeniably, this type of cooperation involves a political dimension. If France and Germany agree to play ball in solidarity with Poland and the eastern countries on gas, the latter will find it difficult to refuse to commit to combating climate change.

Although the final deal reached between Commission, Council and the European Parliament in April 2017 preserves some elements of the regional dimension within 'risk-based groups' defined in a rewritten annex, the intensity of regional cooperation has been largely watered down. Rather than working together on joint preventive action plans within a regional group, member states shall simply draw national preventive action plans including a vague regional chapter. Far from initial ambitions. Put off by this experience the Commission did not display similar courage and propose predefined regional cooperation in its new legislative proposals on risk-preparedness in the electricity sector.

My proposals:
- Structuring regional cooperation around the North Sea in order to create a corridor for deploying 80–100GW of wind power by 2030

(with well-coordinated national or even macro-regional auctions), combined with an ambitious plan to develop the electricity system in the region (managed by an independent system operator); harmonising social, health and safety regulations pertaining to offshore wind power to facilitate cross-border maintenance operations, as has been done in the oil and gas industry; building a single European centre to test new prototype wind turbines more cheaply.

- Strengthening the Pentalateral Energy Forum by examining the possibility of a carbon floor price, joint support schemes for renewables and the promotion of electric mobility; bringing down macro-regions' high degree of overcapacity by coordinating the decrease of coal in Germany and the Netherlands and the decrease of nuclear power in France and Belgium; examining the possibility of expanding the forum to include Italy, Spain and Portugal; developing practical solar and floating wind power projects with north Africa.

- Broadening the scope of regional cooperation in south-east Europe by fleshing out the decision to include electricity, renewables and energy efficiency within the mandate of CESEC; helping these countries to invest in green infrastructure with the aid of guarantees provided by the Juncker Plan (including for countries that are not members of the EU).

- Speeding up the implementation of practical projects around the Baltic Sea, such as the synchronisation of the three Baltic states with the European electricity system, the development of offshore wind power and the conversion of heating networks to renewables.

- Renewing regional cooperation in the Mediterranean basin, including for energy efficiency, with north African countries.

- Making regional cooperation more systematic and organised by means of common plans embedded in community legislation on electricity and gas, in order to enshrine national prerogatives in scenarios shared across macro-regions, drawing on joint working hypotheses and scenarios (including a 100 per cent renewable energy scenario).

CHAPTER 20

FINANCIAL MARKET TRANSITION

The saying that 'money makes the world go round' also applies in the realm of energy. Financial markets have the power to accelerate energy transition, not only by favouring green investment, but also by moving away from investments in fossil fuels and nuclear power. The financial markets are a key catalyst for transition, all the more so since the COP21 Agreement. For this to happen, however, the way these markets work needs to be understood.

Institutional investors at the crossroads

Major investors, most of them from the private sector, play a key role on financial markets. These are known as institutional investors or, in French stockbroker jargon, the zinzins. Right up until a few months before the COP21 conference, they were earning money in the energy sector just as they would anywhere else. These investments were considered as being technology-agnostic, and largely went into oil, gas and coal. Very few of them established any link between portfolio management and the climate, or nuclear accidents. However, for the very first time, at the COP21 conference there were in-depth discussions about the important role of the world of finance in the planet's future. The risks inherent in the stock market value of companies relying on the exploitation of fossil fuels also came to light.

The 'divest/invest' movement was born in the United States, and was

the brainchild of Bill McKibben. In 2008, he set up 350.org, a movement aimed at influencing decision-makers ahead of the Copenhagen
climate conference. Then, in January 2014, 350.org launched media
campaigns directed at US investment funds to encourage them to
divest from coal and later oil.[123] They went on to score an emblematic
success: in March 2016, the Rockefeller fund announced its intention
of divesting from fossil fuels. The legendary American family, which
made its fortune thanks to the oil boom of the late nineteenth century,
thus decided to stop investing in black gold; that is quite a milestone.

When the carbon bubble bursts
In an environment in which government bonds are delivering very
low returns, pension funds are drawn to high-yield shares. In recent
years, this has led to a rush for oil company shares, particularly when
oil prices were well over $100 a barrel, because they paid very high
dividends. Close examination of the portfolios of German, French,
Danish and Norwegian state pension funds, along with Californian
and Canadian private pension funds, reveals that their long-term performance is largely dependent on the scenario of income from shares
in the world's leading oil players.

However, things have changed somewhat today. The value of Shell,
ExxonMobil, BP and their kindred rests on two pillars. The first consists of the proven oil and gas reserves for which they hold drilling
permits. The fact is that these reserves contain approximately five
times more carbon than can actually be burned if we are to remain
within the limits of our carbon budget and restrict the increase of
temperatures to 2°C. The maths is simple: if we can afford to emit
only 565Gt of greenhouse gas emissions out of the 2,795Gt available,
the fossil fuel reserves equivalent to the remaining 2,230Gt ought to
stay in the ground, where their value will be precisely zero. If the Paris
Agreement is to be taken seriously, the first parameter used to determine the value of oil's big guns is therefore extremely fragile.

---

123   See, for instance, Nicolas Haeringer, *Zéro fossile: désinvestir du charbon, du gaz et du pétrole
      pour sauver le climat*, Les Petits Matins, 2015.

The second pillar is the price of oil, which has currently fallen to record lows. Is this simply a temporary trough due to the slowdown of economic activity in China? Or is there something else balancing out supply and demand other than the factors which led to the very high prices of 2007 and 2008? A study by Cambridge Econometrics[124] offers one possible explanation: the impact of energy efficiency measures in transport (passenger cars in particular) in Europe and the USA. These have already driven down the world demand for oil and, more importantly, they have sent a long-term message to the markets: oil demand scenarios are unrealistic and will have to be revised downwards. If China were to adopt electric cars, this effect would be still faster and more pronounced. Energy efficiency and the electrification of transport could result in a world spike in the demand for oil between 2020 and 2025. According to this study, never again will the price exceed $100 a barrel; by 2050, it will settle at $83–$87 a barrel, with estimated consumption in 2030 of 86,000 barrels per day, as opposed to 104,000 barrels per day in the IEA's baseline scenario.

Furthermore, there is also the question of how much it would cost to exploit the reserves held by Shell, ExxonMobil and BP. Any analyst worth their salt will tell you that the related costs are far higher than those of national oil companies Saudi Aramco, Iraq National Oil Company (INOC) or Rosneft. Shell and BP may have deep-water and Arctic reserves, but these very expensive sites will never be profitable, and that's before the enormous environmental costs involved are taken into consideration.

The verdict is therefore without question: sovereign funds and institutional investors, together with all those who have made their fortune thanks to handsome share dividends from major oil companies, are today taking a huge risk, known as the 'carbon risk'. The Bank of England was the first central bank to let the cat out of the bag: in October 2014, its governor, Mark Carney, explained that the carbon risk

---

124 Philip Summerton, Hector Pollitt, Sophie Billington, 'Oil Market Futures', Cambridge Econometrics, 2015.

was a reality that investors need to take into account: 'Most fossil fuel reserves can't be burned'.[125] Things are changing within the European Central Bank, too: by December 2014, my colleagues Reinhard Bütik-ofer and Sven Giegold were asking the ECB to provide more detailed analysis of the carbon risk. This was completed by February 2016 when the European Systemic Risk Board, under the auspices of the ECB, published a report confirming this approach and suggesting stress tests to analyse the exposure of the EU's financial sector to the carbon risk. This is all to the good, since it will result in enormous pressure coming on investors to take this aspect into account in their analysis.

Only the Commission appears to be blissfully unaware of the extent of the risk: its September 2015 paper on the implementation of the Capi-tal Markets Union does not mention the issue at all. Fortunately, thanks to the efforts of MEPs and in particular my colleague Bas Eickhout, in June 2016 it became mandatory for pension funds to take into account 'environmental, social, and governance-related risks' when making in-vestments. This worthwhile battle was won during the revision to the Occupational Pensions Directive, designed to improve how these funds are managed and clarify the information supplied to savers.

If investors turn away from carbon-intensive assets, where will they go? Would it be possible, nationally and at the EU level, to establish a favourable legal framework to redirect the billions formerly invested in energy from below to energy from above (wind and solar power), storage, smart grids and electric mobility? Let's take capitalism at face value: in the wake of the crisis provoked by the collapse of Lehman Brothers, the LuxLeaks and Panama Papers revelations, and the suc-cess of the COP21 in Paris, there is clearly an expectation of transpar-ency and the integration of social and economic risks. Indeed, a new tendency is emerging in the financial world: social and ethical bank-ing. This was in evidence at the annual risk management conference held in Luxembourg in May 2016 at the initiative of ALFI.[126]

---

125 'Mark Carney: most fossil fuel reserves can't be burned', *The Guardian*, 13 October 2014.
126 ALFI is the body that represents investment funds based in Luxembourg, one of the world's leading financial centres.

It was with this in mind that I launched the Luxembourg Declaration at the informal Council of Energy Ministers on 23 September 2015, attended by Elon Musk, Betrand Piccard and Jeremy Rifkin among others. This declaration was drafted with the aid of contributions on the part of a great many financial experts from public- and private-sector establishments. It was also an acknowledgement of the fact that Luxembourg is the world's leading market for the funding of renewables and energy efficiency, thanks in particular to it being home to the European Investment Bank, which has a huge green portfolio – larger even than that of the World Bank.

The importance of capital costs

The deployment of renewables is highly dependent on the weighted average cost of capital.[127] Germany may serve as an example for this. It benefits from around 1,600 hours of sunshine per year – far less than Greece, which enjoys 2,500 hours per year. Despite this, photovoltaic panels are to be found all over Germany and hardly anywhere in Greece. The explanation for this is that the related capital cost is much lower in Germany than in Greece, and the difference in the cost of capital is greater than the difference in sunshine. This reasoning applies to all renewables, since almost all the costs reside in the initial investment (Capex) and not in operating costs (Opex) – simply because neither the sun nor the wind ever send any bills.

I first grasped this at a presentation of the Diacore project, funded by the EU's now-defunct Intelligent Energy for Europe programme. This study drew up a map of the cost of capital across the EU, based on the example of wind power. Costs ranged from less than 6 per cent in Germany, France and Benelux, to more than 11 per cent in Greece, Romania, Hungary and Croatia. Here again, a similar principle applies: windfarm projects are located not on the basis of how long the wind blows for, but on the basis of capital costs.

It is therefore hardly surprising that there has been a lot of

---

127   Also known as WACC.

investment in renewables in Germany. Firstly, there is the positive perception of the related country risk in general, and a friendly regulatory framework due to policies promoting renewables. In the Iberian Peninsula, it may be noted that the cost of capital is higher in Spain than in Portugal, despite both countries having undergone a structural adjustment programme, and both countries having similar climates. Today, the capital costs of wind power are over 10 per cent in Spain, but only 8 per cent in Portugal. How can this be explained in the absence of any decisive geographical factors? The fact is that Spain, unlike Portugal, has carried out retroactive changes in its legal framework without consultation. Indeed, the Spanish government destroyed investor confidence in this manner – and is now paying the price in the form of higher interest rates.

To improve this state of affairs, help must be given aimed at bringing down the cost of capital in southern European, Eastern European and south-eastern European countries, by creating a European renewable energy fund where needed because of high country risk. This 'de-risking' strategy would work as follows: the risk premium would be borne by European public-sector funds. This would allow Romanian investors to benefit from the same terms of access to credit as German investors, helping them to install wind turbines in the Danube Delta, which benefits from perfect wind conditions.

Similarly, Jean-Louis Borloo's Africa Plan is an opportunity for the EU to make a major contribution,[128] along the same lines as the Paris–Lima Action Plan: the idea is to put forward a risk reduction fund worth several hundred million euros. Indeed, the future of investment in renewables in Africa will depend mainly on the cost of capital. Ideally, this fund would be combined with structural dialogue between the Commission and African nations to develop policies that promote renewables. Europe could make no greater contribution to Africa than this: a kind of Juncker Plan II directed at investments outside the EU. This would allow Africans to avoid developing coal, while also

---

128   'Borloo propose un "plan Marshall" pour l'Afrique', *Le Figaro*, 26 April 2015.

reducing their dependence on oil and the related price fluctuations. In doing so, it could stop young Africans 'walking towards the light': being drawn to cities, or indeed Europe, due to a lack of any development prospects at home in the absence of electricity. When it comes to electricity, Africa could achieve the same leapfrogging as it did with telephony. There is no need to wait for a physical network covering the entire territory as autonomous mini-networks would suffice. For wind power, the specific challenge in Africa is the lack of road infrastructure allowing equipment to be transported to appropriate sites, and the absence of cranes to erect the turbines. Solutions are being looked at, however, and projects are starting to be developed in South Africa, Ethiopia, Kenya and elsewhere. The idea of an international de-risking fund for green investment in Africa was taken up by the Commission when it proposed an EU External Investment Plan in September 2016. This legislation is now being examined by the European Parliament and the Council.

A financial framework for energy efficiency

There is also a need for a financial framework conducive to massive investment in energy efficiency in buildings, SMEs and the manufacturing sector. Here, not only is the cost of capital a factor, but the field is also a highly technical one, replete with small-scale projects. In Luxembourg, conventional wisdom has it that 'the EIB doesn't so much as lift a finger for any project worth less than €100 million'. The challenge facing energy efficiency is therefore that of bringing together small projects in order to achieve the critical mass required for banks to take an interest. This calls for better Technical Assistance when putting together financial projects and instruments. The Commission has long understood this. As part of the Intelligent Energy for Europe programme in partnership with the EIB's ELENA fund, it launched Technical Assistance, which bore fruit thanks to the support it provided for local authorities.

Today, the problem is one of expanding Technical Assistance and making it systematic in banks and on the ground in cities, regions and countries, in order to marshal projects together. The EFSI plan is the perfect vehicle for this, and the Greens have fought to acquire €50 billion worth of funding for energy efficiency within the EFSI, which would also include Technical Assistance. Structural funds, which must devote 4 per cent of their funding to Technical Assistance, are also a vital source of leverage. However, this money is actually allocated at the discretion of national authorities. Some play the game, seeking EIB expertise in order to put together efficient financial instruments, while others choose to direct the funds on the basis of different priorities.

The necessary greening of financial centres

The EU's financial centres must become a source of funding for energy transition, with investment being redirected towards green technology. Luxembourg has long been the butt of harsh criticism because of its banking secrecy, but it has made considerable efforts to attract green investment funds, to the point that it is now the world number one address for this type of investment fund, including names such as Akuo Energy and Novenergia. Historically, the Luxembourg stock market has issued more government bonds than any other in Europe.

In 2007, the world's first ever green bond was issued by the Luxembourg Stock Exchange (LuxSE). Just eight years later, 2015 saw the one hundredth such issue – LuxSE holds the world record in this category. Amid the competition between the financial centres of London, Frankfurt, Paris and Dublin, Luxembourg ranks first for microfinance. It is home to two thirds of the world's funds of this type, thanks to a deliberate policy engaged in ever since the early 2000s. This begs the question of how one can be sure that these bonds really are green, and not simply an attempt at 'greenwashing'. To address this, the LuxFLAG initiative ranks investment funds on the basis of sustainability criteria. To provide greater clarity, the government recently excluded nuclear power, coal, first-generation biofuels and large hydroelectric dams from its definition of 'green' funds, on the initiative of environment minister Carole Dieschbourg.

We should be under no illusions: in the absence of sanctions on investments in fossil fuels, only an oil crisis could possibly redirect funds towards renewables and away from oil. As one senior oil official told me, 'renewables earn 5–8 per cent per year. That's not bad but as long as oil brings in over 25 per cent, that's where we'll be putting our money.' That pretty much sums up how people think in that world. As things stand, investors can happily destroy the climate, simply by looking only at short-term financial yields. The solution is for renewables and energy efficiency to become the most profitable investments possible – and this could now well happen. The latest research shows that the mid- to long-term profitability of green investment portfolios is beginning to catch up and in some cases even surpass that of more traditional portfolios.

More ethics in trade relations

Making Europe's financial centres greener is all well and good, but more needs to be done. International finance must also follow suit, by bringing massive tax evasion to a halt, and changing the rules of international trade that today help to make a small minority richer to the detriment of the vast majority. To achieve this, trade agreements must incorporate demanding environmental requirements, as well as aspects pertaining to fiscal and social justice. The planned free-trade agreements between Europe and Canada (CETA) and between Europe and the US (TTIP) are unfit for purpose; they include a high environmental risk, and also threaten to import the bad habits of North America into Europe. That is why I am opposed to them. Take the example of arbitration courts, which allow private-sector firms that feel they have been unjustly treated under a domestic law to engage proceedings against a state before an obscure arbitration court rather than a civil tribunal. When Barack Obama abandoned the Keystone XL oil pipeline, pro-shale gas investors thus took their case before the arbitration court. In Quebec, US firms who felt unjustly treated by the moratorium on exploiting shale gas took the matter to court. Supposing a European nation decided to abandon nuclear power: could the American and Canadian firms that supplied the reactors contest this decision before an arbitration court? And to cap it all, negotiation documents leaked in July 2016 reveal that Europe would be willing to sacrifice its eco-design standards on the altar of free trade, in exchange for the vaguest of self-regulatory procedures for the industrial sectors in question.

This type of dogmatic trade agreement also prohibits any form of local content requirement, i.e. requiring technological components to be built on site as part of an international agreement. For instance, India implemented a requirement for the promoters of photovoltaic projects to include local suppliers, with a view to safeguarding local jobs. The US disputed India's policy in the WTO and won their case in March 2016. This is where unbridled liberalism could take us.

My proposals:

- Restricting access to the Juncker Plan (EFSI) to countries that comply with EU regulations on renewable energy and energy efficiency.
- Establishing a fund dedicated to renewable energy in order to reduce the various risks relating to renewable projects (which result in highly diverse costs of access to capital even within the EU), coupled with an external aspect to encourage the EU–Africa energy partnership.
- Implementing a fully fledged Technical Assistance cluster of excellence together with Project Development Assistance in the field of energy efficiency, bringing together the EIB, national promotional banks and experts funded by structural funds. This would allow small, dispersed projects to be aggregated into standardised portfolios, thereby making them attractive to investors.
- Encouraging institutional investors to be transparent and publish their exposure to the carbon risk, in order to strengthen the links between climate policy and the Capital Markets Union.

CHAPTER 21

STRUCTURING THE OIL, GAS, COAL, ELECTRICITY AND CARBON MARKETS

Over the past few decades, state domination of the world of energy has gradually given way to domination by the markets; in other words, an environment in which prices are determined by the intersection of supply and demand. The oil, coal and gas markets are largely globalised, even if states continue to play a major role in them. By contrast, the electricity market naturally tends to be more regional, or even local. Another market has recently seen the light of day: the carbon market, too – and its first steps have upset its predecessors. This latest newcomer is the controversial capacity market.

Oil, coal and gas are well-established goods

As an energy vector, oil is easy to store and transport, since its market is global, and therefore relatively flexible. Further upstream, in the fields of exploration and exploitation, some countries do jealously guard their reserves for the sole use of state-controlled companies. But in Europe, the only non-market intervention when it comes to oil relates to how it is managed in the event of a supply crisis: the EU has established stock-piling obligations equivalent to ninety days' worth of consumption. In any case, the combination of the massive arrival of non-conventional oil on the one hand, and progress in energy efficiency and renewable energy on the other, has made this market more liquid still. The upshot of this is that there may be a limit on how high oil prices could rise in the future; they could even fall if demand stabilises.

OIL PRICE VOLATILITY

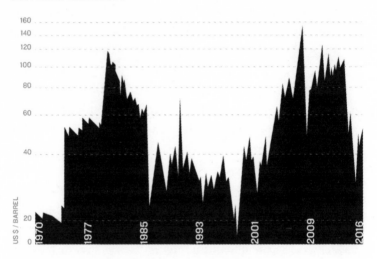

Source: macrotrends.net © REVOLVE MEDIA

Coal, too, is traded on a globalised market. Under the combined effect of the economic slowdown in China and its replacement by shale gas in the United States, the price of coal has fallen considerably of late. As a result, coal mines in Germany, Poland, Spain and Romania are being run at a loss. They have to be kept open on an entirely artificial basis with the aid of billions of euros' worth of subsidies. This makes no sense in economic terms: the coal mined in Europe will never be more competitive than imported coal. Coal also needs to be distinguished from lignite. The recent collapse of the carbon market in Europe means that lignite has become more attractive, and lignite-fired power stations in Germany and Poland have been working flat out in recent years. Since lignite is very cheap to mine, market measures are ineffective, and a whole arsenal of regulatory and legal measures are required to bring an end to its use. Keeping a European lignite and coal industry alive in Europe is also an environmental aberration. The fact is that there is no future for either coal or lignite in a world that takes climate change seriously. The European Commission needs to recognise this, by repealing the regulatory provisions that favour domestic resources and preparing the way for there to be a gradual, ordered abandonment of coal. In exchange, structural funds, in particular the European Social Fund, could be used to make the accompanying social transition as painless as possible.[129]

Hitherto, gas markets have been regional, but they too are becoming more global, particularly due to the increased possibilities for transporting liquefied natural gas (LNG) by means of huge carrier vessels. In addition to Qatar and Algeria, new countries such as Australia, Nigeria and indeed the USA are beginning to enter the LNG export market. In addition, Europe is crisscrossed by gas pipelines linking the continent to Russia, Norway and Algeria, its traditional suppliers. When it comes to gas, Europe has of course suffered from the hardening regime of Vladimir Putin and the constant squabbling about the transportation of Russian gas through Ukraine. However, we need to be sure to fight the right battles: Europe has already improved its crisis management measures considerably, building bidirectional gas pipelines and optimising the use of infrastructure already in place. The real priority is therefore to reduce political support for gas, in line with the Paris Climate Agreement. The use of gas is doomed to decrease in Europe. It is mainly used for heating, and this will decrease as energy efficiency efforts are redoubled. Its second-largest use, in industrial processes, is also set to level off or decrease as a result of gains in energy productivity. The third-largest use of gas is to generate electricity; and while Europe may install new gas turbines to generate electricity in order to add flexibility to the system, these should not be in operation for more than a small amount of running hours a year, so overall amounts of gas used are unlikely to increase. Furthermore, I do not believe that these drastic reductions will be

---

129 See Chapter 24, pp. 317–318.

fully offset by the development of liquefied natural gas transportation, in particular by sea. It is time to wake up to these trends instead of continuing to rely on unrealistic scenarios such as those adopted by the European Commission, but skewered by the European Court of Auditors in a damning report in 2015:[130] 'The Commission has persistently overestimated gas demand during the [2000–2014] period, and needs to restore the credibility of the forecasts it uses.'

Electricity: a market in urgent need of repair

Since 1990s, the electricity sector has also evolved in line with the rules of the market. Some changes have been inspired by neoliberal ideology, one notorious example being when the Thatcher government abruptly privatised the electricity industry in the UK in order to break the power of the coal industry's trade unions. In Germany, a number of private companies have gradually merged to become giants such as E.ON and RWE. In Scandinavian countries, Norway was the first to introduce competition into the sector, even if the dominant company, Statkraft, is still state-owned, as is the Swedish firm Vattenfall. Across Europe as a whole, the 1996 directive deregulated the wholesale market and introduced competition for electricity production. This deregulation was rectified in subsequent directives in 2003 and 2009. In this respect, the 2003 directive enshrined the principle of non-discriminatory access to the transport and distribution network, supervised by independent national regulators. The third Internal Energy Market legislation package, from 2009, added to this new EU regulation the separation of the assets of vertically integrated companies and the establishment of an embryonic EU regulator, ACER.

However, in the wake of this consolidation of the electricity system through the mergers and acquisitions of the 1980s, 1990s and early 2000s came another revolution: that of miniaturisation and decentralisation as a result of renewables. It is important to take due note of this shift and to adjust our regulatory framework by restructuring the

---

130   'Improving the Security of Energy Supply by Developing the Internal Energy Market: More Efforts Needed', European Court of Auditors, December 2015, www.eca.europa.eu.

electricity market, with a particular emphasis on flexibility. This could be achieved by means of a dynamic, intra-day market in which storage would play a large part, and in which demand-side management could be achieved by aggregating consumption. The aim is twofold: bringing an end to overcapacity, which pulls down wholesale prices to levels that are much too low, affecting the viability of necessary investments; and enlisting the electricity sector in the fight against climate change by encouraging renewables. To achieve this end, the electricity market must, in particular, bring an end to distortions in competition, especially those in the form of direct and indirect subsidies to nuclear power and fossil fuels, which benefit from far more public-sector aid than renewable energy does.

The powerlessness of the carbon market when it comes to coal

Why are dirty, coal-fired power stations continuing to operate in the face of an apparent political consensus that they should be shut down? Despite dizzying costs in terms of the climate and health, they benefit from preferential treatment, and somehow seem to be exempt from the 'polluter pays' principle enshrined in EU treaties. The problem is that the collapse of the European carbon market makes it artificially cheap to emit CO_2, at around five euros a tonne. I believe that the reforms of the ETS put forward by the European Commission for 2020–2030 are not enough to restore the fortunes of what could have been a flagship of EU climate policy, but which has been progressively weakened to become little more than a lifeboat. Since every attempt at reform gets caught in the crossfire of German industry and Polish electricity firms, there is little hope of seeing this market emerge from the legislative process any stronger than it was before. In view of this, alongside the ETS, the EU should introduce other schemes designed to ensure a carbon floor price. California does something like this, viewing its carbon market as a safety net, but also deploying tax and regulatory measures.

The first of such measures would be to establish a maximum authorised level of greenhouse gas emissions: an Emission Performance

Standard (EPS). The EPS level should be set in such a way as to rule out the construction of any further coal-fired capacity. For existing power stations, above a certain threshold, power plants would not be allowed to operate, and should either withdraw from the market or carry out the investment required to be compliant with the law. This level would not necessarily have to be the same for the whole of the EU, but could initially be determined on the basis of the energy mix of each member state, and then gradually converge. France, Germany, the Netherlands and several other countries are already examining strategies to enable them to get out of coal. It would be a shame not to look at the strategies together, given their impact on the EU as a whole. If Germany were to get out of coal, what would happen to the resulting surplus ETS allowances? Any new overallocation now would almost certainly be a fatal blow to the ETS as a whole; to ensure things do not come to that, national strategies for abandoning coal should be linked to the cancellation of the corresponding ETS allowances.

In addition to EPS, a carbon floor price must be introduced; initially, this could be done within the Pentalateral Forum. This would also have the benefit of gradually excluding coal from the electricity mix. France very nearly became a pioneer in this respect when French environment minister Ségolène Royal and President Hollande originally committed to such a scheme. Royal instructed a triumvirate consisting of Gérard Mestrallet, Pascal Canfin and Alain Grandjean to come up with a set of proposals for various ways of leaving coal behind. They handed over their final report in July 2016: 'We are therefore in favour of the proposal to establish a price corridor for the European carbon market, with a floor price of €20–€30 in 2020, an annual increase of 10 per cent, and a ceiling price of €50.'[131] Despite this report, the first measures to actually be taken in France have not amounted to much, and the abandonment of coal has been postponed. In the end, it has been much ado about virtually nothing. I believe that a regional strategy involving France, Germany and Benelux is required to address this issue.

---

131   Pascal Canfin, Alain Grandjean, Gérard Mestrallet, 'Propositions pour des prix du carbone alignés avec l'accord de Paris', July 2016, www.engie.com.

Not only should we of course be abandoning coal within the EU, we also need to avoid creating a favourable environment for coal in neighbouring countries at all costs. The greatest risk today is of succumbing to the temptation to import coal-fired electricity from countries bordering the EU, particularly the western Balkans, where the authorities have announced more than 6GW of new coal-fired power plants. The Balkans' pro-coal policy has a sky-high health cost in terms of premature deaths, pulmonary and respiratory diseases and heart failure, evaluated at €8.5 billion in financial terms, and the region is already home to seven of Europe's ten most polluting power stations.[132] To take just one example, the coal-fired power plant in Ugljevik, Bosnia-Herzegovina alone is responsible for 154,385 tonnes of sulphur dioxide emissions per year – eight times over the EU thresholds for this type of installation. The situation in Ukraine is also a matter of concern: the country's leading electricity company, DTEK, is also geared mainly to coal, which it mines locally. At the 'coal dialogue' held in Brussels in June 2016, its deputy commercial director John Woodham announced that DTEK had succeeded in obtaining a guaranteed tariff of €32–€35/MWh from the Ukrainian authorities – higher than the prices observed on the European market. Since Ukraine has good interconnections with the EU electricity market, it is more than likely that part of the Ukraine electricity generated in new coal-fired power stations will sooner or later end up in the EU, thanks to state subsidies – and therefore, indirectly, thanks to EU money, in view of how much Europe contributes to the budget of Ukraine. The EU market is open to neighbouring countries which, despite massive aid, continue to include high-carbon content fuels in their electricity mix, in the face of climate commitments to the contrary as a result of the COP21 Agreement. Whether it's in the Balkans, Ukraine or anywhere else, this cannot be allowed to go on. The only way this exploitation of the system can be brought to an end

---

132   Mike Holland, 'Health Impacts of Coal Fired Power Stations in the Western Balkans', EMRC, HEAL, March 2016, www.env-health.org.

is to introduce border adjustment mechanisms in order to penalise third-country electricity imports generated using coal or lignite.

Nuclear: an unavoidable part of the market, but stripped of its privileges

In addition to the enormous subsidies provided by the UK government for the Hinkley Point C project, there are those being envisaged by Hungary for the Paks power station, in partnership with Vladimir Putin. A letter from the Competition Commissioner Margrethe Vestager on 6 July 2016 devoted to the Paks power plant highlights the nuclear-centric nature of the system: 'If member states choose to invest in nuclear energy, the Euratom's objective to facilitate that investment becomes an objective of common interest that the Commission should take into account in its state aid assessment … the Commission cannot question why other technologies were not chosen.' This is rather hypocritical. Even if the adoption of nuclear power is a national decision, it is the duty of the Commission to ensure that the essential rules of the internal market, including the 'polluter pays' principle, apply to all technologies.

The other scourge in this respect, indeed the main one, is the enormous gifts made to existing nuclear power, even though it now represents a systemic barrier to energy transition as well as a safety risk. Are Europe's existing nuclear power plants competitive? At first sight, one might think that they are; but in actual fact, a large number of external costs have still not been incorporated into the price of nuclear electricity, such as a common liability regime in the event of an accident. In Japan, taxpayers are bearing the financial consequences of the disaster. This is a classic example of what is referred to as privatising profits and socialising losses. The Commission lost little time in burying the promise made by Commissioner Oettinger in the wake of Fukushima to implement a harmonised insurance regime for nuclear operators. Why does Juncker, now at the head of the Commission, continue to consent to a state of affairs in which, in the event of an accident involving the French nuclear power plant at Cattenom on the border with Luxembourg, EDF would not have to bear the related costs?

A second problem relates to decommissioning funds. One of the conditions for granting operating licences for wind farms is a guarantee that the related installations will be fully dismantled once the permit has expired. How do things stand when it comes to nuclear reactors? To date, nothing requires operators to set aside the sums required to fund the decommissioning of their installations or the management of radioactive waste. The European Parliament almost obtained a guarantee of this nature during negotiations on the internal market package in 2003. The Commission had promised, in writing, to address the issue, but nothing has been forthcoming so far, over ten years later. Meanwhile, Germany and Sweden have demonstrated that it is possible to make this responsibility incumbent on operators. The Swedish position on the 'economic' closure of nuclear reactors is well worth examining in this respect. By establishing a regime in which operators must pay a certain amount into a national decommissioning fund, Sweden has made nuclear power plants less profitable, and driven some to close. This exposes nuclear power to market risks and takes the wind out of the sails of electricity companies, always the first to complain about subsidies granted to renewable energy. In the absence of this type of solution, competition on the European electricity market is completely skewed, and it is taxpayers that will be picking up the bill. The credibility of the internal market when it comes to providing 'free and fair competition' is in danger of being left in tatters. If the EU continues along this path, the prospect of tearing up the Euratom Treaty will become increasingly likely. And indeed, Brexit offers a golden opportunity to get rid of this harmful, obsolete agreement.

Towards a new electricity market design

The more renewable energy there is on the electricity market, the more flexibility is needed. Responsive power plants that can adjust to the variations inherent in the supply of renewable energy such as solar and wind power are required. There are four main sources of the flexibility required for the system to be both balanced and secure: inter-connections, demand response, storage and the responsiveness of means of production (e.g. gas-fired power stations that can ramp up and down very quickly). Vertically integrated companies are fiercely opposed to all of these. In France, EDF is seeking to turn France into a bulwark of resistance to system flexibility. At present, France is still a net exporter of electricity to all its neighbours (with the exception of Germany). However, this annual result conceals major seasonal disparities: France has to import significant amounts of electricity during harsh winters, due to its decision to make its heating largely dependent on electricity.

Why, then, is it resisting interconnection with the Iberian Peninsula? I believe that this is first and foremost a preventive measure. For four consecutive days in May 2016, Portugal's electricity mix was 100 per cent renewable and Spain had totally installed renewable capacity that virtually matched its peak domestic demand. Their exports could come into competition with the French nuclear fleet. That is why France has dragged its feet over the issue of interconnection with the Iberian Peninsula, the first new power line to have been built since 1982, inaugurated in 2015 between the two countries.

In this respect, Spain protests rather too much. It is, in fact, quite content with a situation which enables its oligopolies to rake in comfortable margins thanks to their conventional fleet, since the Iberian electricity market has higher prices than the rest of Europe – precisely because of the lack of interconnection. There is no incentive whatsoever for EDF in France, or Iberdrola, Endesa or Gas Natural Fenosa in Spain, to develop interconnections too quickly. That is explanation enough. The real loser in this understanding between France and Spain is Portugal, which is thus condemned to isolation. To escape it, and export their surplus, the Portuguese are therefore looking towards the north African market; a feasibility study for a connection between Portugal and Morocco was launched in 2015.

I very much enjoy walking in the Pyrenees, and fully understand objections to any construction of high-voltage lines that would mar this beautiful landscape. I therefore believe that Europe should help the countries in question to fund the additional costs entailed by a seaward route, such as the project via the Bay of Biscay.

Inflexibility: the Achilles heel of nuclear power

France's nuclear-centric system has an inherent weakness: inflexibility. Nuclear reactors cannot be subjected to rapid, frequent, successive variations in output. While some reactors can operate in load-following mode, the degree of flexibility in the French system remains limited. This means that the French grid requires significant flexible capacity in the form of hydroelectric power, in order to offset this rigidity. Furthermore, little research has been done into the effects of the practice of load following on safety; indeed, the US nuclear regulator has banned it.

Since French hydroelectric power is not enough to balance the system, hydroelectric power plants in neighbouring countries, particularly Switzerland, are also enlisted. One regular practice was for EDF to book capacity long-term on cross-border interconnections. However, the European Court of Justice found against this anti-competitive practice in a ruling handed down on 7 June 2005,[133] on the grounds that the EU internal electricity market directives 'preclude national measures that grant an undertaking preferential capacity for the cross-border transmission of electricity, whether those measures derive from the system operator, the controller of system management or the legislature'. France therefore had to adjust these procedures, which its Energy Regulation Committee (Commission de régulation de l'énergie, CRE) duly did, in a decision[134] dated 1 December 2005. The problem is that the provisions of EU law do not apply between France and Switzerland, which is not an EU member state. EDF can therefore continue its hegemonic practices with impunity, delighted

---

133   Ruling dated 7 June 2005 – Case C-17/03, curia.europa.eu.
134   CRE decision dated 1 December 2005 on the implementation of work programmes known as 'roadmaps' concerning the procedures for allocating interconnection in 2006 and taking into account ruling C-17/03 of 7 June 2005, www.cre.fr

with the fact that the planned electricity cooperation agreement between the EU and Switzerland has bogged down.

French nuclear power is also at the origin of the notorious 'loop flows', as they are known, in Europe. Received wisdom is that renewables are to blame for these loop flows, particularly wind power capacity in northern Germany, as reported in a study by the European Commission.[135] In actual fact, things are much less clear than that: in its 2015 report on the European electricity market, ACER stated that 'many flows may be observed to run in a loop between France, Germany, Switzerland and back to France'. There is undoubtedly a link with renewable energy produced in northern Germany:[136] ACER issued a detailed opinion on the subject in 2015. However, it should be noted that nuclear power is responsible for such loops too, to the detriment of neighbouring countries.

At the end of the day, it is nuclear power itself that is being called into question by energy transition. According to Dimitri Pescia, a researcher working for German think-tank Agora Energiewende, in any event, 'the nuclear fleet will nevertheless need to be downsized and its operation re-optimized'. Even if it were to become technically possible for a nuclear power plant to achieve load-following on an hourly basis, this could not possibly be worthwhile economically: 'nuclear … power plants have high capital costs so these technologies have an economic incentive to run as much as they can'. Pescia predicts that 'in 2030 you have no more baseload in Germany', or even in Europe, thanks to the expansion of renewables.

How can French nuclear power cope with the existence of fifty-eight inflexible reactors in a highly variable system championing flexibility? Amid stable or even declining energy demand,

> there is no more business model to build a new nuclear plant knowing it is likely to run less than 5 to 6,000 hours per year. Operators like

---

135   'Loop Flows: Final Advice', Thema Consulting Group, October 2013, ec.europa.eu.
136   They run through Poland and the Czech Republic to supply the south of Germany, due to a lack of north-south national grid capacity in Germany.

EDF will invest to prolong the operation of their fleet in Europe. Then, I believe they would have no choice than to gradually phase it out and replace it with renewables. They don't want to do it too quickly; the quicker this goes, the more money they will lose.

Demand-side management

Demand-side management is a highly effective means of balancing the electricity system, by adjusting the variable of demand rather than that of supply. Demand-side management may be implicit or explicit, depending on whether demand is brought down automatically at the level of the consumer, by means of a specific type of subscription, or whether consumers themselves activate demand reduction to earn revenues. Of course, this practice relates primarily to major industrial and commercial consumers, but could also be relevant to the residential sector if aggregators were to enable small clients to come together in larger portfolios. The potential is huge, but the business model for aggregators is hampered by anti-competitive practices on the part of the suppliers of energy to the clients in question.

When you order dinner in an Italian restaurant, should you pay the neighbouring Indian restaurant for their corresponding loss of earnings? When you use a bike share scheme, should you pay a premium to Renault for offsetting the non-sale of a car? While clearly ridiculous, this is what is happening in several European nations, including France, on the electricity market: when an aggregator eliminates demand on the part of a portfolio of consumers, it has to pay compensation to the supplier – which all too often, is still EDF – for the unsold electricity. This is absurd, for at least two reasons: firstly, the supplier is not adversely affected in any way, and may even benefit, since the demand-side management implemented in this way brings down wholesale prices and thereby allows it access to cheaper electricity; secondly, by killing aggregator profitability, this system prevents broader extension of the demand-side management market. This is because diffuse demand-side management requires investment. Customers' electricity meters need to be fitted with units allowing their consumption to be halted or reduced remotely – in most cases, without them even noticing – in order to provide the system with the necessary flexibility in the event of high demand or a sudden increase in prices. The EU must move forward on this issue, by prohibiting the principle of compensation, as the US regulator has, in a decision which was upheld[137] in January 2016 by the United States Supreme Court, throwing out an appeal by electricity producers. The reasoning of the US regulator was that the gains generated by demand-side management are greater than any losses incurred by the suppliers.

Over and above compensation, the whole market structure needs to be overhauled in order to grant more space to demand-side management. When TSOs seek to engage services for a whole series of markets pertaining to system-balancing, demand-side management operators are often excluded, either explicitly or implicitly, by the products in question being defined in such a way as to be incompatible with the latter's characteristics. For instance, why force operators to guarantee service for a whole hour, during a one-week period, if the flexibility service is only required for a period of fifteen minutes? The review of the EU's Internal Market in Electricity Directive must clarify the situation and ensure that the true worth of the immense potential of demand-side management is allowed to emerge. This is a vital contribution to achieving an electricity market that is flexible, responsive and dynamic, together with other components such as batteries, hydro storage and interconnections. These solutions must be preferred to 'must runs' – power stations with inflexible production.

Capacity markets – a new source of distortion?

The European electricity market rests on the principle of 'energy only'; in other words, producers are paid for electricity sold on the basis of a price per megawatt-hour. However, a parallel market has emerged in recent years, remunerating production capacity simply for existing, even when it is not producing any electricity. This involves the now

---

137   Supreme Court of the United States, 'Federal energy regulatory commission v. Electric power supply association *et al.*' 25 January 2016, www.supremecourt.gov.

notorious capacity mechanisms. From 2013 onwards, electricity firms clamoured for these capacity mechanisms in the wake of the erosion of their profit margins. According to the Magritte Group, 'Capacity Remuneration Mechanisms (CRM) do not constitute subsidies but form part of a new market model, paying for a service that consists in providing qualified availability for the purpose of ensuring security of supply'. In other words, they are simply singing the same old song: there will be blackouts or brownouts if they are not granted subsidies. Simply put, it is blackmail on the part of major energy firms. Of course, Eurelectric and the Magritte Group hide behind the pretext that capacity mechanisms not only benefit conventional power stations, but are open without distinction to all types of production, as well as to demand-side management and demand response operators. This is a green figleaf, as it were: nothing more than a device designed to conceal the strategy of the operators of coal, lignite, gas-fired and nuclear power stations aiming to provide themselves with new sources of revenue other than the electricity market itself. This strategy involves artificially extending the lifespan of their creaking power plants, despite these being light-years away from the responsiveness and flexibility required in today's world of energy.

I believe that the best way forward would be to produce a detailed analysis of the next ten to fifteen years, with common criteria for the EU as a whole, concerning credible production needs and the expected demand at the macro-regional level, not simply national levels. This would provide an answer to the question as to whether there are problems of supply or overcapacity. This analysis should be transparent and open to all forms of discussion by experts, as well as stakeholders in electricity's new world. The real issue is that of having an appropriate system, rather than appropriate means of production. Such a system must include storage, demand management and interconnections, as well as appropriate production resources. The problem must be looked at holistically, and not simply from the perspective of production facilities. There is little doubt that an objective analysis of the adequacy of the system across macro-regions would bring to light the huge overcapacity of existing production resources.

ENTSO-E is currently carrying out research into the adequacy of production, but is coming under criticism with respect to its demand-forecasting scenarios, which have been systematically overestimated in recent years. If Europe's TSOs were to invite energy efficiency experts to join in the work, they would be less likely to get it wrong. At the end of the day, the aim of any analysis should be that of allowing the cheapest and least market-intrusive decision to be taken. In Denmark, research by Energinet shows that opting for a limited strategic reserve is ten times cheaper than establishing a fully fledged capacity market.[138] In Germany, Secretary of State for Energy Rainer Baake has negotiated an agreement with neighbouring countries in which shortages are resolved by the market, by means of price signals. In the event of a shortage in one country, the price goes up, algorithms respond and electricity converges to this country, using cross-border interconnections to their full capacity. At the same time, there are small national reserves in each country against the event of an extreme shortage. This is a promising system that can solve the problem of adjusting supply and demand, quickly and cheaply. It offers a way out of a system full of overcapacity, by having existing power stations aid energy transition towards a system based on renewables and energy efficiency.

However, in its report on capacity markets, the European Commission recommends a capacity payment model based on the UK example, which favours existing, legacy power stations and new fossil fuel capacity. Poland will have no scruples about exploiting these conclusions to find a solution to its pressing problem, which is that of building new coal-fired power stations even when electricity prices are low and banks are increasingly reluctant to commit to fossil fuel projects. Since direct subsidies for coal are prohibited by the guidelines on state aid (indeed, the European Commission has defended

---

138   'Market Model 2.0', Energinet, 2016, www.energinet.dk.

this position in the G20), Poland now has a ready-made solution: it can simply copy the UK market, which has already been greenlit by DG Comp, to pay for its coal. With the ink on the Paris Agreement hardly dry, this is at best nonsense and, at worst, a provocation. It is up to Competition Commissioner Margrethe Vestager to bring order into this chaos.

The approach put forward by the European Parliament in its resolution of 13 September 2016 is more reserved: capacity mechanisms are permissible only for specific cases, and limited in time. Firstly, prior regional analysis must be carried out. The risks of an electricity shortage must be properly proven, by means of a transparent process, and not simply alleged by the stakeholders in question. Secondly, the absence of a less expensive and less market-intrusive alternative, such as strategic reserves maintained by network operators, must be evidenced. This gradual approach has been approved by a significant cross-party majority in the Parliament. Despite this, DG Comp has dug its heels in; the final report of the sectoral inquiry into capacity markets published in November 2016 delights in favouring complex, costly models, such as the French and UK markets.

What will be the system in the EU in the future? On the plus side, the Commission has proposed that there should be legislation on capacity mechanisms, and that these should be based on system adequacy assessed at the regional level. This is a good starting point, although the devil is in the detail: very close attention will need to be paid to the methods used to calculate regional system adequacy.

My proposals:
- Internalising the external costs of fossil fuels (greenhouse gas emissions, costs to public health) and of nuclear energy (decommissioning, waste management and insurance in the event of accidents) in order to put an end to their privileges.
- Abolishing subsidies for fossil fuels, which are currently guaranteed in particular by member states having the option of requiring at least 15 per cent of electricity producers' fuel to be domestic (in

general, this is coal); barring the way to new subsidies being allocated under the guise of capacity markets.

- Organising the progressive abandonment of fossil fuels on a regional basis, establishing emission performance standards and a carbon floor price.
- Developing a dynamic, liquid, intra-day electricity market, with bids as close as possible to real time and time slots that are as short as possible.
- Transitioning towards electricity prices being formed dynamically in such a way as to reflect the cost of scarcity; improving the transparency of electricity bills for all types of consumer.
- Promoting demand-side management by allowing operators to penetrate all the necessary markets (e.g. balancing services and ancillary services) and abolishing the obligation to compensate suppliers.
- Putting an end to the vertical integration of energy suppliers who also own distribution networks, on the same basis as the separation of assets implemented for electricity transport system operators, with de minimis clauses to protect cities and local authorities engaged in both the production and the distribution of electricity.

CHAPTER 22

THE GREAT UNKNOWN: WILL ELECTRICITY COMPANIES BE ABLE TO BOUNCE BACK?

There are two things at which electricity oligopolies excel: putting together projects that are large-scale and complex both financially and in engineering terms; and monopolising (or even perhaps skewing) technical and economic information regarding energy issues so as to influence policymakers, the media and society as a whole. These two factors explain the dominance of national monopolies, or in some cases cross-border oligopolies, in the world of energy, whether state-owned (such as EDF, Vattenfall and CEZ) or private (e.g. E.ON, RWE and Enel).

However, the sector is changing. The structural dominance of electricity firms has begun to ebb away due to a combination of three factors: the obligation to separate the management, and sometimes even the ownership, of electricity transmission networks and electricity production; the advent of decentralised technologies such as onshore wind power, photovoltaic solar power and biogas, which have democratised electricity production; and the fact that electricity companies no longer have a monopoly on information, coupled with the fact that some industry leaders have lost credibility in the eyes of the authorities, journalists and public opinion.

The twilight of the old world

What sort of future might the electricity companies envisage? Deregulation of electricity markets in the mid-1990s established competition, but the electricity firms responded by expanding, seeking to acquire elsewhere market share that they were in danger of losing on their domestic markets. The resulting wave of mergers and acquisitions was mostly funded by nuclear piggybanks, and resulted in the creation of cross-border oligopolies. At the same time, energy transition began to speed up. Amid stable demand for electricity, the dispatch of 20 per cent more renewable energy into the electricity system between 2005 and 2015 disrupted the status quo and shrank traditional stakeholders' margins, even as the number of competitors increased dramatically. Today, the oligopolies have their backs to the wall, having mistakenly banked on the assumption that renewables would remain marginal in Europe in the medium term. The economic fundamentals of the electricity sector have changed far beyond anybody's expectations. Times are changing, and business models need to change too.

There could be no better embodiment of this decline than the former boss of RWE, Jürgen Grossmann. Having become a billionaire in the 1980s and 1990s after buying the former steelworks in Georgsmarienhütte for a token Deutschmark, he became a shareholder in the German energy firm RWE, and then, in 2006, its CEO. At that time, he was so influential that he managed to put an end to an internal war within the German bosses' union BDI, between the electricity-intensive industrial firms working in steelmaking, chemicals and aluminium, and the energy oligopolies (RWE, E.ON, Vattenfall and ENBW), in which the former were accusing the latter of subjecting them to prices that were too high.

In Brussels, Grossmann exerted his influence to the full during the negotiations on the 2008 Climate and Energy Package. Whereas the European Parliament, the Commission and some governments were seeking to allocate CO_2 allowances by means of auctions, he conducted a ferocious lobbying campaign promoting the extension of the CO_2 allowances awarded free of charge as part of phase III of the ETS.

Indeed, this was the only way of him recouping the recent investments in his production fleet, largely based on coal (and partly decided by his predecessor, Harry Roels). CO_2 allowances obtained free of charge could be resold on the market at their market value, which in 2007–2008 was around €20. This clearly constituted a state subsidy to polluting industries: Grossmann and his cronies were laughing all the way to the bank as they polluted the planet. However, the policy-makers were no longer willing to provide electricity companies with hundreds of millions of euros' worth of profits in the form of free allowances. In December 2008, the law therefore put an end to this huge privilege, despite Grossmann playing every card he had, calling Angela Merkel right before her final press conference at the European Council in an attempt to wrest a more favourable compromise.

Chancellor Angela Merkel and RWE's boss, Jürgen Grossmann, clink their glass together to the future of German nuclear © PICTURE-ALLIANCE / DPA / THISSEN

In March 2011, the Fukushima disaster spelt the end of yet another dream for him: in the build-up to the German elections in 2010, the boss of RWE had managed to convince the future winners (Merkel's CDU party and Philipp Rösler's Liberals) to renege on the historic. 2002 Schröder–Fischer–Trittin agreement committing Germany to abandon nuclear power. In autumn 2010, the new Merkel–Rösler government made good on this pledge and decided to extend the lifespan of the power plants in question. This created a huge storm in the media, because it would have generated billions of euros' worth of additional profits for the electricity companies. The general public found this even harder to swallow as the result of a photo that went the rounds on social media: in the weeks following this disputed decision, Merkel and Grossmann inaugurated a coal-fired power station, where they could be seen toasting each other with Schnapps.

Seeing the diminutive Chancellor next to the giant of a man was an eloquent depiction of the balance of power. However, there was to be a complete U-turn just a few months later. In the wake of Fukushima, Merkel no longer had any option: pragmatic as ever, she sacrificed nuclear power in order to hang onto political power. The death knell for German nuclear power marked a defeat for the electricity companies, both in the media and in financial terms. Despite all his efforts, in the space of just a few years Grossmann witnessed the collapse of everything from which the oligopolies drew their strength: the monopoly of information about energy, the lucrative arrangements in the corridors of power and control of the electricity market. In 2011 and 2012, over 1 million German citizens took their revenge by becoming owners of their own little power station, with Germany installing almost 40GW worth of solar panels. The market share of traditional energy firms on the profitable German renewables market fell to just 5 per cent. In summary, the energy revolution in Germany had begun, never to be reversed.

E.ON and RWE: a change of heart or greenwashing?

Some traditional energy firms are shifting towards a new business model based on a service offering, which includes the supply of electricity but in which the latter is no longer the primary focus. The question remains as to whether they will be the best at implementing this model. What will happen when Google, Apple, Facebook and Amazon, the so-called GAFA firms, enter the market? Ikea has already ventured into solar panels, and is another, potentially major, competitor.

I met the CEO of E.ON, Johannes Teyssen, on the fringe of the COP21 summit in Paris in December 2015. He was the first of Germany's leading electricity bosses to have taken radical measures, splitting his company into two distinct subsidiaries: the first, which has kept the E.ON name, looks after renewables, distribution networks and new energy services; the second, Uniper, is rather like a bank for junk bonds, in which he has lumped coal and gas-fired power stations. The value of these legacy power stations is so low that the German authorities have forced Teyssen to put his nuclear power stations in the 'new' E.ON; they are afraid that Uniper's stock market value may not be enough to cover the nuclear debt (in other words, the funds required to pay for the decommissioning of nuclear power plants and waste management). I would not like to be the captain of an ocean liner on the high seas in bad weather who has to offload a large proportion of their crew.

Today, like his colleagues, Teyssen has changed his views on distribution networks. Admittedly, this part of the business is regulated, and the regulators often restrict return on investment to 8–10 per cent. That amounted to a pittance in the old energy world, in which giants like E.ON could legitimately aspire to margins of 20 per cent or more. Now, however, electricity firms have become enamoured with their grids: they generate stable, constant revenues, and as such they constitute a blue-chip asset on which the parent company can rely. Teyssen also believes that the decentralisation of energy, digitalisation and connected objects will make distribution networks an invaluable platform for data gathering. He is undoubtedly correct in this, although the role of electricity firms on this new market will clearly be a matter for debate, particularly as regards issues of data protection and competition.

Refocusing on renewables will be a long and difficult task. Indeed, even if the new E.ON is doing its best to drastically bring down its operating costs by making its decision-making structures more responsive and more decentralised, competition is stiff, with dynamic SMEs such as WPD leading the charge, boosted by lower overheads due to increased specialisation. According to Teyssen, E.ON's chief asset will thus be the development of new energy services. Many private individuals have started to produce solar electricity, but they lack technical capabilities, and are therefore keen to benefit from professional management services. As a result, his company has dipped a toe back into the decentralised solar power market via its PV Energy Solutions division, which installs and looks after solar panels. In truth, this is an attempt to repatriate clients who, by embarking on self-generation, are about to leave the ambit of traditional electricity firms (or indeed already have done); in France, EDF has done something similar with its new 'Mon soleil & moi' offering. As a well-known, respected brand, E.ON can certainly hope to attract clients via its website. During my conversation with Teyssen, however, I pressed him as to how many people were flocking to the E.ON Internet portal – the firm's point of contact with potential clients. He looked at me with a rather startled air and wanted to know why I was asking. The fact is that on the market of services to private individuals, E.ON is not only in competition with similar firms such as RWE and EnBW; it is also in competition with the GAFA giants and new players from the world of retail distribution such as Ikea. If E.ON's aim is to position itself in this sector, it will have to outdo brands that attract huge amounts of visitor traffic to their websites and social media feeds. All this gave Teyssen pause for thought.

E.ON does look to be better placed on the B2B[139] market. The firm has just signed agreements with Lidl, Aldi and other supermarket chains to help the latter bring down their energy wastage (e.g. in lighting and the cold chain) and put together solar power projects for the vast expanses of roof space on top of their stores. E.ON has also launched consultancy services for small businesses and industrial firms, dealing with energy services and energy management project funding. I think this could be a promising niche. Indeed, I worked hard to introduce energy savings obligations as part of the

---

139   B2B (business to business) refers to services to businesses, as opposed to B2C (business to customers).

EU Energy Efficiency Directive in order to encourage this type of market to emerge. Teyssen is also intending to branch into facilities management for retail and service buildings, as well as the transport market: in the aftermath of Dieselgate, the latter will undoubtedly be accelerating its technological shift in favour of electric mobility. As I left our meeting in Paris that evening, I left a man humble enough to acknowledge the disruption the electricity firms are undergoing.

RWE is going down a similar path, too. Jürgen Grossmann handed over the reins of the firm to Peter Terium, who appears to be seeking a change of model, in similar fashion to his competitor E.ON. In April 2016 a new firm, Innogy, was born, taking on RWE's renewable energy portfolio, its network business and activities relating to retail. Innogy's initial public offering in October 2016 was the most successful on the Frankfurt stock market since the year 2000, raising €5 billion by opening up 25 per cent of its share capital. This gave the firm a stock market value of €20 billion, compared to some €8 billion for its parent company RWE! Have E.ON and RWE managed to get on board and follow the winds of change in time, or have they missed the boat? Only time will tell.

The business case for specialisation

In 2005, as the result of the merger of a number of local operators, the Danish energy company Dong Energy was born. In a rapidly consolidating sector, there was a need to bring together the smaller Danish entities that were at risk of being bought out by bigger fish from Germany and Sweden. Most of the capacity owned by Dong Energy was in coal, part of which was used to fuel heat distribution networks, in line with a strategy implemented by Denmark in the 1980s in a response to the oil bust.

The company went on to diversify its portfolio, moving into onshore wind power, and more particularly, offshore wind power. Within a very short space of time, by concentrating on the North Sea wind power market (Denmark, the UK and Germany), it became the leading wind power provider, well ahead of the German oligopolies, and French firms EDF and Engie (which were very late in entering this promising market). Today, Dong Energy excels in offshore wind power logistics and engineering, and has brought down costs by carrying out mass purchasing. In 2012, the firm concluded a historic agreement with Siemens for the purchase of more than three hundred wind turbines over a four-year period, as scheduled offshore wind farms were deployed off the shores of the UK.

What is more, Dong Energy also excels in financial engineering. As a small structure that needs to invest hundreds of millions of euros in its projects, it cannot hope to do so with its own capital alone. Its business model involves developing a project, operating it for one or two years to prove that it works, and then selling it on to institutional investors, such as Danish pension funds. This model benefits such investors, since it requires them to shoulder only a small amount of the risk by buying the assets once their reliability and profitability are assured; it also benefits Dong Energy by providing it with significant cash revenues. This model is burgeoning, particularly as pension funds seek to diversify their portfolios in the light of declining bond yields.

The business case for internationalisation

'We have lost huge amounts of revenue in Europe, but gained huge amounts of revenue elsewhere,' says Francesco Venturini, the CEO of Enel Green Power. This illustrates another strategy used by groups such as the Italian giant Enel (and its Spanish subsidiary Endesa) and the Spanish firm Iberdrola (and its UK subsidiary Scottish Power): internationalisation beyond Europe's borders. In April 2016, Enel Green Power won the contract for one gigawatt of solar power in Mexico, at a price of around €45 per megawatt-hour. The previous year, the Italian company had commenced construction of 136MW of solar power in Chile and 450MW of wind and solar power in Brazil. Enel is also very active in Morocco. At the same time, Iberdrola won major contracts in Mexico and Brazil, and is on track to have a portfolio of 888MW in these two countries by 2020, as well as in the USA. This is of course excellent news in terms of European leadership in the industry and the development of renewables on a worldwide scale. However, attention must be drawn to the inconsistency of such groups who, on the one hand, are dragging down the EU's regulatory framework and on the other, complaining about Europe's lack of appeal for them.

The internationalisation model is beneficial in terms of the learning curve, preparing future bids, and identifying new partners. However, to consolidate this model, it is important for these firms to continue to invest in Europe as well, so that they take their place in dynamic markets at home. Groups such as Enel Green Power and Iberdrola are at something of a crossroads: they need to decide whether they are going to leave Europe altogether, or allow the European market to benefit from the experience they have acquired elsewhere. It is to be hoped that they choose the latter. In recent months, Iberdrola has announced new wind projects in Spain. This is a step in the right direction, but much more needs to be done.

The business case for innovation

It is also worth drawing attention to some newcomers on the electricity market who have proved the worth of innovation-based business models in Germany. EWE is active in northern Germany, more specifically in Schleswig-Holstein and Lower Saxony. Its share capital belongs to local authorities, and it is also a mobile telephony operator. Having been involved in the boom in wind power in northern Germany, it is now seeking to be a pioneer in bringing together energy and digital technology. In late 2014, it launched one of the largest pilot projects in the world to test the electricity grids of tomorrow, combining 100 per cent renewables, electric vehicles and domestic electricity storage; the research project is being co-funded by the German government.

Another example is WPD, created by a German environmental activist in the late 1990s; it began by investing in wind power. Today, the firm employs one thousand people in Bremen, and is active in seventeen countries in Europe, as well as in Taiwan, South America and Africa. This wind farm project developer is beating yesterday's giants hands down thanks to its swift positioning on these markets, and lower overheads.

Lastly, there is MVV Energie, in which the city of Mannheim is the majority shareholder, and whose subsidiaries include directly managed municipal companies (Stadtwerke) in Kiel, Offenbach and Ingolstadt. MVV is involved in smart grids, and installs batteries in city neighbourhoods, with a focus on electricity storage. In Bavaria, the Munich municipal company combines large international projects with small local ones to enable the city to transition rapidly towards '100 per cent renewables' for electricity and heating.

How is France doing?

Suez was in many ways an internationalised European energy firm before its time. In the 1970s and 1980s, the firm was virtually invisible on the European market, but had invested all over the world. In 2005, it bought out the Belgian firm Electrabel. When the merger between Gaz de France and Suez/Electrabel was announced in 2008, I had a good feeling about it: it could, I thought, strengthen the presence on the French market of Suez, a player with a greater interest than most in future technologies such as wind power; furthermore, one year previously it had bought out a very dynamic SME, la Compagnie du vent. But GDF-Suez never really managed to get established on the wind power market – indeed, perhaps it never really tried.

In June 2013, at a time when Gérard Mestrallet, the CEO of GDF-Suez, was announcing a firm commitment to energy transition, I was more than happy to agree to meet him. I invited him to back us on at least two measures: the introduction of a CO_2 emission performance standard, which would rule out the dirtiest coal and lignite-fired power stations; and a CO_2 floor price, to give the advantage to gas ahead of coal on the European electricity market. However, I felt that he was not very open to the idea of renewable energy. Later events were to prove me right: the Magritte Group, which he set up at the same time, revealed what was really going on. GDF-Suez had embarked on a crusade with the intention of mitigating energy efficiency targets and the roll out of renewable energy in Europe. It was keen to keep its conventional power stations going as long as possible, and slow down the emergence of competition from renewables on its domestic market. At the same time, the media campaign conducted by the firm in Belgium resulted in a fear of blackouts (the narrative being that the lights were in danger of going out if the country were to seek to do without nuclear power), an attitude deemed 'hysterical'[140] by none other than the former Prime Minister, Johan Vande Lanotte. The campaign was, however, successful: Mestrallet managed to persuade the liberal Belgian government to extend the lifespan of its power plants. In 2015, in an attempt to improve its image, the new group started calling itself Engie, bought out Solairedirect, and appointed Isabelle Kocher to head it up. Did this indicate a new commitment in favour of green energy, or was it nothing more than a marketing ploy?

EDF has been a perfect partner for GDF-Suez when it comes to slowing down energy transition. Indeed, why on earth would EDF's CEO, Jean-Bernard Lévy, decide to plunge headlong into the Hinkley Point endeavour, instead of making the most of the ageing French fleet and the momentum generated by French environment minister Ségolène Royal's Energy Transition and Green Growth Act to move on from nuclear power? There is only one rational explanation: he had little option if he was intent on preserving his company's nuclear-centric model. After all, the cumbersome giant EDF is in a fragile state of health, so a mega-subsidy of €120 per megawatt-hour for a period of thirty-five years was not be turned down lightly. Abandoning Hinkley Point would have revealed the complete lack of any alternative to the EPR reactor in the group's strategy. Indeed, EDF is in an increasingly perilous financial situation: both the extended lifespan and the closure of its power stations will come at a high price. The 'major refit' plan to extend the lifespan of certain nuclear power plants by a further ten years will cost the firm a fortune, requiring it to bring these reactors up to current standards. The alternative of

---

140   'Electrabel "profite de l'hystérie autour du black-out"', *Le Vif*, 4 December 2014, www.levif.be.

closing them down also represents a money pit, and the sums set aside for this purpose fall far short of the amount required to cover proper decommissioning of the reactors. Will Hinkley Point be enough to save EDF? Nothing could be less certain. If the UK EPR turns out to be an industrial failure, Jean-Bernard Lévy will have achieved for EDF what Anne Lauvergeon has managed to accomplish for Areva: bankrupting a state-owned company due to a failure to anticipate structural changes in the sector.

My proposals:
As an MEP, I do not wish to interfere in the strategic decisions of Europe's major industrial companies. It is up to them to reinvent themselves, and shift towards new business models that are compatible with energy transition.

CHAPTER 23

LOCAL AUTHORITIES: GRASSROOTS CONNECTIONS MAKE ALL THE DIFFERENCE

In Europe as elsewhere, not only are cities active in the field, they are also key political stakeholders when it comes to governance of energy transition. During my visit to the United States in 2009, I noted how the most powerful lobbies in Congress, alongside those from traditional sectors such as gunmakers (the NRA), coal and oil (such as Exxon Mobil), were those supporting America's cities. This is not particularly new, but the representation of local authorities to the US Congress is flourishing, both through representative bodies such as the National League of Cities and by means of direct lobbying, a practice in which several hundred medium-sized cities are engaged. According to recent American–Danish research,[141] Texan cities alone have spent $17 million on advocacy in Washington between 2006 and 2010. Imagine how much the grand total must be across all fifty states.

Why should the various networks of European cities not be exercising similar influence on the EU Parliament? We tested out the idea with the vote on the Juncker Plan in April 2015. To win a crucial vote in the ITRE Committee on earmarking part of the EFSI money for

---

141   Matt W. Loftis and Jaclyn J. Kettler, 'Lobbying from inside the system: why local governments pay for representation in the US Congress', *Political Research Quarterly*, vol. 68, 2015.

energy efficiency, I enlisted the support of a number of cities, who wrote to their respective MEPs, explaining that if they supported a budget allocation for energy efficiency guarantees worth €5 billion, the EIB would have more money to invest in infrastructures for their cities. The test was conclusive: we won the vote. As and when we manage to increase the strike power of forward-looking cities and local authorities, we will have a lobby capable of withstanding the oligopolies.

Cities get organised in the wake of the Earth Summit

In the 1980s, in response to the oil crisis, local energy agencies began to see the light of day thanks to programmes supported by the EU budget. The aim at that time was to encourage cities and their inhabitants to invest in bringing down oil consumption. Sometime later, this embryonic movement grew and gave birth to the French transitioning cities network Réseau des villes en transition, in which residents could join forces to act together in initiatives such as community gardens, local currencies, energy investments and so on.

For my part, I shared this 'think global, act local' perspective on my return from the Rio Earth Summit in 1992. It was there that for the first time, there was a real sense of engagement in favour of the climate and the protection of natural resources. Admittedly, the conference itself was a failure, with President George Bush declaring that 'the American way of life is not up for negotiations', and the UK exercising its power of veto to bury the European project of a carbon tax. However, local initiatives did emerge all over Europe: the Climate Alliances. These formalised a commitment by cities and local authorities to bring down their carbon footprint, as well as a partnership with oppressed and indigenous peoples suffering from conflicts generated by the pillage of natural resources by multinationals and due to agricultural pressure.

For my part, I set up the Luxembourg Climate Alliance in 1993. Initially, only six municipalities joined. Subsequently, the movement gathered momentum, following the example of the German-speaking countries. Two of the Luxembourg mayors who were among the first six signatories went on to have ministerial posts. In 2012, as a minister Marco Schank created the Climate Pact, a programme that put in place a three-level set of specifications enabling municipalities to receive state subsidies for the thermal renovation of buildings, the modernisation of heating networks, and the launch of informational campaigns. His successor, Secretary of State for the Environment Camille Gira, was similarly committed. The Luxembourg Climate Pact is now something of a template. Within Europe, it is one of the most sophisticated agreements between a government seeking to reduce its country's carbon footprint and municipalities. Today, 95 per cent of Luxembourg's territory and population is covered by this Climate Pact.

Meanwhile, in France Gérard Magnin set up Énergie-Cités (later to be known as Energy Cities) in 1990. Today, around a thousand towns and cities belong to this association. In that same year, major cities across the world got together to create the International Council for Local Environmental Initiatives (ICLEI), now active in eighty-four countries. A few years later, in 2006, C40 was established, bringing together forty major cities engaged in combating climate change, including New York and Copenhagen. The mayor of Paris, Anne Hidalgo, has recently assumed the chairmanship of this network.

This local dynamic is represented in Brussels by the creation of a new instrument, the Covenant of Mayors. Initially, such an undertaking was entirely without precedent.

The Covenant of Mayors: a revolution

Back in 2003, I helped to set up the Intelligent Energy Europe[142] programme. François Lamoureux, at that time director-general for Energy, had grasped the benefits of promoting renewables and energy efficiency, and the need for this to come from the local level. Indeed, decentralisation is an important aspect of energy transition, in terms of both technology and stakeholders: a bottom-up approach that

---

142   See Chapter 1, p. 19.

opens up the way for cities and energy cooperatives to become involved. François Lamoureux agreed with this concept and set up the IEE programme, the purpose of which was thus to give cities and local authorities a greater role in energy transition. A number of initiatives were launched on this basis to allow examples to emerge at the local level. However, the projects in question were relatively few and far between. Nevertheless, the process did spur the Commission and the European cities in the Energy Cities association, with the backing of Commissioner Piebalgs, to launch a fully fledged instrument in 2009, just after the adoption of the Climate and Energy Package: the Covenant of Mayors. Right from the outset, the central idea was clear: in addition to member states, the Covenant of Mayors would spearhead the promotion of energy transition at the local level on behalf of the EU. The method is simple: cities submit a commitment, in figures, to bring down their greenhouse gas emissions to the European Commission's Joint Research Centre (JRC). The JRC then checks the quality of the project and oversees its implementation. In return, cities benefit from advice to improve their public policy, and can use the Covenant of Mayors label in their communication.

Gérard Magnin, one of the founding fathers, explains the extent to which this concept was innovative as far as the European decision-making process was concerned:

> This approach acted as a catalyst for policy-making; as a result, the Commission eventually ended up agreeing to risk bending the subsidiarity principle a little in order to address local authorities directly … Indeed, when it comes to energy, genuine subsidiarity involves finding the nearest local solutions: bringing down consumption, identifying the resources obtained outside the system, and seeking to work gradually outwards to obtain what you need.[143]

It was a resounding success from the beginning.

---

143   *Enerpresse*, issue 9819, 11 May 2009.

Now with a membership of over 6,700 European cities, the Covenant of Mayors is accelerating energy transition. Within the cities themselves, residents are mobilised via a platform. The Covenant is not solely devoted to energy; urban planning also includes issues such as green mobility, the thermal renovation of buildings and street lighting. By committing to energy transition, cities like Munich, which is seeking to be 100 per cent renewable by 2025, represent potential markets for innovative SMEs. Even Pope Francis has called on mayors to take action, signing a joint declaration[144] with some of them. The system we have put in place is extremely efficient: it is harder for energy oligopolies to influence 36,000 French mayors than one single energy minister. Cities thus act as a counterweight to governments, and even to the European Union's Council of Ministers, and could constitute an influential lobby in the European Parliament.

The only cloud on the horizon is that the secretariat of the Covenant of Mayors is currently underfunded by the Commission, resulting in a lack of financial support for the cities committing to it; they therefore have to bring other resources to bear to support their transition. For municipalities making commitments to achieve this, it needs to be easier for them to obtain access to EU funding.

An overall plan for cities
In the run-up to the COP21 summit, the focus was on cities' commitments to 2020. Now, the horizon is 2030, or even 2050, which is indicative of a genuine long-term vision. Under the leadership of Anne Hidalgo and Michael Bloomberg, city networks are drawing together, resulting in a Climate Summit for Local Leaders at the COP21 in Paris on 4 December 2015. Ideally, an alliance between different city networks, such as ICLEI, C40 and others, on a global level, would make it possible to start heading towards the goal of 100 per cent renewables by 2050. Indeed, this dynamic led to the birth of the

---

144 'Pope and mayors sign declaration on climate and trafficking', Vatican Radio, 22 July 2015, en.radiovaticana.va.

Compact of Mayors in September 2014, drawing inspiration from the workings of the Covenant of Mayors.

The Commission appears to have understood that the Covenant of Mayors is a huge source of leverage for change, particularly at the international level. Christopher Jones, deputy director-general of DG Ener, is an enthusiastic supporter of its internationalisation. He is keen to export it to China and Egypt, linking it directly with the export strategy for Europe's green technology. In April 2016, alongside the signature of the headline COP21 Agreement, Energy Union vice president Maroš Šefčovič began negotiations in New York with a view to sealing a partnership between the Covenant of Mayors and the Compact of Mayors, in order to raise the profile of these initiatives and develop synergies. I am not opposed to this in principle, provided that it does not involve letting go of the key to the success of the Covenant of Mayors: a bottom-up approach in which mayors are free to innovate, or even be a little provocative, without being brought to heel by a centralised management in Brussels. In this respect, I am rather sceptical about the establishment of a steering committee for the purposes of managing this initiative. Who could be better placed to decide on mayors' commitments than the mayors themselves?

The External Investment Plan (EIP) put forward by the Commission on 14 September 2016 could be a new source of leverage for international change. It could bring down the financial risks relating to renewables and urban investments; this is a much-needed strategy, given the extremely high cost of capital in developing countries. It would allow cities in those developing countries which are the least favoured by the financial markets to attract investments promoting local economic development. At the same time, the know-how of green cities and European technology could be exported too. Indeed, if there is one thing Europe is really good at, it is the mobilisation of local authorities. Within Europe, smart cities and communities are a showcase for technology; they serve as full-scale laboratories, thereby creating a market for the deployment of state-of-the-art techniques and life-size demonstration projects. More needs to be done, however. Some at the Commission, such as former energy commissioner Günther Oettinger, are suspicious of the political dimension of the Covenant of Mayors, and thus seek to restrict local initiatives to purely technological aspects in Europe's major cities, such as the Smart Cities and Communities initiative. I do not share this attitude. On the contrary, I believe that technological innovation should comprise a political dimension, with both large cities and smaller towns being involved.

There's still work to be done in Europe

Other barriers also need to be removed. In particular, cities could be encouraged to join forces for joint purchases of green technology, such as electric buses. This would allow some technologies to achieve critical mass. Similarly, the de minimis clause in the guidelines on state aid for environmental protection and energy already allows mayors that commit to 100 per cent renewables to directly support local projects without having to go through the auction processes managed by ministries. In this respect, it is vital that DG Comp should stop promoting technology-neutral auctions, as they prevent cities and local authorities from committing to renewable energy projects.

Lastly, local authorities are committed to Energy Performance Contracts, which are deemed to constitute services by Eurostat. These contracts are considered a public debt according to the Maastricht Treaty, even though they are nothing more than operating expenditure, just like a water or electricity bill, so the risk is borne by the third-party investor. The current arrangement acts as a strong deterrent against municipalities using such schemes because strict rules apply to their debt. This hinders energy efficiency in public buildings and is thus in blatant contradiction with the Energy Efficiency Directive, which establishes targets in this area. Eurostat must re-examine this question.

In this respect, there is a glimmer of hope at the European Commission. In its Energy Union Strategy adopted in February 2015, the first two pages are devoted to the role of cities and citizens. This is thanks to Peter Van Kemseke, the member of vice president Šefčovič's team responsible for drafting the text, who is strongly in favour of mobilising cities and local authorities (he is also a councillor for the Belgian municipality of Vilvoorde). To accelerate energy transition and ensure that the Energy Union has a grassroots dimension, the Commission must now allocate significant funds to networks of cities.

My proposals:
- Allowing cities and their inhabitants to continue to invest directly in renewable energy projects by setting up a more favourable regime for small investors and local authorities, alongside the auction system for larger projects.
- Revising the Eurostat interpretation of European accounting standards to exclude Energy Performance Contracts taken out with third-party investors from public debt calculations, qualifying them as 'off-balance-sheet' items.
- Generalising green public procurements, with adequate Technical Assistance to help central and local government handle the complex procedures involved in procurement.
- Mobilising existing networks of cities such as Energy Cities, Climate Alliance and Eurocities, together with the six thousand members of the Covenant of Mayors, providing them with the human and financial resources required to continue to exercise leadership in the energy transition debate; restoring a programme along the lines of Intelligent Energy Europe to assist with energy transition and support social innovation and systemic integration; making membership of the Covenant of Mayors an eligibility criterion for cities to have access to research and innovation funds such as Horizon 2020, structural funds and investment funds such as the Juncker Plan.
- Developing a higher level of initiatives internationally, along the lines of Sustainable Energy for All (SE4ALL), launched in 2011; expanding the Covenant of Mayors beyond the EU, while preserving its bottom-up approach, with no centralised decision-making structure.

CHAPTER 24

NEW QUALIFICATIONS AND JOBS WITH A FUTURE: WORKERS HAVE EVERYTHING TO GAIN

Contrary to received wisdom, energy transition is a source of new jobs within the European Union. It has already been determined[145] that over 1 million direct and indirect jobs have been created in the sector of renewable energy with almost half of them in wind and solar power. Despite regional disparities, every member state has benefited from new jobs, not just Germany and Scandinavia. There are 18,500 jobs relating to solid biomass in Poland, 8,300 in biofuels in Belgium, 1,200 in biogas in the Czech Republic, 4,000 in solar power in Romania, 2,200 in small hydroelectric facilities in Italy and 18,000 in wind power in Spain. Worldwide, it is estimated that 7.7 million people are employed in jobs relating to renewables.

Energy efficiency does almost as well, employing just under 1 million people in jobs relating directly to energy services in Europe. According to a study[146] carried out for the European Commission, this figure could even increase fivefold by 2030 if incentive policies are implemented. Such policies would therefore be good, both for the

---

145 '15e baromètre bilan', EurObserv'ER, www.eurobserv-er.org.
146 Cambridge Econometrics, 'Assessing the Employment and Social Impact of Energy Efficiency', November 2015, ec.europa.eu.

environment and for unemployment figures. What is more, this is one of the areas in which the EU has a definite competitive advantage compared with other economies.

Energy transition: a sector with a future

Europe is a pioneer in wind power, solar power and grid integration, with unique expertise in cutting-edge technologies. Its leading industrial firms export worldwide. The same cannot be said, however, when it comes to information technology and some forms of manufacturing industry, particularly electronics. In IT, the EU is struggling to catch up with the leaders (the USA, Japan and Korea), having made a late start in the field. It is declining in the realm of manufacturing industry, in particular due to a lack of investment and modernisation in production plant in the wake of the excessive austerity policies implemented in recent years.

The success of the COP21 summit is of great benefit to Europe. The EU is already home to 40 per cent of the world's patent applications relating to renewable energies. What is more, it is the world leader in exports of environmental goods and services, ahead of China, bringing in €35 billion a year. Despite significant imports, especially of solar panels made in China, there is still a pronounced trade surplus in this area. What is lacking is an integrated vision. Europeans are present in a somewhat haphazard manner, whereas our American, Canadian and Korean competitors are organised, as embodied for instance by the US's 'Green Export Enabler Program'. Back in 2003, the European Renewable Energy Council EREC (now defunct) was suggesting that a European export strategy should be implemented. Unfortunately, we are still waiting for the European Commission to deliver any such strategy.

Social transition has begun
Coal mines and coal-fired power stations
Even if transition creates more jobs than the old world of centralised energy, some sectors could of course suffer as a result of transition being poorly handled, perhaps abruptly and without any social

provisions. With the collapse of the CO_2 market, the lifespan of historic coal- and lignite-fired power stations is being artificially extended, but we will soon see an absolute avalanche of closures. This process needs to be accompanied and structured at both the local and regional levels, with the planning of successive, ordered shutdowns of these legacy power stations and unprofitable mines, instead of ignoring the evidence and thus the bearing the brunt of a major social crisis at the very last minute.

Those working in the oligopolies whose leaders have committed strategic errors are the most exposed to this. Some groups are attempting to mobilise in order to avoid massive job losses, in partnership with the trade unions. For instance, a major European social agreement was signed by Engie and the trade unions in April 2015, setting aside €100 million per year for employee training: 'Engie is committed to providing recognised skills training to at least two-thirds of employees, every year.' Dong Energy offers proof that gradual change is possible: between 2006 and 2015, the proportion of renewables in their portfolio rose from 15 per cent to 55 per cent, decreasing the group's emissions from 638 to 334g CO_2/kWh – and did so without any job losses at all. Indeed, the company now has a workforce of 6,700 compared to 4,600 in 2006.

Massive job losses are hardly new in the mining industry. It's just that energy transition is simply speeding up a phenomenon that is already well underway. Even Poland's mines[147] are no longer profitable in a sharply declining market. The workforce in these mines has decreased from 280,000 people twenty years ago to 170,000 in the 2000s. Some former coal-mining regions have achieved successful transition, such as Wales. In this traditional land of coal, in 2015 the Welsh Assembly adopted a moratorium on new mining permits for opencast coal mines, and a prohibition on hydraulic fracturing. The Welsh energy strategy, 'a low carbon transition', focuses on renewables (accounting for 13,000 local jobs in 2012) and energy efficiency, with

---

147   'Polish Power Sector Riding on the Wave of Megatrends', Forum for Energy Analysis, January 2016, www.fae.org.

particular help from European Structural Funds.[148] The Ruhr district is also a historic coal-mining region in which transition is underway and it will have closed its last three working coal mines by 2018. New jobs have successfully been created in healthcare, new technologies, tourism and other fields. Spain's mines are also condemned to close in the next few years, on both economic and legal grounds. Will the new Spanish government be capable of putting forward a gradual transition plan?

During the 'coal dialogue' held in Brussels in June 2016, D-G for Energy, Klaus-Dieter Borchardt, signalled his agreement with the view that there is no future for coal. Over and above this acknowledgement, I call on the European Commission to consider how to accompany the social consequences of the end of lignite and coal in the regions in question, by mobilising structural funds and the European Social Fund.

Sources of jobs for the future

Halting a nuclear power plant results in a decommissioning process that lasts fifty to sixty years. A large number of nuclear power stations will have to be decommissioned in the years to come – not only in France, where the fleet is ageing, but everywhere else in the world, too. This could become a sector of excellence for France and Europe as Areva and EDF could position themselves as experts in the field. In Italy, for example, the Trino Vercellese power station ceased operations in 1990, but decommissioning only began in 2012 and will not be completed until 2024 at the earliest – thirty-four years after shutdown. This offers scope for long-term employment in the region. Instead of injecting huge amounts of money to help EDF invest in the UK, the French government should be thinking about the end of the French nuclear fleet and setting up a top-level processing chain to carry out decommissioning.

Another promising sector is that of bio-refineries. Once Europe's

---

148   'A Low Carbon Transition', Energy Wales, March 2012, gov.wales.

obsession with diesel has finally been brought to an end, traditional re-fineries could be converted into bio-refineries – provided of course that the available biomass is exploited sustainably. Oil and gas giant Total is already heading down this road. In 2015, it decided to invest €200 million to create Europe's largest bio-refinery in France by repurpos-ing a facility formerly used to process crude oil, a highly loss-making activity. Total's grounds for this turnaround are also interesting; against a backdrop of declining demand, it invoked overcapacity due 'in part to the environmental commitments made by the EU'. As a result, of the 450 jobs that would have disappeared if Total had closed the site instead of redeveloping it, 250 will remain.

Agriculture and forestry also offer sources of employment. The failure of the agricultural lobby's strategy of exporting our agricultural produce must be acknowledged. Seeking to flood the entire world with European dairy products is an illusion, one for which the sector is now paying a heavy price. However, biomass can also be turned into biogas, thereby supplying stable revenue to farmers and mini-mising the social consequences in this highly exposed sector. GRDF and others are already working on biogas and biomethane develop-ment scenarios in France, which could cover most of the country's gas consumption requirements. By 2030, 16 per cent of all biogas should be being dispatched into the network from 1,400 sites, with the aim of increasing this to 73 per cent by 2050. This development also calls for the creation of many new jobs: there are 1,700 related jobs in France today, and almost 16,000 direct and indirect jobs are forecast by 2020.

Meanwhile, at a time when energy and transport are entering the digital age, could European companies be capable of positioning themselves on this segment of excellence – or will the GAFA firms of the US (Google, Apple, Facebook and Amazon) win the day? The industrial stakes here are high. The EU is suffering from a shortage of personnel in information technology. If we want qualified labour, we need to attract young people and train engineers to this sector, and encourage universities to embrace this prospect.

Training: a vital component

The biggest challenge, however, is in the construction sector, where the largest numbers of new jobs are expected. For installers, heating engineers, maintenance managers, energy auditors, urban planners, engineers, architects and others, training will be a vital key to the future. Construction is a very difficult sector in which to be employed, with its poor social status, pay and demanding working conditions. It is therefore important for genuine social dialogue to begin in order to examine how the EU can help increase the amount of training in the sector and disseminate best practices.

For instance, the outstanding EU project BuildUp Skills is striving to support member states as they implement roadmaps for training labourers and artisans and promote good practice. Luxembourg offers another example to follow, with the Construction Sector Training Institute (Institut de formation sectoriel du bâtiment, IFSB) rolling out an ambitious training policy, enabling trained labourers to secure pay increases. In France, despite some imperfections, an agreement on training professionals in energy savings in buildings has enabled over 25,000 people to be trained each year, and earn the 'certified environmental steward' accreditation (*reconnu garant de l'environnement*, RGE).

In this respect, it is unfortunate that Employment Commissioner Marianne Thyssen has not included construction as one of the EU priorities for training. In the communication adopted by the Commission in June 2016 entitled 'A new strategy for skills for Europe', the sector is not dealt with at all beyond being the subject of subsequent evaluation, and the same applies to renewables and green technology. This is a missed opportunity. However, the Commission has declared itself favourable to an EU initiative as part of European Social Dialogue aimed at improving both the sector's productivity and related worker compensation. What's more, these two proposals are high on the list in the memorandum I drafted in 2015 in partnership with my colleague Jude Kirton-Darling, the former confederal secretary of the European Trade Union Confederation (ETUC). The construction industry is often reluctant to innovate, which is why every available source of leverage must be used to encourage it to change.

My proposals:
- Extending training across the board for construction workers, artisans and installers, engineers and architects in new energy management techniques, using programmes co-funded by employers, with a particular emphasis on the least-qualified workers.
- Establishing an entitlement to training in green services and technologies for workers and the unemployed, in order to improve their employability in the fields of renewable energy, energy services, and information and communications technology.
- Opening up funding possibilities for social partners seeking to make the workplace greener, for instance through employees committing to energy savings policies and green mobility in and around the workplace.
- Stimulating social dialogue, both nationally and at the European level, in order to organise the implementation of these proposals through tripartite discussion forums along the lines of a 'Green Growth Forum' and sectoral roadmaps.
- Organising transition to the post-coal era with the help of networks to exchange know-how and good practice, allowing the impacted regions to be redeveloped gradually.

CHAPTER 25

450 MILLION CITIZENS SHOW THE WAY

Our responsibility as policymakers is to remove the barriers preventing those individuals who so wish from reducing and sorting their waste, renovating and insulating their homes, bringing down their energy use, using green mode transport, installing solar panels on their roofs and banding together to install community wind turbines. A critical mass of citizens committed to energy transition would be enough to change the entire system. The fact is that successful projects spawn offspring. When an individual plays an active part in the energy system, they become an ambassador who can attract other individuals: friends, neighbours and colleagues.

In the EU's Energy Union Framework Strategy, the opening pages give the impression that citizens are at the heart of its concerns. Not before time. Hitherto, citizens had been left out of the deregulation of energy markets and European climate strategies. But thanks to energy transition, they can now play a growing role in transforming the system – several roles, in fact.

Stakeholder citizens

Here's how my interest in energy-related issues came about. In the late 1980s, there was a plan for a high-voltage power line in my native region, near Diekirch in Luxembourg. The manager of the municipal utility company held that this power line was completely pointless, with no added value for residents, despite featuring in the national electricity company Cégédel's strategic plans. I succeeded in getting hold of the plans, and sought to oppose the power line by launching a public petition. People could sign the petition on one condition: they had to buy two low-energy light bulbs. Local shopkeepers and supermarkets delightedly seized the opportunity and helped me pass round the petition and sold hundreds of lightbulbs in a single month. No one had ever seen anything like it. We succeeded in blocking the construction of two planned high-tension power lines using this strategy. To ensure we were not seen simply as opponents of change, the strategy was accompanied by a positive initiative, which was the Energy Park cooperative set up in Redange. This led to community wind turbines being installed in 2003, along with a dozen or so community solar power projects. It was at that time that we launched our first energy management campaign, subsidised by government: 'Let's save electricity together'.

In short, a touch of humour went a long way to helping me win out against the almighty Cégédel in this instance. I entered politics because I became aware that friends getting together could have an impact on policy – and have some fun along the way.

Prosumer citizens

Millions of EU citizens have become energy producers. Denmark saw the first wind turbine cooperatives and Germany's EEG Act has facilitated similar developments thanks to feed-in tariffs. These changes have brought plenty of criticisms with them, particularly the perception that such schemes only helped 'rich folks' who had enough capital to invest, while the 'poor' were being asked to do little more than pay for the related subsidies. In Flanders, consumer associations attacked solar power along these lines. Indeed, only house owners could start self-producing, thus benefiting from tax exemptions and lower grid fees; these were offset by price hikes for everybody else. Overall, however, I believe that the entire population of Europe can benefit from energy transition. Indeed, that is precisely why new models are emerging to enable tenants, including those in social housing, to have the opportunity to become 'prosumers' themselves. For example, there is the 'rent-a-roof' initiative in the UK, experimental solar panel leasing and consortiums made up of social housing residents. In such cases, tenants join together in a self-generation project that covers an entire building or neighbourhood. Self-generation is becoming more democratic. Each individual should have the right to develop grassroots energy – in other words, to produce, store, resell and use their production of electricity, energy and heat, and manage their use of all these.

Self-generation has to find a balance between autonomy when it comes to production and consumption, and solidarity when it comes to contributing to system balancing via transmission and distribution networks. How can the right balance be found between autonomy and solidarity? Distribution and transmission networks can be optimised, but it takes solidarity to fund this. Is it really worth installing a battery in each cellar, or could storage be aggregated out across an entire neighbourhood? In each case, individual decisions should be coordinated with the common interest at heart.

Spain offers an example of what not to do. The solar tax levied by the conservative government has prevented the inhabitants of the European country with the most sunshine from having their own solar panels. It is somewhat as if market gardeners were to encourage the government to tax private individuals growing tomatoes in their own garden for their own consumption. Indeed, this solar tax was set up at the request of the oligopolies in order to lock in the Spanish market and prevent the emergence of a degree of competition, and the 'German scenario' was their worst nightmare. I, on the other hand, believe that consumer-stakeholders should be duly recognised, and encouraged to self-generate by benefiting from specific, secure assistance. That includes priority access and dispatch to the grid, appropriate support schemes and a fair contribution to network management costs.

The issue of personal data
Another important aspect is the fact that self-producers need to have a smart meter. This goes hand in hand with any photovoltaic installation,

so that the system is informed about their production and consumption data. The question is how to ensure that this data is both exploitable and confidential. Smart meters enable distributors to achieve huge efficiency gains, not only with respect to metering and measurement, but also when cutting off electricity as call-outs to cut off or reconnect subscribers are no longer required. Individual citizens should have the right to use their data themselves, and make it available to market stakeholders who have committed to a policy that protects privacy. Smart meters therefore offer a huge opportunity for consumers, but also for other stakeholders. They are a gold mine for network managers, suppliers and more generally for any company that loves personal data – including the GAFA giants (Google, Apple, Facebook and Amazon).

European consumer organisation BEUC is fully aware of both the opportunities and the threats involved here and has thus established free, individual choice as a core principle: 'Consumers should freely choose if they want to use smart meters in their homes. This is particularly important where consumers are required to pay for it. When consumers do not accept a smart meter, they should not bear any additional costs.'[149] BEUC has also put forward a strict framework for the data gathered, stating that these 'should be stored at the consumer premises by default'. Distribution system operators are engaged in intense lobbying to be officially designated as the regulated entities in charge of data collection and processing. Why should they have a monopoly on this, especially as many of them are not really distinct from the vertically integrated oligopolies? How can we be sure that Enedis will act independently of EDF when it comes to managing the data of millions of subscribers? To overcome this difficulty, I have proposed a hybrid model, in which consumers automatically supply the information that is strictly necessary for the grid to function properly and remain free to supply the rest of their data to third-party providers, without necessarily having to go through the system operator. Data protection would also need to be strictly managed in this scenario, too.

---

[149] 'Protecting and empowering consumers in future smart energy markets', BEUC, February 2013, www.beuc.eu.

Consumer stakeholders contributing to energy efficiency

Europe is witnessing an alarming spread of energy poverty. According to research by the European Commission, almost 10 per cent of European citizens do not have the resources to heat their homes adequately.[150] First and foremost, this phenomenon is due to a general impoverishment of the population, particularly in the states that have been the most exposed to the austerity policies implemented in the wake of the 2008 economic crisis. A number of measures that need to be taken urgently to halt this trend include better-insulated homes to make drastic reductions in monthly utility bills possible. However, many programmes promoting energy efficiency are designed for the middle classes, both in terms of access to information and the grants available when an initial payment is required. It is therefore vital to democratise these programmes in order to reach the most vulnerable, such as tenants in social housing (through schemes like France's social housing landlords association Union sociale de l'habitat) as well as low-income homeowners, particularly in Eastern Europe. In an initiative spearheaded by my Hungarian colleague Tamás Meszerics,[151] the European Parliament adopted a resolution on this issue in April 2016. This 'calls on the member states and the EU to provide microcredits or loans free of interest or at low rates via (e.g. the EIB) to low-income households to support them in the upfront investment in renewables or energy efficiency, such as insulation, solar energy and energy efficient appliances'.

In addition, for the purchase of household appliances, in 2003 energy labelling introduced transparency in the form of a performance label assigning categories from A to G. Now, consumers can buy appliances in full awareness of how much they will save energy and bring their bills down. Combined with eco-design, energy labels for a whole range of products including radiators, boilers and heat

---

150   'Energy Poverty and Vulnerable Consumers in the Energy Sector Across the EU: Analysis of Policies and Measures', Insight-E, May 2015, ec.europa.eu.

151   Published in December 2016, the *Energy Poverty Handbook*, ed. Tamás Meszerics, reveals that energy efficiency policies benefit citizens and that ecology has an intrinsic social dimension.

pumps can bring down the annual energy bills for an EU consumer by an average of €275.

If the authorities play ball, by providing alternatives to individual car use and safe infrastructures, consumer-stakeholders can also reduce their carbon footprint by making much more use of urban public transport, bikes and car-sharing. Just one other issue remains, and it is often a taboo subject. It also is a delicate topic for politicians, who quickly find themselves accused of meddling in what consumers eat. It is meat, the overconsumption of which is one of the factors contributing to global warming. Consumer-stakeholder citizens could really make a difference here by adjusting their diet and changing their consumer habits. To help them in this, there could soon be an EU label to provide proper identification of vegetarian products.

Cattenom, Fessenheim and Tihange: the reactors of strife

The Fukushima disaster happened despite reassuring declarations as to how impossible a nuclear accident was in the high-tech land of Japan. Henceforth, EU leaders have been much more circumspect. Among them is the director of France's Nuclear Safety Authority (Autorité de sûreté nucléaire, ASN), Pierre-Franck Chevet. In March 2016, he made the following statement: 'We have to envisage the prospect of a Fukushima-style accident happening in Europe.' When it comes to a decision as to whether or not to use nuclear power, countries have full national sovereignty. The consequences, however, do not stop at borders. Citizen-stakeholders need to engage with this issue. People living in the vicinity of Cattenom, Tihange and Fessenheim are becoming increasingly concerned, staging multiple demonstrations and instigating court proceedings. The inhabitants of the various countries in question should have a voice when it comes to halting a dangerous reactor located close to a national border.

Citizen investors

I would like to see space for investment by individual citizens and cooperatives in the forthcoming EU Renewable Energy Directive, and in national plans to develop renewable energy. The de minimis rules in the guidelines on state aid currently allow smaller projects (of under 1MW for photovoltaic power and 18–22MW for wind power, equivalent to six medium-sized wind turbines) to be dealt with separately and thus escape the auction system imposed by DG Comp. Renewables are also accessible to retailers, farmers, SMEs and small municipalities without any excessive red tape, provided that national governments make the most of this room for manoeuvre.

Examples of this abound. The island of Sein off the coast of Brittany is striving to develop its 100 per cent renewable energy project, despite the obstacles strewn in its path by EDF and its fuel-oil-powered generators. Cooperatives in Luxembourg, Germany, Denmark and Belgium are flourishing, and benefit from widespread public acceptance of onshore wind power. The socialist/liberal/green government in Luxembourg has even created a special feed-in tariff to help support electricity produced by grassroots cooperatives. All of this has created a positive dynamic with farmers being among the first to be promoting decentralised wind power, which brings in additional revenue for them. Similarly, if a school installs photovoltaic panels on its roof as part of an educational project, this raises the awareness not only of the children, but also of their parents.

I am patron of the European Federation of Renewable Energy Cooperatives (REScoop). With the help of the Intelligent Energy Europe programme, the REScoop project has brought together different renewables cooperatives: Enercoop in France, Ecopower in Flanders and many others besides. REScoop currently consists of 1,240 cooperatives, totalling 300,000 individuals. In Scotland alone, 500MW of wind power is already in the hands of citizens, either individually or in cooperatives. Friends of the Earth are also highly engaged in this area, through their 'Community Power' campaign, implemented in twelve European countries including Poland, where fifteen community biogas programmes are currently under development. According to one study, 264 million 'energy citizens' could produce almost half of all electricity consumed in Europe by 2050.[152]

---

152   'The Potential of Energy Citizens in the European Union', CE Delft, September 2016, www. greenpeace.org.

Citizen savers

Lastly, people are increasingly asking questions about where their savings are going: should I invest my money in a bank that is ethical? Green? Transparent? What are the yields like? The answer is that ethical funds perform as well if not better than traditional finance in terms of pure financial performance. There are even cooperatives that offer shares in grassroots projects: investment funds take out shares in local cooperative projects, such as Énergie partagée in France, which has already brought in €11 million from a large number of investors, including over 4,500 individuals.

My proposals:

- Including a citizens' right to self-generation (producing, consuming, storing and selling their electricity) in the revision of the EU's Renewable Energy Directive, based on appropriate support schemes and priority access and dispatch to the grid.
- Mobilising the guarantees available under the Juncker Plan (EFSI) to facilitate the access of grassroots cooperative projects to funding.
- Setting targets for the proportion of energy generated by individual and corporative projects in Europe, and including this indicator in the annual State of the Energy Union report.
- Implementing educational awareness-raising programmes devoted to green energy in primary and secondary schools.
- Setting up decentralised debates on the Energy Union, with a series of 'citizen summits' in all EU countries, in order to garner the views of individuals, cooperatives and local communities.
- Collecting more than 1 million signatures in order to launch a grassroots European initiative promoting renewable energy.

FROM BREXIT TO THE 'WINTER PACKAGE': THE TRAVAILS OF 2016

The night of 23–24 June 2016 was to mark the genesis of a historic event. The departure of the United Kingdom, the world's fifth-largest economy, from the EU. The British public voted on Thursday 23 June and by 3.30 a.m. on Friday morning, it was clear that the Leave camp was bound for a win, with the odds from the bookies suddenly tilting in favour of Brexit. Many in London, Scotland and Gibraltar voted to remain in the European Union, but it was not enough. By 4:30 a.m., with the pound falling to less than $1.40, nobody was left clinging to the illusion that Brexit could not possibly happen. One hour later, the pound fell to a thirty-year low. Brussels woke to a terrible hangover: 17.4 million UK citizens had voted to leave the EU, while 16.1 million had voted to remain. At 6 a.m., David Cameron announced victory for the Brexit camp – and his own resignation. Abandoning ship, he left the Brexiteers to fight among themselves. Despite the fact that he himself was largely responsible, having used the referendum as an electoral tactic since January 2013, his attitude was *après moi le déluge*.

The implications of Brexit: pro-climate, pro-nuclear
While the United Kingdom has always been 'half-in, half-out' of

the EU, there's never been any doubt about the fact that its presence within the Union has had a substantial impact on the definition of European climate and energy policy. Together with the Scandinavian countries, Germany and France, UK leaders have undeniably been among those most strongly in favour of the EU's pro-climate commitment. Tony Blair set a precedent in this respect, opening up the way for the EU's first Climate and Energy Package at the informal summit held at Hampton Court in October 2005. In the person of Ed Davey, the coalition government of David Cameron and Nick Clegg had an indefatigable warrior against climate change.

When it came to the internal market, Her Majesty's Government made a major contribution to the regulation of the electricity market in 2003, supporting the separation of assets between networks and production activities, over and against France and Germany, as well as the setting up of an independent regulator responsible for supervising system operators' neutrality. However, these efforts on the part of the UK were offset by two other factors: on the one hand, a vision focused on the carbon market as the sole instrument for bringing down greenhouse gas emissions, leaving no room at all for other policies provided for in the treaties with regard to energy efficiency and renewables; and then, of course, the nuclear issue. The only European nation apart from France to have nuclear weapons, the United Kingdom sees atomic power as being of strategic importance. It is hardly surprising that renewables and energy efficiency have paid a price in this respect: indeed, it is hard to reconcile a pro-nuclear policy with making the system more flexible and bringing down energy consumption.

Lobbying – an English term

There can be no doubt that the British are formidable lobbyists. Indeed, the most effective lobbyist in Brussels has not been Exxon Mobil or Shell, or even Angela Merkel, but Her Majesty's network. Hinkley Point C is a prime example of this.

Since the lingua franca of the Brussels microcosm is English, the British have made the most of this privilege to get close to all those who matter at the Commission, the Council and the European Parliament. I have seen more UK ministers and secretaries of state in my office than I have representatives of my own Luxembourg government. In the Council, the UK has worked closely with member states that share similar agendas, in particular the Visegrád group of countries and the Baltic states. Then too, there is Malta, a former colony, which is benefiting from the support of a great many UK functionaries as it exercised the EU presidency in the first half of 2017. Pragmatism does have its advantages.

The British make up only 3.8 per cent of the Commission workforce, despite representing 13 per cent of the population of Europe. But while they may be numerically in the minority, they are always strategically placed. To take the field of energy alone, Christopher Jones, the brains behind the deregulation of the electricity and gas markets in 2007–2008, is now deputy director-general. Three Brits have been in key positions in the Secretariat General preparing the 2030 Climate and Energy Framework: Peter Handley is head of unit for Resource Efficiency (including the Energy Union), Jonathon Stoodley was for long head of the Evaluation, Regulatory Fitness and Performance Unit (also known as 'better regulation'), and Duncan Johnstone is deputy head of unit for Impact Assessments. Then, too, there is Paul Hodson, head of unit for Energy Efficiency, and Jonathan Taylor, vice president of the European Investment Bank. And last but by no means least, Catherine Day, Irish but beholden to UK interests, occupied the position of secretary-general for a decade. Not to mention members of commissioners' cabinets and seconded national experts appointed to key positions at DG Ener and DG Comp. The lobbies have clearly understood the benefits of playing the sort of game and, in an irony of history, the CEOs recently appointed by the European Wind Energy Association and SolarPower Europe are both British.

Splendid isolation – at a price

Who will be the winners and losers in this divorce? I am not alone in thinking that the UK has more to lose than it has to gain. In a May

2016 study entitled 'UK Unplugged', researchers from the Chatham House Institute explored various options for the relationship between the UK and the EU, working on the principle that 'the UK is increasingly reliant on imports, including from and through continental Europe, and its energy market is deeply integrated with that of its European neighbours'.

Indeed, the United Kingdom is more dependent on the EU than the other way around. One of the reasons the Indian giant Tata Steel is closing its steelworks in the UK rather than one in the Netherlands is undoubtedly the unduly high energy costs there. Indeed, these are linked to several very British issues. The wholesale electricity market price is around €60 per megawatt-hour, almost twice that in continental Europe (€30–€35/MWh for the same period). There are several reasons for this difference. In 2013, the British introduced a carbon floor price of approximately €18/MWh for the production of coal. Half of the observed difference can be accounted for right there.

As to the other half, it can be attributed to the policy conducted by David Cameron's Conservative government. Under pressure from UKIP populists, it abandoned all investment in the cheapest technology, onshore wind power. Instead, public-sector support concentrated on the most expensive technology on the market: nuclear power and the Hinkley Point C EPR power station, with a guaranteed feed-in tariff of €120/MWh, indexed to inflation, for a period of thirty-five years.

Another aspect to be taken into consideration in this respect is the instigation of excessive competition at every level of the economy. For instance, when offshore wind power project developers submit a bid, they are placed in competition for all the grid connection costs. This is an expensive approach, since it adds risk for investors. Countries such as the Netherlands and Denmark have taken the opposite approach: the system operator, a public-sector entity, identifies favourable sites and provides the required cables; developers therefore do not need to shoulder these costs. The result is that the costs of offshore wind power have tumbled and regional planning is coherent.

Having observed the increasingly large gap between electricity prices in the UK and the rest of Europe, the British system operator National Grid developed a plan to improve interconnections. Projects such as North Sea Link (NSL) with Norway, BritNed with the Netherlands, Viking Link (VL) with Denmark, and Cross-Channel Cable (CCC) with France are beginning to emerge. However, it is perhaps a little late to try and moor the UK to the Continent.

Hinkley or not Hinkley?

On 4 July 2016, without making the details public, EDF put its case to its central works council. Brexit, it announced, would not call into question the huge, risky investment in Hinkley Point C. The group's board of directors approved the project at the same time. However, their joy proved to be short-lived. The enthusiasm of EDF and the French government was about to be doused: after having forced the issue through internally, Theresa May's new government dithered before postponing the decision. Indeed, the UK government opted to take another look at the arguments, and its new Secretary of State for Business, Energy and Industrial Strategy, Greg Clark, had inherited a complex situation. The previous climate and energy minister had always claimed that nuclear power was cheaper than offshore wind power, but this is no longer the case today in at least two European nations. Denmark is building an offshore wind farm for €50/MWh, while the Dutch are doing the same for €72/MWh – both projects are much cheaper than the €120/MWh promised for Hinkley Point. The latest offshore wind tender in Germany was even awarded to a 0€/MWh bidder! At the end of the day, the decision to go ahead with Hinkley Point C was not taken in London or Paris, but at Hangzhou, on the fringes of the G20 summit. As the world's leaders were meeting in September 2016, the Chinese insisted on a successful conclusion to their investment, granting them a wide-open door to bring the nuclear industry to the European market. And a few days later on 15 September 2016, Theresa May agreed that the project should continue. Will this arrangement withstand the turmoil of Brexit? Will the government guarantees pertaining to the project take into account the risks to which the pound is now exposed?

Brexit: soft or hard?

When it comes to renewables and energy efficiency, the United Kingdom could certainly make the most of its long-sought-after flexibility to continue to keep these two sectors at arms' length – without having to worry about annoying Brussels. The corollary of this is that it will no doubt be easier to achieve political majorities in the European Parliament and the Council for genuine energy transition without the United Kingdom and its ability to interfere. Not only that, it could be argued that when it comes down to it, David Cameron's veto of binding national targets at the European Council meeting in October 2014 has been rendered obsolete. Why not open up this debate again? There is still time to establish binding targets of 40 per cent energy efficiency and 35 per cent renewables, implemented nationally. Europe could even draw inspiration from Scotland and its government, so committed to renewables that it is seeking to have them cater for 100 per cent of domestic demand.[153] The Scots would be very welcome to join in the discussions!

In terms of climate policy, the United Kingdom may remain within the European sphere, in which case the country will have to continue to do its bit to ensure the EU fulfils its international obligations with regard to combating climate change. Indeed, such arrangements are in place for Switzerland and Iceland. Norway and Switzerland have signed a partnership agreement with the EU to be part of the ETS, and the UK could go down a similar road. However, it is uncertain whether it will still be part of the European Economic Area. This would clearly be the model with the most economic benefits for both parties, enabling British products to be marketed in Europe without customs tariffs and vice versa. However, this would involve the British accepting almost all EU standards, without having any say in how they are

---

153   '2020 Routemap for Renewable Energy in Scotland', www.gov.scot.

drafted. Similarly, the European regulations governing state aid apply to European Economic Area member countries. Ironically, in this scenario Brexit would result in less UK sovereignty rather than more; it is certainly the end of 'having your cake and eating it'. As European Council president Donald Tusk said in December 2016, during Brexit negotiations, 'There will be no cakes on the table for anyone. There will only be salt and vinegar.'

Lessons worth learning

Brexit has resulted in major upheaval in Europe, and in particular, a realisation on the part of European policymakers that nothing is as it was before. There must now be a rethink of European policies, placing citizens at the heart of priorities. The 'Winter Package' announced by the Commission on 30 November 2016 offered an ideal opportunity to implement these promises, and finally take a giant step towards energy transition by speeding up efforts in the direction of renewable energy and energy efficiency for the benefit of all Europeans. Have these promises been kept? What is in the 'Winter Package' proposed by the Commission?

The 2016 'Winter Package': the lobbies strike back

On Wednesday 30 November 2016, vice president for Energy Union Maroš Šefčovič and the Climate Action and Energy Commissioner Miguel Arias Cañete took the floor at a press conference with an air of triumph. Both pleased as Punch, they unveiled the concept of their proposals for the Energy Union, complete with an attractive tagline that nonetheless had rather cynical overtones: 'Clean energy for all Europeans'. In theory, these eight legislative proposals[154] are supposed to place citizens at the centre of the energy system, with the right to self-generation; make energy efficiency a top priority; and enshrine

---

154   Revision of the Renewable Energy Directive, revision of the Energy Efficiency Directive, re-
       vision of the Energy Performance of Buildings Directive, revision of the Internal Market in
       Electricity Regulation Directive, revision of the Regulation founding ACER, a new Regulation
       on risk-preparedness in the electricity sector and a new Regulation on the governance of the
       Energy Union.

President Juncker's promise to make the EU world number one in renewable energy. At the same time, a fair and functional organisation of the European electricity market is supposed to happen. The facts, however, fall far short of these lofty ambitions.

After their carefully prepared number, the two speakers struggled rather more at the hands of the media. The journalists remained unconvinced by the patter of the two commissioners, and their questions took a critical turn. The same central issue emerged from them all: if the duo really believed in the virtues of energy transition, why restrict the growth of renewables to a 27 per cent target in 2030, and have an energy efficiency target of just 30 per cent for the same period? The two stooges did their best to support their position with a swath of statistics, but it was impossible: the proposed targets for 2030 represent a bare minimum. Worse still, the related governance marks a huge step backwards. The 2020 targets included specific allocations for each member state, with binding national targets, whereas the 27 per cent target for 2030 is nothing more than a simple aspiration, entirely dependent on the goodwill of national governments.

A coordinated attack by the Magritte group, BusinessEurope and Eurelectric

In fact, this legislative package almost failed to see the light of day at all and when did, it almost emerged without a key component: the revision of the Renewable Energy Directive. Indeed, the preparatory work was marred by a great many incidents. DG Ener had to fend off the usual attacks on the part of the anti-renewables lobbies, headed up by the Magritte Group – a group that has been with us throughout this book, and is still there, more active than ever.

A few days prior to the adoption of the legislative package by the Commission, the CEOs of Centrica, Cez, Engie, Fortum, Iberdrola and Innogy staged an event at the European Parliament, with the official purpose to demonstrate their commitment to reforming the European carbon market. However, this public event also provided an opportunity for them to rain criticism on the EU's targets for energy efficiency and renewable energy. Iberdrola's boss Ignacio Galan declared that 'everything on consumer bills other than the price of energy itself must be done away with' – i.e. the cost of renewable energy support schemes. Iain Conn of Centrica went further still: 'I hope that in the future, we will no longer have to live with a confused system based on three targets; this would be regrettable.' It was left to Pekka Lundmark from Fortum to have the last word: 'The ETS must remain as the only instrument.'

In short, the same attacks, the same criticisms, and the same mistruths that the oligopolies have been putting forward since spring 2013. And these attacks have found their target. The Magritte Group itself gleefully acknowledged as much, back in April 2015: 'The assessment of the energy industry made two years ago by the Magritte Group is now widely shared. In particular, the European Commission's strategy on a European Energy Union marks an important step forward in this regard.'[155] On 22 November 2016, not only did the representatives of the Magritte Group organise a public event at the Parliament, they also held a closed-doors meeting with commissioners Šefčovič and Arias Cañete. So just what was said behind those closed doors?

The previous day, vice president Šefčovič had been subjected to recriminations from Europe's bosses. The general secretary of BusinessEurope delivered an all-out attack on any kind of aspirations to energy efficiency: 'It is key to make sure the system is not undermined by an overly ambitious energy efficiency target. To sum-up, we maintain our views that an indicative 27 per cent energy efficiency target, as part of the overall energy and climate policy design, remains the best and most cost-effective option.'[156] Given that energy efficiency is a source of both growth and competitiveness, it can be legitimately wondered which entrepreneurs BusinessEurope is speaking on behalf of.

Eurelectric made the most of the opportunity too. The electricity

---

155 'Magritte Group calls for more convergence and integration in European energy policy', 21 April 2015, www.engie.com.

156 'Intervention by Director General Markus J. Beyrer at the European Social Partners meeting on the Energy Union', 21 November 2016, www.businesseurope.eu.

companies' lobby also published its recommendations just a few weeks before the Commission's legislative proposals in a document entitled 'Winter Package Solutions'. Here again, the language used reflects the energy firms' usual anti-renewables bias. In addition to calling into question support schemes, there is a clear desire to abolish priority access for renewable energy, an intention to restrict the extent to which renewables are deployed by having recourse to technology-neutral auctions, and a call to bring an end to binding national targets. In an ultimate act of hypocrisy, Eurelectric advocates more Europe where it suits, and less Europe where it wishes national electricity companies to be able to preserve their room for manoeuvre. As far as renewables are concerned, 'alignment of support schemes' and 'partial opening across borders' are requested, while 'an EU-wide harmonisation approach to distribution tariffs is not advisable'.

The enemies within

Attacks from the energy oligopolies were only to be expected, and indeed are consistent with the conservative agenda being pushed by organisations such as the Magritte Group, BusinessEurope and Eurelectric; but alongside them came much more insidious offensives from hardened adversaries of energy transition within the European Commission itself such as the Regulatory Scrutiny Board, the legal service and DG Comp.

When the Commission presents new legislation, it has to submit an impact assessment study in which various possible options are examined and their economic, social and environmental consequences analysed. In practice, this is a fastidious task which involves attempting to provide scientific support for political decisions. In order to ensure this is done properly, these assessment studies must be submitted for the approval of a special committee, the Regulatory Scrutiny Board. The problem is that this board is anything but technical: on the contrary, it is a highly political body with significant power. A negative opinion from the RSB can considerably weaken the credibility of proposed legislation.

This board has had the gall to request a review of the impact assessment study for the Renewable Energy Directive – twice. The first submission was thrown out in September 2016, following which DG Ener had another go, presenting a revised, consolidated version. The RSB rejected it once again, and did so on highly dubious grounds, including the belief that 'a different mix of EU and national measures might arguably be more efficient and effective, notably in light of the political decision of the European Council to move away from national legally binding targets'. Furthermore, the RSB indicated that any renewables directive over and above other measures 'might be a disproportionate way to deliver the Union's target for renewable energy', and took the view that renewable energy support schemes should not be included in the directive because 'the existing state aid guidelines already address most of the issues'.

This direct attack on the Renewable Energy Directive is unfortunately not the only one to have come from within the Commission itself, sometimes in the face of a political consensus on the part of the commissioners. Indeed, this was also the case when it came to renewable support schemes. To make these mechanisms more stable, and therefore provide better visibility for investors, the German and French governments made an approach to the commissioners in charge of this issue: Maroš Šefčovič and Miguel Arias Cañete for Energy, and Margrethe Vestager at Competition. The idea was to agree to the basic principles to be used to govern financial support for renewable energy, at the political level. To achieve this, a new article was proposed in the directive in order to grant member states the right to support their development of renewables through specific support schemes for each type of technology, by means of appropriate resources, such as auctions for major projects and guaranteed tariffs to encourage grassroots investment. The concept was backed by the German government and approved by the three commissioners.

However, when DG Ener submitted its draft directive for interdepartment consultation, with the aim of other departments in the Commission having an opportunity to make comments, the response from DG Comp was unequivocal: 'DG Comp strongly objects the in-clusion of provisions on support schemes in the draft directive.' Two main reasons were invoked for this: firstly, it would contravene DG Comp's monopoly for determining whether state aid was legal or not, and secondly, it would disrupt the 'institutional balance'. Not only was this an arrogant attitude, it was also a gauntlet thrown down by the Commission's officers to the commissioners themselves. DG Comp's position appears to be that European energy policy should be deter-mined solely by civil servants, and not by the commissioners, member states and MEPs. That is not exactly democracy.

Another argument put forward was that 'provisions on support measures in the directive will hinder adaptations in a rapidly evolving market'. To address this, the draft directive specifies that 'member States must review their support schemes every four years'. Oddly enough, two weeks prior to this text being approved by the Commission, the very same DG Comp had agreed to the French capacity mechanism for ten years. In addition, DG Comp also managed to destroy the principle of technology-specific auctions, to the benefit of technology-neutral schemes. This is another ridiculous idea inspired by the ultra-liberal theory of the 'invisible hand': how can a member state possibly plan its future energy supply and network extension if it is not allowed to determine which renewable sources it seeks to benefit from?

The legal department played its part in this concerted attack, too. It aligned itself with DG Comp's analysis, declaring that 'the EU leg-islator does not have the competence under the treaty ... to set out requirements for the implementation of the state aid measures grant-ed in the form of support schemes'. In no uncertain terms, it expressed its horror that these provisions 'could and even very likely would be modified and made even more flexible by the Council and the Par-liament in the legislative procedure'. Surely this is what co-legislators are supposed to do? Here too, the ultra-liberal proponents of exces-sive competition have brought the very same arguments to bear – yet again – in an attempt to put an end to national support schemes for renewables. This guerrilla warfare has been going on since 2008 and the Climate and Energy Package, continued during the development of the guidelines for state aid in 2014, and is now being waged as the 2030 Climate and Energy Framework is being defined.

The progressives respond

Faced with this concerted attack from the gravediggers of energy transition, the progressives mobilised, enlisting the support of civil society. By happy coincidence, the Marrakesh climate conference (COP22) took place shortly before the Commission's adoption of this 'Winter Package'. The Climate Action Network made the most of the COP summit to point out the inconsistencies in Commissioner Arias Cañete's position: while posing as a champion combating climate change in Marrakesh, he was simultaneously undermining energy transition targets in Brussels. Indeed, this paradox led to the Commission being awarded the 'Fossil of the Day' prize on 16 November – rather an embarrassment right in the middle of a climate summit.

© PETER DREDGE

For my part, I quickly realised that I would need to focus my action on the few key points that could still be rescued. Aware that the

Commission was going to take due note of the conclusions of the European Council meeting of 24 October and invoke its freedom of initiative, I had no hope of any possibility of raising the targets above 27 per cent for renewables and 30 per cent for energy efficiency. I therefore concentrated on improving the regulatory framework for grassroots producers of green energy, since the Commission's working hypotheses in this respect were contradictory. On the one hand, individuals have the right to self-generation, but on the other, priority access to the grid and priority dispatch for electricity produced from renewable energy sources was only optional. In a second line of attack, I tried to restrict the possibility of subsidies to fossil fuels as much as possible, by means of emission performance standards and close oversight of capacity mechanisms.

A lost decade for energy transition?

The final outcome is disappointing, to say the least. The Commission has stuck with the target of 27 per cent renewable energy in 2030, which is far below the level called for by the issues. According to the Commission's own calculations, this amounts to a significant decrease in investment in the sector. In the decade from 2005 to 2015, Europe saw average annual investment in this sector of €68 billion; a 27 per cent target is likely to see only €25 billion invested on average each year. When was the last time a 'world number one' had a declining domestic market?

How could things have turned out any other way? The approach is even more infuriating than the outcome. The Commission's working hypotheses are breathtakingly wrong. They are based on the following belief: after years of subsidies, renewable energy is now mature enough to be fully exposed to the market. Consequently, the 'privileges' from which it benefits, such as subsidies, along with priority access and dispatch to the grid, should be done away with. In actual fact, the market being referred to here is so skewed that it is incapable of ensuring fair competition between different technologies. As we have seen throughout this book, the carbon market is depressed, and coal does not pay for the pollution it generates. This overcapacity has led to wholesale electricity market prices going into free fall. Nuclear power benefits from preferential treatment, given the absence of any related European insurance regime, or any obligation to set aside sufficient funds to ensure decommissioning of installations and waste management. In view of this, significant political action in favour of renewables is vital.

Here again, the figures used by the Commission are open to challenge. The impact assessment study assumes a carbon price of €38–€42 per tonne, whereas the market has been hovering around the €5 mark for the past six years. The Commission also bases itself on completely unrealistic costs for renewable technologies, citing €110–€205/MWh for offshore wind power, despite the two most recent contracts in the Netherlands and Denmark being awarded for €72/MWh and €50/MWh respectively (without even speaking of the €0/MWh bid recently awarded in Germany, as specific conditions related to that project do not reflect the general market situation of renewables throughout Europe). The same bias is apparent when it comes to solar power: in November 2016, a joint German–Danish contract was concluded at a price of €54/MWh; the hypothesis used in the Commission impact assessment study is €79–€148/MWh.

The two-pronged attack from the traditional lobbies and DG Comp has also made its mark. The final text of the proposed Renewable Energy Directive has been reduced to a bare minimum: the lowest of targets, little in the way of binding requirements, limited priority dispatch and poorly dealt with support schemes. Another disappointment is that the legislative proposals say nothing at all about nuclear power. Indeed, it is not mentioned even once in thousands of pages' worth of new legislation put forward by the Commission. There is nothing about decommissioning funds, nothing about any insurance regime and nothing about compensation for early closures. Finally, in spite of the inclusion of a maximum level of greenhouse gas emissions of 550g CO_2/kWh – which, admittedly, represents significant progress, since it automatically rules out the construction of new coal-fired power plants in Europe – there is no proposal as to how to escape the current problem of overcapacity, which is largely due to existing coal- and lignite-fired power plants.

However, there are some encouraging aspects. The Commission's legislative proposals deal with the issue of energy efficiency very well. A 30 per cent target has been proposed. While this is below the optimum target of around 40 per cent, it is a step in the right direction, especially given the woefully inadequate 27 per cent target mentioned by the European Council in October 2014. There are also the beginnings of a response to the issue of grassroots energy, with some provisions designed to encourage EU citizens to commit to producing, consuming, storing and reselling their electricity.

The need for a collective awakening

After two years of bitter internal strife and external pressure from all sides, the Commission has now commenced work on the largest European legislative undertaking of all time in the realm of energy and eight pieces of legislation are now on the table. Staff at the European Parliament and the twenty-eight national governments will now be looking at them, presided over by Malta and Estonia in 2017 followed by Bulgaria and Austria in 2018. In the European Parliament, the broad coalition between the Social Democrats and the Conservatives has once again done its bit; the two major groups have ensured they will have a firm hold on the main texts under discussion. After a two-year marathon, these negotiations run the risk of getting bogged down and producing only marginal changes at the end of the day – a gloomy prospect.

Personally, I am more inclined to hope for a collective awakening, one that creates a dynamic and speeds up energy transition at the grassroots level. The primordial role of energy efficiency is now widely accepted, as is the prospect of future energy production being green. The costs of wind and solar power are inexorably declining and many companies have taken the strategic decision to transition; fuel-oil boilers will inevitably be replaced by solar thermal power, geothermal energy, sustainable biomass and heat pumps. The 'pro-climate' movement has gathered momentum in Europe's cities and municipalities since the COP21 summit. And we are moving more swiftly towards electric mobility in the wake of Dieselgate.

Millions of people are getting involved, either individually or collectively, through the cooperatives springing up all over Europe. What is more, the alliance forged in Brussels between consumer associations, environmental protection groups and grassroots cooperatives will mean that ultimately, there will be no remaining barriers to stop individuals and small businesses investing wholeheartedly in decentralised, renewable energy.

The only thing left to overcome is the conservativism prevalent in political spheres, be it at the European Parliament or in national parliaments and governments. Nothing less than a credible, visionary plan will rally them to our cause. This plan must entail the following four elements:

1. Ambitious regional scenarios:
   As I have done my best to explain throughout this book, I am a firm believer in the virtues of regional cooperation at an intermediate level between purely national policy and the twenty-eight member states taken as a whole. Working at this scale offers reassurance to national governments seeking to retain control, at the same time as helping to disseminate the practice of systematic cross-border cooperation. The Commission should improve its standing by examining 'high-efficiency/high renewables' scenarios at the level of five European macro-regions: the Baltic Sea, western Europe, the North Sea, the Mediterranean basin and southeast Europe. Furthermore, cooperation between member states in a region can bring down the costs of rolling out renewable energy, grid extensions and system-balancing. This would show that renewables could cater for much more than 50 per cent of electricity used in 2030, whatever the Commission would have us believe.

2. Flagship projects:

The economic meltdown is largely to blame for EU citizens' disenchantment with the European project. Many leading economists, among them Thomas Piketty, Peter Bofinger and Mariana Mazzucato, are convinced that Europe's declining competitiveness is closely related to a lack of investment in promising sectors for the future such as digital technology, building renovation and electric mobility, and in the replacement of our ageing infrastructures. Jeremy Rifkin has also said as much, and just as compellingly. It is therefore vital to see some flagship projects emerge, with the financial and political backing of the EU, such as desynchronisation of the Baltic states from the Russian electrical system, combined with the construction of wind farms in the Baltic Sea; the conversion of heating networks powered by fossil fuels to 100 per cent renewable networks; the emergence of European electric mobility corridors powered by renewable energy (after all, there's no point in having electric cars powered by coal-fired or nuclear electricity); the construction of cross-border wind farms in the North Sea with on-site maintenance; and European investment in the south-east Europe region to exploit the huge potential for renewables there, benefiting from lower costs of capital. Each of these major challenges offers scope for demonstrating the added value Europe can provide.

3. Achieving political compromises to leave coal and nuclear power behind:

The first thing to do is to increase the 2030 targets so as to achieve more ambitious goals in terms of reducing greenhouse gas emissions and increasing both renewable energy and energy efficiency, thereby creating a dynamic for green growth – and a chance to keep global warming beneath 1.5°C. More contentious issues will need to be addressed, too. There is no future for coal; governments and workers in this industry should be left under no illusions in this respect. This means there must be no compromise on the prohibition of new coal-fired power stations; at the same time, by the end of 2017 a plan must be prepared to assist with the gradual abandonment of coal and lignite, bringing together available sources of funding and organising a network of experts to redevelop coal-mining districts.

Similarly, nuclear power must no longer be given a free pass. If the European electricity market is to have a future, the issues of insurance, decommissioning and radioactive waste-handling all need to be addressed. The taboo subject of cross-border risks from nuclear power must be discussed, too. Having absolutely no say with respect to a nuclear power station on one's doorstep (but in another country) is a far more intrusive issue in everyday life than even the most annoying of EU directives.

4. Creating Europe's positive energy with the help of its citizens and cities:

The people in Europe who are losing confidence in the EU need to be persuaded that the Energy Union is worthwhile. This will involve a financial effort, helping the most motivated citizens to invest in solar power, wind power and heating networks managed by cooperatives or by local authorities. There is no doubt that this would result in an army of enthusiastic supporters of the European vision.

The numbers of architects of energy transition are increasing, but the saboteurs are still on the scene. Will the future see a return to the 'Enlightenment' years, or are we set for an extension of the 'Dark Ages'? How the story goes on from here is partly up to the lawmakers – but regaining control of the system is also a job for innovative companies, local authorities, workers and millions of citizens – and that includes you.

POSTSCRIPT

Ceci n'est pas un livre

I got involved in energy because of my opposition to a high-voltage power line. I thought it was it ugly and useless. Today, I am fighting to promote wind turbines and solar panels, and find myself confronted with some people who think they are ugly and useless.

I became involved in climate issues after a class given by somebody who is now the chief lobbyist in Europe for nuclear power – a type of energy I am against for a great many reasons.

I entered the European Parliament after having dreamed of working there to pursue my commitment to a better world, as an extension of my engagement as an environmental activist, which had taken me from Friends of the Earth in Luxembourg to Friends of the Earth Europe in Brussels.

In view of all this, this is not a book about climate policies as we know it, in that it makes no claim to objectivity. While some parts may be difficult to get into, the idea is to shed light on the complex world of energy – and the equally complex world of EU politics.

Ceci n'est pas un livre: it is 'not a book as we know it'; rather, it is the story of fifteen years' worth of struggles, joys, occasional disappointments and unrelenting passion. The European Parliament is a fascinating place; an atypical assembly with shifting majorities. For each piece of legislation, a handful of MEPs analyse texts put forward by the European Commission, discuss them with stakeholders from civil society and then work with their respective political groups to introduce hundreds of amendments. These are then debated and voted on, in order to reach a common basis of negotiation. Producing legislation in this way is a fastidious job; but it is both useful and important, impacting the lives of 500 million Europeans.

As a member of a small political group, the Greens, I have had the privilege of being involved in almost all the major negotiations with respect to energy policy since 1999. MEPs work as part of a team. I work with my colleagues and advisers from my parliamentary group, academics, other experts, lobbyists, civil society and MEPs – not only those of the same political persuasion, but also some from other parliamentary groups. Then, too, there are the European Commission's civil servants, often top specialists in their field, as well as European commissioners, ministers and their officers from twenty-eight countries, all different and often with extremely different energy cultures. And there are the journalists who enjoy exploring all these backroads, but for whom the space and time required to get to grips with European democracy are constantly being squeezed.

This is not a book as we know it, and neither is it mine alone. It represents the sum of contributions from dozens, or indeed hundreds of people who have helped me gain a better understanding of the world of energy in order to have a more informed influence on decisions. I would like to thank my successive staff members Michaela, Fred, Esther, Jérémie, Olaf, Meris, Denise, Theresa and Linda, as well as all the interns who have assisted this great team. I would also like to thank the Green group advisers Gratten, Heike, Terhi, Charlotte, Karolina and especially 'Mich', the amazing amendment engineer. Thank you to Mechthild, Britta, Fiona, Kathleen and Peter, along with all the other MEPs from different political groups with which we have put together robust majorities, as well as to the MEPs who challenge me on a daily basis, including Jerzy, Herbert and Markus: sometimes our arguments give birth to great ideas! Thanks too, to the academics and experts who know far more than I do and from whom I learn something new every day: Bernard, Felix, Antony, Uwe, Mario, Gustav,

Yamina, Gérard, Hélène, Jorge, Julian and Pete. I would also like to acknowledge the advocates of green energy and the environment who unceasingly remind me of my militant origins: Dörte, Frauke, Claire, Josche, Brook, Stefan, Magda, Paul, Jean-François, Jorgo and others; and to express my thanks to the innumerable officers of the European Commission and national governments who have stood by me for fifteen years now – and who I cannot name without upsetting their superiors.

This is not my book alone, since it would never have come into existence without the indispensable aid of Hughes. His journalistic experience has brought order and structure into a constant profusion of ideas, and created a carefully crafted guiding thread; his legendary straight talk has spared readers from some particularly bitter invective directed at my political opponents. Last but by no means least, this book would never have seen the light of day without Jérémie, brought by fair winds and new technology straight from a rugby pitch in Kosovo to my office, two years ago now. His writing skills, rational thinking and humour, together with his experience at the Commission and in French administration, have made this joint effort by the two of us a most enjoyable experience.

INDEX